The Mother-Child Interaction in Psychosomatic Disorders

THE
MOTHER-CHILD
INTERACTION
IN PSYCHOSOMATIC
DISORDERS

Ann M. Garner
and Charles Wenar

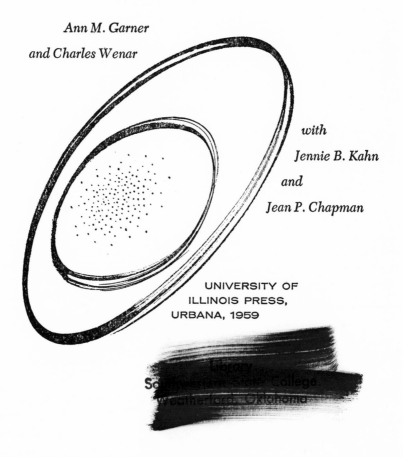

with
Jennie B. Kahn
and
Jean P. Chapman

UNIVERSITY OF
ILLINOIS PRESS,
URBANA, 1959

To Solveig and Ross

Acknowledgment

In designing the project to be described in this book, we frequently found that it was impossible to realize certain ideal goals and that we had to lower our sights in order to make the study practicable. Of all these enforced compromises with reality, however, the one we must make now is the most difficult. Surely our wish is to acknowledge individually everyone who helped in the different phases of the research: the psychiatrists and psychologists who contributed to the theory and design, the physicians and educators who gave us entree to medical and educational facilities, and the many psychiatrists, pediatricians, social workers, psychologists, teachers, and nurses who assisted in the actual locating of the mothers and children who participated in the research. Not only did these people give of their time, but their interest in the project also helped counteract the frustrations and fatigues which seem an inevitable by-product of extensive investigation. Unfortunately, such a complete listing of individuals would far exceed the limits imposed by practicality, and we must make one final compromise by naming only a few. Our gratitude, however, extends to all.

We are particularly grateful to the late Dr. Margaret W. Gerard and to Drs. Francis J. Gerty, David Shakow, Julius B. Richmond, and Samuel H. Barron for their many contributions to the theoretical aspects of the study as well as for their help in its practical implementation. Many physicians in medical centers opened their facilities to us; Dr. Heyworth N. Sanford of the University of Illinois Research and Educational Hospitals, Drs. Roy R. Grinker and B. M. Kagan of Michael Reese Hospital, Dr. Joseph B. Kirsner of Billings Hospital of the University of Chicago, and Dr. Hugh McCulloch of LaRabida

Jackson Park Sanitarium were particularly generous in this respect. Dr. Raymond Robertson and the staff of psychiatrists, psychologists, and social workers at the Institute for Juvenile Research were continually helpful in locating mothers and children for the Neurotic control group. We wish to thank Dr. Frances A. Mullen of the Chicago Board of Education and Mrs. Olive P. Brunner of Spalding School for giving us access to a number of physically ill, non-psychosomatic children. Drs. Robert S. Mendelsohn, Mitchell Spellberg, and Bessie L. Lendrum were particularly interested and cooperative individual physicians. Finally, we are grateful to Dr. Marion Wieman for supplying us with a much needed auxiliary intellect in regard to problems of evaluation and interpretation of results.

Those to whom we are most indebted, however, are those who must remain anonymous—the mothers and children who participated in the study. We wish to record here our deep gratitude for their continued cooperation on tasks which were often difficult and demanding, and always time-consuming.

We wish to thank the Department of Psychiatry of the University of Illinois College of Medicine for making its facilities available to us. This investigation was supported by a research grant (M-823) from the National Institute of Mental Health, of the National Institutes of Health, U.S. Department of Health, Education and Welfare.

Contents

PART ONE

1---Introduction

The research project to be described in the following chapters derives from the principal investigators' experience as psychologists on the ward for psychosomatic children which is part of the Department of Psychiatry of the University of Illinois. The ward served as an invaluable source of theoretical ideas and empirical observations, since it was established for the twofold purpose of providing a therapeutic milieu for children with psychosomatic disorders and simultaneously making an intensive study of their personalities.

In order to fulfill this dual purpose, everyone connected with the ward had both a therapeutic and a research function. The social worker obtained extensive case history material from the mothers and, in most instances, involved them in casework therapy. The psychologists evaluated the children and, whenever possible, their parents, by means of personality and intelligence tests. The nurses and aides were trained both to meet the children's needs and to make extensive notes of their behavior. The pediatrician, tutor, and occupational therapist likewise recorded the children's attitudes toward illness, toward the demands of schoolwork, and toward recreational activities. Each child was in psychoanalytically oriented therapy, the therapist keeping a running account and periodically making an evaluative summary of the sessions. Since the research was aimed at intensive rather than extensive understanding, the census was never more than nine, but the children usually stayed on the ward a year or more. However, care was taken that a number of different psychosomatic diagnoses were always represented in the population.

Integration of these rich and diversified pictures of mother and child took place at weekly staff meetings which were conducted by the late Dr. Margaret W. Gerard, who was psychiatric consultant for the ward. Dr. Gerard was not only extremely skillful in her suggestions as to how to handle the many problems which constantly arose in such a setting, but she also had a keen interest in understanding the dynamics of the mother-child relationship. Thus, during the staff discussions she would discuss possible interpretations of the interaction of mother and child and relate these to broader theoretical concepts.

The psychologists, in addition to doing diagnostic evaluations and therapy, were particularly interested in deriving testable hypotheses about the etiology of psychosomatic disorders in children from such staff discussions. This took considerable time since some behaviors of the children proved to be transient rather than permanent characteristics, and some interpretations were later discarded or re-evaluated. However, certain ideas not only stood the test of time in that they were continually relevant to observed behavior, but also were comprehensive enough to unify a number of diverse observations. Most prominent of these was the idea that mothers of children who later develop psychosomatic disorders lack "motherliness" in caring for their infant during the first year of life. This became the central hypothesis of the present research.

In order to test this rather elusive hypothesis, a new sample of outpatient children was drawn. The research to be described, therefore, while inspired originally by ward observations, is based on groups of children living in their home situations, attending public schools, going about their own neighborhoods with their own friends. Many of them have had periods of hospitalization and will probably have more, but none is a patient on the psychosomatic ward.

Dr. Gerard and Dr. David Shakow made stimulating contributions to the theoretical implications of the hypothesis. Dr. Ann Magaret Garner and Dr. Charles Wenar were chiefly responsible for designing the experimental procedures, administering the psychological techniques, and evaluating the results. Mrs. Jennie B. Kahn was the social worker who obtained case history material from the mothers and later evaluated the mothers' personalities from a clinical point of view. Mrs. Jean P. Chapman, the statistician, not only analyzed the results but also provided valuable and, at times, lifesaving, insights into the data. Dr. Julius B. Richmond and, later, Dr. Samuel H. Barron were the pediatric consultants who clarified for the psychologists many of the baffling points of medical diagnosis and also made sure that the children used as subjects were correctly diagnosed.

Since the research was designed to test a central hypothesis, the theoretical underpinnings of the project will be discussed in the next chapter. The remainder of the book will be concerned with the methods used to test the hypothesis and the interpretation of the results obtained. The book is so organized that Part I is a descriptive account of the procedures, findings, and conclusions, while Part II contains the more detailed and technical presentation of methodology.

A final word regarding the authors' philosophy in planning, executing, and reporting the study remains to be recorded. We have tried, over the years which this investigation spans, to preserve the clinical significance of our material without sacrificing methodological and statistical considerations. At every step this has proved a difficult task. Indeed, it has often seemed impossible. Where we have thought that our uncertainties, compromises, and inadequacies would assist others who might undertake similar research, we have reported them: Chapter 12 is probably the most easily accessible summary of our thinking regarding the difficulties inherent in this type of investigation. Despite these shortcomings, however, we continue to share, with an increasing number of contemporary writers, the conviction that clinically significant variables can be studied within the framework of an essentially experimental approach.

2---Basic Considerations

Research activity consists to a large extent in making choices. Some of these choices are comprehensive and crucial: what questions to ask of nature, what governing point of view to maintain toward the phenomena studied, what samples of these phenomena to select for investigation. Some of the choices are more restricted but no less crucial: what methods of inquiry to use, what confidence limits to set in evaluating results, what degree of generality to demand of the findings. Many of the necessary choices, such as those concerned with guiding theoretical orientation, may involve alternatives which are exceedingly complex and ambiguous. A few, such as those related to methods of data analysis, may depend upon alternatives which are comparatively clear-cut. Certainly the choices made at each step in a research program reflect the particular training, experience, preferences, and probably even the personality structures of the investigators.

In the present research, the authors have considered the prior and basic choices to be those of theoretical orientation and hypothesis formulation. The literature of child pathology, perhaps more than any other area of personality psychology, abounds in clinical studies of disturbed persons, fascinating in their narrative detail, but frustrating and exasperating in their diversity of method, in the ambiguity or absence of explicit hypotheses to be tested, and in the contradictory conclusions. This is not to decry the value of such studies. Indeed, without the rich background of published clinical observations to add to the limited experience which any one investigator can amass, no more precise studies would be possible. But the present need in research on childhood pathology seems to be for explicitly stated hypotheses, precisely tested.

If the potential advantages of such a philosophy are great, so also are the potential dangers. Contemporary personality theories are not the rigorous, consistent systems which the term "theory" implies. Some of the most promising orientations—the psychoanalytic, for example—contain much that is ambiguous and more that is at present untestable. Such broad orientations invite the construction of hypotheses which are exceedingly general, and they may encourage as well the *a posteriori* reinterpretation of the original theory if results are not quite in accord with predictions. A different sort of danger is just as great. A strict hypothesis may drive a research program with too tight a rein. Findings contrary to the hypothesis are then dismissed as negative, without further study of their possible significance. Interesting incidental results which inevitably emerge are ignored as irrelevant. To walk the narrow path between undue generality and stifling specificity is the difficult task of the hypothesis-guided investigator.

Despite these difficulties, it has still seemed important to the present authors to choose a theoretical orientation, to specify an hypothesis for testing, to devise a central explanatory construct, and to make definite predictions concerning the behavior of young children who suffer from psychosomatic disorder. The broad theoretical background is psychoanalytic. The guiding hypothesis states that the conditions antecedent to psychosomatic illness develop during the first year of life, within a particular context of mother-infant interaction. The central explanatory construct is that of "motherliness." The predictions concern the performance of young children and their mothers in a series of behavioral situations devised for the purpose of testing the hypothesis. The following sections describe these basic considerations in greater detail.

GENERAL FRAMEWORK OF THE RESEARCH

Psychosomatic illness as a variety of behavior disorder involves many problems of interpretation. To begin with, the rather unfortunate label which these disorders have earned seems to imply a dichotomy of bodily and social dysfunction which does violence both to the organization of human beings and to the richness and sophistication of contemporary personality theory. It is fast becoming a truism in psychology—here repeated only for clarity—that the many systems of reaction available to human beings, from thinking, fantasying, and speaking to breathing, digesting, and evacuating, operate together in an organized and interdependent manner. Frightening dreams have their concomitants in increased heart and respiratory rates; artificially induced states of hypoxia are accompanied by reports of intense anxiety feelings. It is scarcely necessary to reaffirm a basically monistic position in this field today. Indeed, it is precisely the simultaneous study of the many different reaction systems forming a pattern of intrapersonal behavior which defines the psychosomatic approach to illness.

The more challenging questions concerning psychosomatic disorder, particularly where young children are involved, are the questions of etiology of the particular organ dysfunction which presumably occurs within a total context of emotional difficulty. The widespread disruption of respiratory responses which defines asthma, for example, or the pervasive digestive malfunctioning of duodenal ulcer, suggests that a total response system has somehow become disarticulated from an otherwise organized pattern of behavior. Most contemporary theories of behavior pathology distinguish between the disarticulation which characterizes psychosomatic disorder and that which typifies hysterical disorder. The extensive use of repressive techniques in hysteria, for example, and the symbolic significance given the hysterical symptom, are ordinarily considered absent from, or at least not crucial to, the definition of psychosomatic illness. Rather there seems to be, in psychosomatic disorder, a physiological disorganization; a widespread bodily system does not function in the smoothly integrated fashion characteristic of healthy persons. The apparent disorganization of basic responses which thus defines psychosomatic disorder is one element which led the present authors to postulate the beginnings of the difficulty in the early months of life. It is, after all, very early in life that these elementary somatic processes are laid down, and their severe disruption argues for very early etiology.

But this is still only a beginning. The infant is vulnerable to a wide range of influences which might conceivably predispose it to organ dysfunction. Nutritional difficulties or infectious agents, for example, may have more profoundly traumatic effects upon the immature organism than upon the more developed and physiologically more stable one. Allergic sensitivities may be present from birth and may alter drastically the usual patterns of digestion or respiration. Constitutional factors, whether hereditarily based or not, may determine levels of infant activity and responsiveness, as well as susceptibility to certain sorts of disease. The impact of close interpersonal relationships and of wider cultural patterns also makes itself felt extremely early. What it means to be a child of a particular mother, in a particular family, in a network of parental hopes and anticipations, must be clear, at a simple level, from the first months of life. A complete investigation of psychosomatic disorder in children would study all these early factors and many more.

The present research makes no claim to completeness of this sort. For practical reasons, if for no other, any investigation of this problem will necessarily focus on just one of the hypothesized factors. This does not mean that other factors are rejected, dismissed, or ignored. It does mean that, for the sake of cleanness and simplicity of research design, one possible determinant wins the spotlight, and others are either controlled or assumed to vary randomly. In this investigation, it is the mother-child relationships which become central. Instances of known allergic, infectious, or nutritional difficulty have been excluded; broad cultural and ethnic groupings have been controlled; and only constitutional or hereditary factors—impossible to control by means of the techniques used here—have been assumed to vary randomly.

The supposition basic to this research, then, is that psychosomatic illness is a developmental disorder. The effect of early infantile experiences, particularly the character of the infant's relationship to the mother, is crucial in determining susceptibility to the later development of psychosomatic disorder. While the consequence of early infantile events for later personality development has been most thoroughly explored by Freud and his followers, most contemporary developmental psychologists, regardless of theoretical orientation, accept this view as well. A growing literature testifies to the steadily increasing emphasis upon the importance of early life, of parental—especially maternal—figures, and of the principle of developmental pre-eminence in studies of child behavior.[1] Still, the bulk of published

---

[1] A review of these studies is beyond the scope of the present report. The reader is referred to the excellent summaries of the literature by John Bowlby, *Maternal Care and Mental Health* (Geneva: World Health Organization Mon. Series No. 2, 1951); in Sylvia Brody, *Patterns of Mothering* (New York: International Universities Press, 1956); and by Kenneth Soddy, *Mental Health and Infantile Development* (2 vols.; New York: Basic Books, Inc., 1956). Typical reports illustrating the trend toward systematic observation and interpretation of the events of early childhood would include those of Paul Bergman and Sibylle

research and clinical observation on psychosomatic disorder is written today within the context of psychoanalytic theory. Contradictory and controversial as this material is, it forms the background against which new contributions to the problem of psychosomatic illness must be evaluated.

Although there are many psychoanalytic approaches to the subject of psychosomatic disorder, it is to the work of Margaret Gerard [2] that the present research owes the major part of its theoretical basis. We turn now to a consideration of the basic hypothesis of the investigation.

THE BASIC HYPOTHESIS

Psychosomatic disorder is the consequence of disturbance in the early development of the individual. Presumably these early developmental difficulties involve both organ systems and character structure. An infant may sustain real organ injury at the hands of an inept mother, for example, and may therefore be unable to integrate the functioning of that system with the rest of his bodily reactions. But the same maternal behavior which favors organ injury will result also in emphasizing or calling forth certain social reactions from the infant which may end in a particular character structure later in life. Viewed in this way, psychosomatic disorder is a complex maladaptive pattern, involving both organ vulnerability and special difficulties in the interpersonal field.

Escalona, "Unusual Sensitivities in Young Children," in *The Psychoanalytic Study of the Child*, eds. Anna Freud, Ernst Kris, and Heinz Hartmann (New York: International Universities Press, 1949), III-IV, 333-52; of Sibylle Escalona, "Emotional Development in the First Year of Life," in *Problems of Infancy and Childhood*, Transactions of the Sixth (1952) Conference, ed. Milton J. E. Senn (New York: Josiah Macy, Jr. Foundation, 1953); Sibylle Escalona and Mary Leitch, *et al.*, "Early phases of personality development: A non-normative study of infant behavior," *Mon. Society for Research in Child Development*, 17 (1952); David M. Levy and Audrey Hess, "Problems in determining maternal attitudes toward newborn infants," *Psychiatry*, 15 (1952), 273-86; René A. Spitz, "Hospitalism: An Inquiry into the Genesis of Psychiatric Conditions in Early Childhood," in *The Psychoanalytic Study of the Child, op. cit.*, I (1945), 53-74; and René A. Spitz and Katherine M. Wolf, "Anaclitic Depression," in *The Psychoanalytic Study of the Child, op. cit.*, II (1946), 313-42; Robert R. Sears, Eleanor E. Maccoby and Harry Levin, *Patterns of Child Rearing* (Evanston, Ill.: Row, Peterson and Company, 1957).

[2] Margaret W. Gerard, *The Emotionally Disturbed Child* (New York: Child Welfare League of America, Inc., n.d.).

For the present studies, the basic hypothesis states, more specifically, that susceptibility to psychosomatic illness in children develops
in the first year of life, when somatic response patterns are first laid
down. This is a twelve-month period which, for rapid and pervasive
physiological development, is unparalleled in the life history. The
neonate is an organism, and as an organism has a certain unity and
stability, but many of the early responses seem disjoined and even
erratic. Such easily observable phenomena as breathing irregularities,
digestive inadequacies, ill-defined states of sleeping and waking, and
movements which seem random, testify to the relatively unorganized
state of the young infant. The gradual development of these responses,
over the first months of life, into smoothly functioning patterns of
behavior, is one of the most dramatic events in the human growth
cycle. It is during this crucial period that the seeds of psychosomatic
disorder are sown.

According to the hypothesis, the early susceptibility to psychosomatic illness flourishes within a field of a particular sort of mother-
infant interaction, where the mother is lacking in what we here call
"motherliness." For reasons which must be highly individual, the
mother is unable to assist her infant effectively in developing and integrating the smooth patterns of somatic response—breathing, digestion,
elimination, for example—which enter into the behavioral repertory
of the healthy infant. Perhaps she is unable to meet her infant's needs
promptly enough. She cannot comfort his crying, for example, until
the point of gasping, choking, or frighteningly irregular respiration
has been reached, and then maternal anxiety and frustration com-
pound maternal ineptness. Or perhaps she cannot provide food at the
time or in the manner or within the affectional context that insures
relaxed feeding and easy digestion; again, the infant's inefficient sucking, air-swallowing, spitting, vomiting, and general tension increase
the mother's anxiety and frustration and encourage a cycle of infant-
mother maladjustment. Or the mother finds the infant "hard to handle"
in the intimate situations of fondling, bathing, and dressing: she holds
him tensely, roughly, or uncertainly; she bathes him infrequently or
hurriedly; she forces dressing routines or delays and then prolongs
diaper- and shirt-changing. Again, the infant's early distress in these
situations—his crying, withdrawing, wriggling, or stiffening, perhaps
even his development of skin rashes—will certainly add to the severity
of maternal frustration.

It is clear from these examples that we hypothesize a particular sort of disturbance between mother and infant as basic to the development of psychosomatic susceptibility. The postulated mother-infant relationship is a close one; there is no continual psychological distancing, no chronic neglect, no overt rejection involved. On the contrary, the mother is concerned over her infant, attempts to satisfy his physiological requirements, remains a significant part of his social field. But she is unable to meet his needs smoothly and effectively. The consequence for both mother and child is an increasingly frustrating relationship. The mother-child interaction hypothesized here, therefore, is not only close but mutually frustrating.

How such early lack of gratification of basic needs may find later expression in the psychosomatic symptomatology of childhood must, in the absence of careful longitudinal studies, remain in the realm of speculation. The conceptualization of this process of breakdown presented by Grinker [3] is the one which has been followed in the present study. Grinker places psychosomatic illness in a broad framework of human growth and development, with particular emphasis on the organism's response to stress. The neonate at birth functions viscerally as a whole, with global reactions to all stress. Intrapersonal physiological development proceeds through differentiation and reintegration at a more complex level. This intrapersonal development begins before the advent of psychological object-awareness, and such intrapersonal events are termed the "body ego." As the infant develops, the "psychological ego," with its capacity for symbolic ideation, thinking, and differentiation of objects in time and space, becomes increasingly prominent.

If no untoward events occur, the physiological organism can function efficiently, and the ego can invest its energy in the task of adapting to the external environment. The untoward events which can occur are many. One of the most crucial, in this theory, is a negative mother-infant transaction. If physiological integration is hampered by such negative events, two important consequences follow: the ego is burdened with the task of managing the physiological vulnerabilities of the organism, and thus has less energy to invest in dealing with external reality. Such lack of energy then, in turn, produces a greater vulnerability to breakdown under stress. The critical stress may be either largely physiological or largely psychological; in either case, the

----

[3] Roy R. Grinker, *Psychosomatic Research* (New York: Norton, 1953).

ensuing breakdown is viewed as a return to the early global visceral responsiveness.

Grinker's emphasis upon early intrapersonal physiological development is clearly reflected in the present view of the organization or disarticulation of early physiological responses as a determiner of health or psychosomatic illness. His account of breakdown under stress as a return to a primitive, undifferentiated state of early infancy (again a viewpoint stemming from early Freudian concepts of anxiety) parallels our emphasis upon this developmental period as crucial to psychosomatic disorder. And his use of a transactional approach is seen in our recognition of the many interacting facets of person and environment which enter into the development of psychosomatic disorder.

In contrast to Alexander (who will soon be discussed), neither Gerard nor Grinker postulates a specific emotional conflict as underlying a specific psychosomatic disorder. This leaves the question of the mechanisms involved in the choice of one particular psychosomatic illness unanswered. However, their general theoretical orientation permits speculation on this point. Of the possible factors implicated, we might mention (1) the differential physiological vulnerability of the child (perhaps some children have lower thresholds for gastric than for colonic reaction, for example); (2) the differential tolerances of the mother for malfunction in different organs (perhaps some mothers can tolerate vomiting better than diarrhea in their infants); or (3) the nature and timing of events in the child's life history (perhaps the mother's tension at the time of weaning has different organ effects on her infant from those resulting from maternal tensions at the time of beginning toilet training). It is thus not impossible to construct hypotheses concerning organ choice within the total theoretical orientation of this research. Thus Gerard speculates that the mother, in her anxious, irritable caretaking activities actually damages the infant organism, the specific organ damage depending on the function the mother finds most disagreeable to minister to. She suggests therefore a microscopic examination of the mother's actual caretaking activities with the infant.

All such speculation, however, views the infant as a passive, helpless recipient of general and specific trauma. In a sense this is true, but the present investigators wonder if it is the whole truth. It is difficult for them to imagine an organism in a state of extreme distress which does not attempt some means of diminishing it. Granted that the infant is helpless in that he does not have the usual defenses available to him, he does have a repertoire of physiological responses. Defecation, a tensing or "freezing" of the body, breath-holding, may offer some temporary relief from generalized distress; the type of withdrawal and physiological depression noted by Spitz [4] might also serve this purpose. As is generally true, any such response which diminished pain would tend to be reinforced and repeated in times of distress. Thus, a delimited physiological response would protect the entire organism from being flooded with noxious stimuli. Again it is possible to speculate that the added stress placed upon the particular organ system performing this function would be instrumental in its eventual breakdown.

From the point of view of investigative method as well as of comprehensive theory, the work of Franz Alexander [5] must also receive mention. While this is not the place for a summary and evaluation of his contributions, it is appropriate to indicate where and why the theoretical orientation of the present research differs from that of Alexander. Some of the disagreement may be the consequence of the different types of patients seen. Alexander's hypotheses stem largely from work with adult patients suffering from psychosomatic illness, while the present study is rooted in observations of sick children. Certainly the emphases and expressions, if not the basic elements, of crucial conflicts in adults would be expected to differ from those to be found in young children. Furthermore, the patients' reactions which determined the particular form of Alexander's hypotheses were often obtained in the situation of psychoanalytic interview therapy. Consequently, more unconscious fantasy and dream material obtained from interviews with adults could enter into his descriptions of the determining conflicts in the various psychosomatic disorders than was the case in the present investigation.

There are two major junctures at which the viewpoint of the present investigation diverges from that of Alexander.

The hypothesis of specificity of conflict underlying the various psychosomatic diagnoses—the heart of Alexander's theoretical system

----

[4] René A. Spitz, "Hospitalism: An Inquiry into the Genesis of Psychiatric Conditions in Early Childhood," in *The Psychoanalytic Study of the Child, op. cit.,* I (1945), 53-74; René A. Spitz and Katherine M. Wolf, "Anaclitic Depression," in *The Psychoanalytic Study of the Child, op. cit.,* II (1946), 313-42.

[5] F. Alexander and Thomas M. French, *Studies in Psychosomatic Medicine* (New York: Ronald Press, 1948); F. Alexander, *Psychosomatic Medicine* (New York: Norton, 1950).

—is not part of the present study. The assumption here is rather that the conditions giving rise to psychosomatic disorder in children are general rather than specific. It is the general nature of the early mother-child relationship that determines vulnerability to psychosomatic illness. This position is the inevitable outcome of specifying early infancy as the critical period for the development of psychosomatic disorder: the range, variety, and specificity of conflictual situations in the young infant are meager indeed by contrast to, say, those available to the three-year-old child. It should be added, however, that again our work with children on the psychosomatic ward did not persuade us of the diagnostic specificity of the conflicts which seemed to be causing their difficulties. Perhaps one girl who suffered simultaneously from both ulcer and ulcerative colitis, in defiance of the specificity hypothesis, influenced the research team unduly.

The assumption made by Alexander that psychosomatic symptomatology develops within a personality structure which is essentially neurotic is at variance with the hypothesis of this research. This is probably the point at which the two views differ most sharply, and it is related closely to the problem of specificity. To implicate the first year of life as crucial in the development of psychosomatic disorder is to rule out, by strict Freudian theory, the occurrence of neurotic personality organization. According to classical psychoanalytic theory, of course, neurotic predispositions develop considerably later, when problems of handling parental prohibitions on specific impulses become acute. The formulation of the development of psychosomatic disorder in this study resembles much more that of psychotic than of neurotic organization. We shall return to this point later.

MOTHERLINESS: THE CENTRAL CONSTRUCT

The explanatory construct employed in this research on psychosomatic illness in young children is that of "motherliness." We define motherliness, for purposes of our predictions from the basic hypothesis, as *maternal gratification of the infant's needs for body care and pleasurable stimulation in ways that also provide the mother herself with satisfaction.* The motherly woman derives personal gratification from child care. She provides her infant with the close physical contact and protection he needs for survival and growth. But she does more than this. She is able, in the service of her own maternal need, to make spontaneous, unexpected, "extra" gestures of giving to her child. At the same time, she can separate her child's identity from her own: she does not submerge her own personality in his, nor his in hers. It is the absence or distortion of motherliness, so defined, in infancy which sets the stage for the development of later psychosomatic disorder.

A detailed evaluation of the form of this construct, its usefulness in prediction, and of the whole problem of construct validity in contemporary research is best reserved for a later technical chapter. At this point, the sources of the construct and its major properties in terms of presumed maternal and infant behavior deserve description as an introduction to the statement of the explicit predictions made in this research.

Motherliness as here defined owes a great deal to the formulations of Therese Benedek.[6] Her early descriptions of mother-child symbiosis, following Balint, her structuring of the mother-child relationship as a primary psychosomatic unit, and her subsequent analysis of the concept of inadequate mothering in its relationship to the depressive constellation have all influenced our definition and use of the construct of motherliness. Inevitably, of course, not only this rich literature but also first-hand clinical experience with mothers and their disturbed children has entered into the present choice and definition of the construct.

The salient feature of motherliness is the genuinely mutual, two-way interaction which it implies. Not only the mother's effect upon her infant, but also his simultaneous and reciprocal effect upon her enter into the development of motherly attitudes. Whatever its strong biological sources in female structure and function, maternal behavior develops, over a period of time, in the context of a woman's interaction with her baby. If the infant learns in response to maternal behavior, so also does the mother modify her reactions at the hands of her infant. "The capacity of the mother to receive from the child, her ability to be consciously gratified by the exchange and to use this gratification unconsciously in her emotional maturation is the specific quality and function of motherliness."[7] In a more than semantic sense, mother and child are members of a functioning unit; the subsequent

----

[6] Therese Benedek, "The psychosomatic implications of the primary unit: Mother-child," *Amer. J. Orthopsychiat.*, 19 (1949), 642; *Psychosexual Functions in Women* (New York: Ronald Press, 1952); "Toward the biology of the depressive constellation," *J. Amer. Psychoanal. Assn.*, 4 (1957), 389-427.

[7] *Ibid.*, p. 421.

personality organizations of both reflect the reciprocal interaction between them.

While this mutual interdependence is important at any time in the life history, it is probably of particular significance when the infant is young and the mother as yet inexperienced with this particular child. The woman who is able to receive gratification from her new baby wins a sense of confidence in dealing with him, and this confidence will have significant repercussions in her relationship with her child as well as in her own sense of fulfillment as an adequate woman. She deals with her infant with increasing sureness, the baby is able to respond with increasing smoothness, and the resulting relationship is one of mutual satisfaction and pleasure. Such a stable early relationship should provide, for both mother and child, a reservoir of confidence and optimistic expectation which would make later catastrophic breakdown unlikely.

On the other hand, the woman who is unable to receive gratification from her new baby fails to develop the sense of confidence in him or in herself as a mother which would advance her feminine maturation. She is inadequate in her motherliness, as the term is used here. Because she deals with her infant uncertainly, the baby is unable to respond smoothly, and the vicious circle of mutual frustration begins. This is the background of the later psychosomatic disorder in the child; but it is the background also of persisting disturbances of maternal function in the mother.

The foregoing considerations make it plain that the particular behavior which constitutes motherliness is highly individual. More than anything else, it is the mother's capacity to recognize and evaluate the needs of her own child, and her ability to achieve gratification within her own unique personality pattern, which determine the development of adequate maternal behavior. Consequently, we cannot be concerned exclusively or even largely with over-all patterns of child rearing which seem healthy or pathogenic. The needs of the particular child for activity, rest, food, fondling, or relief from discomfort are crucial. So also are the needs of the particular mother for response, quiet, giving, and relieving, as well as her wider needs to fulfill the feminine role of motherhood as she has structured it throughout her unique life history. If, therefore, the statement of the central construct of motherliness seems highly general, it is because, in our thinking, it must be so.

On the basis of the foregoing discussion, certain differences between children with psychosomatic disorder and those who develop psychotic or neurotic behavior might be expected. Because our knowledge of the etiological factors in all these disorders is somewhat limited and certainly tentative, many of these differences can be presented only as speculation. Some, however, have been examined in the light of present data.

Psychosomatic Disorder and Psychosis

According to the hypothesis, both childhood psychosis and childhood psychosomatic disease begin in the earliest developmental period. Consequently, one would expect the same underlying character structure in both groups. One group, the psychotic, is disturbed in its relationship to reality, while the other group, the psychosomatic, is disturbed in the integration of somatic reactions within the total bodily organization.

Many factors may contribute to the differences in symptom development between these two groups. The variables of underlying differences in physiological sensitivities and the mother's differential responses to various aspects of the infant's bodily functioning may play a role in predisposing the infant to psychosomatic disorder rather than to psychotic disorganization. Because it seems that children with psychosomatic disorder have undergone considerable ego development (by contrast, in theory at least, to the psychotic children), it may be that the mothers of psychosomatic children were able to provide their offspring with some of the elements of ego-building. This is a complicated and intriguing problem, about which much remains to be discovered.

The study in this volume is being extended, at present, to include severely disturbed children. It is hoped that the results will throw light on some of the features of the mother-child relationship which differentiate this group from children who develop psychosomatic disorders.

Psychosomatic Disorder and Neurosis

Childhood neurosis and childhood psychosomatic disorder presuppose different developmental etiology. Neurotic predisposition presumably develops somewhat later in the life history than does susceptibility to psychosomatic disorder. Consequently, we would expect the character structure of neurotic children to be different from that of either psychotic children or those with psychosomatic symptoms.

There are certainly many factors which must contribute to the differences between neurotic children and those with psychosomatic illness. Perhaps the mothers of neurotic children are better able to provide body pleasure than are the mothers of psychosomatic children, for example, so that the neurotic children learn early to integrate the various organ functions. On the other hand, it may be that mothers of neurotic children are more sensitized to difficulties involved in the control of aggressive, hostile, or sexual impulses than are the mothers of psychosomatic patients. The responses of a control group of neurotic children in this study provide some answers to these questions.

Psychosomatic Disorder and Other Chronic Illness

Many children suffer from chronic physical illness which entails suffering, restriction, and even long-term hospitalization, but which is still not considered psychosomatic in character. One may then raise the question of differences between children with psychosomatic disorder and those suffering from other long-term physical illness. Here the major difference is, as usual, one of etiology. In this instance, however, the crucial question would seem to be the nature of the causative agent. Perhaps in chronic non-psychosomatic illness the contribution of emotional or psychological factors is relatively small, and the contribution of infection or physical trauma relatively great, while the relationship is reversed in psychosomatic disorder. We would therefore expect that the concept of "being sick" would be different in the chronically ill child from that developed by the child with psychosomatic illness. Again a control group of children with chronic non-psychosomatic illness furnishes some answers to these questions.

While the addition of a randomly selected control group would have located the three groups studied here in the general population, it is not particularly relevant to the specific hypothesis studied.

PREDICTIONS DERIVED FROM THE MAJOR HYPOTHESIS

The guiding hypothesis of this research, depending heavily upon the construct of motherliness, has been translated into a number of specific predictions. In each instance, the predictions are tested by means of investigative techniques which are tailor-made for the hypothesis. For the most part, the results offered in the following chapters have been evaluated against predictions made and recorded in advance of the gathering of data. Inevitably, however, unexpected results emerged. We have sought to preserve the richness of our material by evaluating and reporting these results as well. In such cases, however, we have recorded the fact that the result was unanticipated and not related directly to a definite prediction.

An hypothesis which makes statements about the early months of life should most properly be tested by means of direct observation of maternal and infant behavior. In the same way, statements about the continuity of behavior should be tested by continuing longitudinal methods. Probably the most unwelcome choices made by the investigators were the decision to deal with school-age children rather than with infants, and the decision to do a cross-sectional rather than a longitudinal study. The reasons for these choices are considered in detail in subsequent chapters. Paucity of appropriate case material in infancy, the waste involved in waiting for the appearance, in unselected samples, of disorders known to be rare, and a sense of urgency about attacking the problem of psychosomatic illness at some point, all contributed.

Consequently, those predictions involving details of the first year of life have been tested by means of retrospective and reconstructive techniques applied to the mothers. The investigators are well aware of the distortions which enter into recalled events. The need to change facts on a defensive basis is only one of many possible sources of invalidity. The early feelings and attitudes of the new mother about her infant may never have achieved verbal expression, and their recall cannot help being hazy and incomplete. Subsequent children born to the same mother inevitably confuse the picture she constructs of the early years. The emotional tone of other intervening events—the child's illness, marital discord, periods of prosperity, and times of hardship—may change the recalled character of the crucial early months. The investigators are aware also of the impoverishment of data which may occur in this field when lengthy studies of unconscious processes, preferably within a psychoanalytic setting, are not made. The final studies on these points remain to be done. But the results obtained here from a retrospective, cross-sectional approach will undoubtedly supplement and modify those critical future researches.

The following predictions, derived from the major hypothesis, were made:

(1) If the mothers of children with psychosomatic disorder are lacking in "motherliness," then the mother-infant relationship in the first year of life will be distorted (Chapter 4). The mothers' fantasies regarding pregnancy and childbirth will reveal distortions, over-emphases, compensatory attitudes, and other signs of disturbance in motherliness (Chapter 5). The mothers will show a distance from the early events of their children's lives, either because of initial lack of involvement or because of subsequent repression (Chapter 4).

(2) If the infant has received inadequate mothering, then his later attitude toward maternal figures will be one of ambivalence, char-acterized by feelings of rage, fear, and mistrust, along with longings for tender protection. More specifically, the child's fantasies about being mothered will be characterized by a decrease in positive feel-ings and an increase in negative and ambivalent feelings (Chapter 7). Because of his ambivalence he should be mistrustful of affection which is offered him (Chapter 8), while his unfulfilled longings for closeness should intensify his interest in primitive, sensory experiences (Chapter 17).

(3) If the infant has been damaged at the earliest level of forming interpersonal relationships (in the mother-infant setting), then he will show, in his later social behavior, distance, inhibition, and inability to relate spontaneously (Chapter 8).

(4) The present mother-child interaction will show mutual frus-tration of need (Chapter 6).

3---Population and Procedure

The postulation of a common factor in all childhood psychosomatic illness means that the group of psychosomatic children studied must contain a number of different disease entities. But there are many other considerations. The hypothesis specifies certain kinds of psychological disturbances in the case of psychosomatic illness which contrast with those found, for example, in neurotic disorder. Consequently, adequate testing of the hypothesis requires a comparable sample of neurotic children to serve as a control group. If psychosomatic illnesses have their roots in a traumatic mother-child relationship during earliest infancy, then mothers of psychosomatically ill children should lack basic maternal warmth in their attitude toward infant care. Their children, reciprocally, should be mistrustful of intimacy and have deeply ingrained doubts about being loved. By contrast, if neurotic disturbances theoretically originate at later stages of the child's development, then neurotic children and their mothers should have fewer problems in the area of early mother-infant intimacy. Their pathology rather should center on such problems as identification and socialization. Comparisons between Psychosomatic and Neurotic groups can then assess the validity of the characteristic kind of disturbed mother-child relationship hypothesized for the Psychosomatic group.

Not only psychological disturbance but also physical illness occupies a special status, according to this hypothesis. Vulnerability to physical disease is seen as a consequence of the physiological trauma of faulty care during early infancy. However, once the actual illness develops, its severity and chronicity may have significant effects on the child's personality which are relatively independent of the hypothesized traumatic antecedents. Therefore a second control group of children suffering from comparably severe but non-psychosomatic physical disorders is needed to control for the effects of physical illness upon personality.

Although strict definition and careful selection of the three groups were legitimately imposed by the hypothesis, in actuality many practical problems arose. As is inevitable in psychological research, a variety of considerations determined the final membership of the three groups. The 78 children from whom the conclusions have been drawn represent, as nearly as can be determined, random samples of cooperative psychosomatic, neurotic, and physically ill patients, with cooperative mothers, referred by cooperative agencies. The problems and compromises involved in the selection of these samples will now be discussed in detail.

Psychosomatic Group. The disease entities included in the Psychosomatic group are bronchial asthma, rheumatoid arthritis, ulcerative colitis, peptic ulcer, and atopic eczema. The choice of these particular diseases was made on purely historical grounds—they are most frequently considered psychosomatic by experts in the field. Granted that such a criterion leaves much to be desired, one is almost forced to use it in an area so young that all research is exploratory rather than definitive. The present grouping, then, is to be considered something more than arbitrary but something less than ultimate.

Although the inclusion of certain of the disease entities might be questioned, the diagnostic evaluations themselves were done with rigor and care. The pediatric consultant for the project reviewed each medical history and, in doubtful cases, conducted his own examination of the child. His diagnostic criteria for each disease were as follows:

Bronchial asthma. A chronic pulmonary disease characterized by repeated and prolonged respiratory difficulty and wheezing with the production of chronic pulmonary emphysema.

Rheumatoid arthritis. A chronically, permanently deforming involvement of the smaller and some of the larger joints of the body with characteristic X-ray findings or fusiform swelling of the smaller joints and with remissions and exacerbations of the pathological process. There is no evidence of other organic system involvement or any demonstrable etiologic agent.

Ulcerative colitis. A disease process of a protracted nature with proctoscopic evidence of ulceration of the colon, X-ray evidence of modification of the normal haustral markings. There is a chronic secondary anemia and in some cases the secondary complications of arthritis, pyelitis, or severe malnutrition. No specific cause, allergic, infectious, or parasitic, could be demonstrated.

Peptic ulcer. A demonstrable, persistent ulcer crater on X-ray examination with or without the demonstration of melena.

Atopic eczema. A chronic recurrent skin involvement usually of the face and flexural surfaces of the arms and legs, occurring usually in individuals with an allergic family and aggravated by infections and the contact or ingestion of specific allergenic substances.

Certain theoretical considerations also came into play when deciding whether a child should be included in the Psychosomatic group. Even though a disease is labeled "psychosomatic," such non-psychological factors as heredity, physical or ecological conditions, and infection play a role in the physiological breakdown of the organism. There are cases in which these non-psychological variables predominate and the illness can, in a large measure, be accounted for in terms of them. For example, in a number of asthmatic conditions the allergic factors predominate, and in certain instances of ulcerative colitis, bacterial or parasitic infestation play a leading role. Such cases were eliminated from the Psychosomatic group on the practical grounds that the emotional component might be particularly obscure or difficult to tease out. It would seem more fruitful first to study those children in whom the non-psychological factors are minimized and the emotional ones predominate.

The majority of the cases were obtained from the outpatient clinics of the Research and Educational Hospitals of the University of Illinois in Chicago. A few came from other Chicago hospitals, from the Institute for Juvenile Research, and from physicians in private practice. None of the children in this group, or in the non-psychosomatic illness group, was hospitalized at the time of the experiments. Exploratory studies indicated that hospitalization strongly biased the projective material of both mother and child. The mothers were preoccupied with themes involving hospitals, and the children frequently projected their longings to return home. Such preoccupations masked the more abiding characteristics of the mother-child relationship.

Another consideration in both the Psychosomatic and non-psychosomatic illness groups was the extent of the handicap. In regard to fine motor coordination, no child could be so crippled that he could not manipulate the simple toy material which was part of the experimental procedures. The child also had to be able to locomote within the confines of the playroom. Since both requirements were not very stringent, only the most severely crippled children were eliminated.

Neurotic Group. The choice of a neurotic rather than a "normal" control group meant stacking the cards against finding dramatic group differences. Since faulty mother-child relationships are theoretically characteristic of both psychosomatically ill and neurotic children, the experimental techniques had to be sensitive to differences in kind and degree of disturbance. This is certainly more demanding than differentiating psychologically healthy from unhealthy children. However, the specific nature of the hypothesized disturbance in the Psychosomatic group required that the more stringent test be made.

All the Neurotic cases came from the outpatient clinic of the Institute for Juvenile Research in Chicago. The mothers had been interviewed by a psychiatrist and a social worker, the children had been interviewed by a psychiatrist and tested by a psychologist, and the final diagnosis had been arrived at on the basis of a staff discussion of all findings.

The children's problems included phobias, learning blocks, minor delinquencies, and such signs of unmastered anxiety and hostility as restlessness, night terrors, hyperactivity, disobedience, and aggressiveness. At no point in the diagnostic procedure was the question of a severe psychological disturbance raised. There was no history of any psychosomatic disorder or any chronic, non-psychosomatic disease. Neither was there any evidence of organic brain damage. Finally, cases were excluded if the mother was in treatment or if the psychiatrist thought her too disturbed to participate in the experiments.

Non-psychosomatic Illness Group. Ideally each psychosomatic illness should have been matched with a non-psychosomatic disease resembling it in its objective and subjective manifestations, its chronicity and severity. Thus asthma should have been matched with a similar respiratory disease, arthritis with a similar joint disease, and so on. There is some question as to whether this is a medical possibility; in the present study it was clearly a practical impossibility. Instead, a number of different disease entities were included on the assumption that the variety of diagnoses would minimize the effect of any one disease on the group results. In addition, the groups could be equated for severity and chronicity of illness by comparing medical histories and using such criteria as age of onset, number and duration of hospitalizations.

It was further decided that this group would be defined solely in terms of the disease entity without reference to the emotional status of the child. This was done primarily to make the group comparable to the Psychosomatic one, which had also been defined solely in terms of physical diagnosis. In addition, the results could be generalized to a wide range of physically ill children instead of being limited to a segment specially chosen for the adequacy of its psychological adjustment.

However, the decision to disregard emotional status also raised certain unanswerable questions in regard to prediction. The child's emotional status is strongly influenced by the mother-child relationship, and it is this relationship which is the central focus of the research. With the Neurotic group, predictions could be made about the nature of the mother-child interaction on the basis of a sizable body of clinical and experimental evidence. But what could one predict when the child had a non-psychosomatic illness? Here there is no theory or research comprehensive enough to serve as a guide.

This quandary was resolved by making two common-sense assumptions. In regard to etiology the most conservative assumption would be that the disease struck at random in respect to the mother-child relationship. Now the thoroughgoing psychosomatist might object that emotional disturbances contribute to susceptibility to any disease. Two points are relevant in this connection. One can agree that emotional factors are important in the etiology of all disease but still maintain that they play a more prominent role in some illnesses than in others. Thus, psychosomatic versus non-psychosomatic does not mean presence versus absence of emotional factors, but refers to the relative importance of these factors. If this is granted, then it is legitimate to distinguish a group of diseases which, from all present evidence, are caused by a predominance of non-psychological factors. The second point is that the congenital diseases included in this group would not be subject to such an objection even from a psychosomatic extremist.

Even if one grants the assumption that the disease struck at random in respect to the mother-child relationship, the stress of illness itself might increase the chances of psychological difficulties. Because of this, it was further assumed that this group would be less well adjusted than a truly random sample of mothers and children. Such an assumption can be backed up by a fair amount of empirical and theoretical work concerning the effects of chronic illness on interpersonal relations. Unfortunately there is no way of estimating more precisely the degree of disturbance. The essential question of whether this group would be more or less disturbed than the Neurotic group could not be answered.

This dilemma had one important methodological consequence. It meant that predictions could be made only for the Psychosomatic and Neurotic groups, and that the design could not be as clean as was desired. However, there was some compensation in the fact that the results might throw light on an important area of inquiry—the psychological effects of severe non-psychosomatic illness on the mother-child relationship.

Most of the cases for this group were obtained either from the Research and Educational Hospitals of the University of Illinois, or from Spalding School, which is one of the Chicago public schools for handicapped children. Only two cases were obtained from physicians in private practice. As with the psychosomatic cases, the pediatric consultant made sure that the diagnosis was clearly established and that there was no evidence of psychosomatic disturbances. In cases which had inadequate histories, a special check list of symptoms was sent to the mothers and later evaluated by the pediatrician. Congenital malformations without illness or severe injuries such as burns were excluded on the grounds that they might have different psychological and social meanings to the child. Also, no terminal illnesses were included, on the assumption that these might engender attitudes of guilt or defensiveness which would mask the nature of the prior mother-child relationship.

DESCRIPTION OF THE POPULATION

The age range of the children was from six to twelve. Ideally it would have been better if a younger age range could have been used, since the hypothesis stresses the mother-infant relationship. However, the paucity and unreliability of appropriate psychological techniques made it impracticable to use very young children. In addition, the incidence of psychosomatic disorders is lower in very young children and this would make the search for cases an even more time-consuming job than it was.

The three groups were equated for intelligence, sex, race, socioeconomic status, and family constellation. Relevant data are presented in Table 1.

Table 1

DESCRIPTION OF TOTAL POPULATION

	PSYCHOSOMATIC (n 26)	NEUROTIC (n 26)	ILLNESS (n 26)
AGE			
Mean	8–1	8–5	8–4
Range	5–11 11–7	6–4 10–10	6–0 10–11
SEX			
Male	11	12	12
Female	15	14	14
RACE			
White	21	22	22
Negro	5	4	4
INTELLIGENCE			
Mean IQ	107.15	104.19	105.27
Range	85–133	78–133	85–137
SOCIOECONOMIC STATUS			
High	1	1	
Middle	15	13	12
Low	10	12	14
FAMILY INTACTNESS			
Parents living, married	24	21	24
Broken home	2	5	2
SIBLINGS			
None	4	3	4
One	13	8	11
Two	5	8	5
Three or more	4	7	6
SOURCE OF REFERRAL			
U. of Ill. hospital	15		12
Other hospitals	4		
Private practice	4		1
I. J. R.	3	26	
Spalding School			12
Other			1

Table 1 (concluded)

	PSYCHOSOMATIC (n 26)	NEUROTIC (n 26)	ILLNESS (n 26)
DIAGNOSES			
	8 Asthma	11 Aggressive [a]	7 Poliomyelitis
	9 Rheumatoid arthritis	11 Anxiety	6 Congenital cardiac malformation
	6 Ulcerative colitis	5 Delinquency	3 Nephrosis
	2 Eczema	3 Withdrawn	2 Legg–Perthes
	1 Ulcer	4 Sex problem	2 Sickle cell anemia
		1 Immaturity	2 Hemophilia
		1 Learning block	1 Charcot-Marie-Tooth disease
			1 Pott's disease
			1 Fibrocystic disease
			1 Bronchiectasis
SEVERITY OF ILLNESS			
Age diagnosed			
Mean	4–4		3–11
Median	4–0		4–0
Range	6 mos.–9 yrs.		1 yr.–7 yrs.
No. hospitalizations			
Mean	1.1		3.3
Median	1		1
Range	0–5		0–39 [b]
Days hospitalized			
Mean	44		58.8
Median	21		16
Range	0–330		0–216

[a] These diagnoses include the following behaviors:
Aggressive—temper tantrum, fighting, disrupting class, antagonistic, stubborn
Anxiety—phobias, fearfulness, tense, insecure, night terrors
Delinquency—stealing, fire-setting, lying, truancy
Withdrawn—no friends, daydreaming, shy
Sex problems—masturbation, feminine behavior in boy
Immaturity—babyish, cling to mother, crying
Total N is greater than 26 because more than one diagnosis was often made.
[b] This extreme number is due to a single case of a boy with hemophilia.

The most important shortcoming is the failure to obtain children from the upper socioeconomic levels. This is to be expected when cases are drawn primarily from clinic populations. The number of Negro children is also somewhat low. With these two exceptions, the results to be presented can be generalized to an urban population of mothers and children.

This is an especially important point in view of increasing evidence in the literature that particular attitudes and techniques of child rearing seem to accompany membership in particular social or racial classes.[1] The absence of significant intergroup differences in class membership means that maternal attitudes to be described later as characteristic of the various groups must be attributed to factors other than the mores of a given social or racial class. Recent indications that psychosomatic disorder—at least in adults—may occur differentially in different social groups [2] also make the successful equating of the subjects on sociological variables important.

As the statistical tables show, both the total N and the equating of the groups were satisfactory. However, some more subtle characteristics of the population remain unknown and even unknowable. Of prime importance is the question, "What larger population was really sampled by the mothers and children who finally presented themselves as subjects?" After the first few months of research it was clear that a random sample of psychosomatically ill, neurotic, and non-psychosomatically ill children was a practical impossibility. Instead, the population represented a random sample of cooperative mothers and children referred by cooperative clinics and physicians. A more precise definition of "cooperative," then, would be highly desirable in order to determine what biases this factor introduced into the sampling. Unfortunately such a precise definition is not possible and one can only speculate about this matter.

In regard to the cooperativeness of the referral sources, all that can be stated is that clinics and physicians differ greatly in their accept-

---

[1] See, for example, Allison Davis and Robert J. Havighurst, "Social class and color differences in child rearing," *Amer. Sociol. Rev.*, 11 (1946), 698-710; Robert R. Sears, Eleanor E. Maccoby, and Harry Levin, *Patterns of Child Rearing, op. cit.;* Martha C. Ericson, "Social Status and Child Rearing Practices," in *Readings in Social Psychology*, eds. Theodore H. Newcomb and Eugene L. Hartley (New York: Henry Holt, 1957), pp. 494-501.

[2] See, for example, Thomas A. C. Rennie and Leo Srole, "Social class prevalence and distribution of psychosomatic conditions in an urban population," *Psychosomat. Med.*, 18 (1956), 449-56.

ance of the psychosomatic approach. Obviously no subjects could be obtained when this orientation was rejected. It was fortunate, that, in the present instance, most of the hospitals and physicians were co-operative. The Department of Special Education of the Chicago Board of Education also helped in providing subjects through its schools for handicapped children. Thus at the level of agency co-operativeness there was no striking evidence of bias. The fact that cases were obtained from a number of sources also means that the population is more representative than if it had been drawn from a single clinic.

There was some selectivity introduced by the fact that the phy-sicians or clinic personnel were asked to judge whether a mother were too disturbed emotionally to participate in the research. No statistics are available on the number of mothers eliminated on this basis, but it seemed to be small. In most cases the question itself was not relevant and, even if it were, participation in the research could still be recom-mended on the basis of the contribution the results might make to understanding the mother-child relationship.

In a like manner, the number of direct refusals to participate on the part of the mothers was low. There were nine in all, four from the Psychosomatic group, two from the Neurotic, and three from the Ill-ness group. There was no consistent pattern in these refusals and no differences among the groups. There were two cases of passive resist-ance (saying "Yes," but not showing up), three cases of refusals on the basis that the child was too upset, and four cases of direct hostility on the part of either the mother or the father.

It is more difficult to tease out the characteristics of the mothers who did cooperate. The common denominator in all first visits seemed to be a desire to get help. In spite of the social worker's structuring of the project purely in terms of research, the mothers either directly or subtly expressed the hope of obtaining further psychological or medi-cal advice. In light of the genuine distress the child was causing the mother, this seemed to be a "realistic distortion."

More puzzling were the mothers who continued to return for subse-quent appointments after they realized that the project had little direct help to offer. Generally speaking, the stress on research and the appeal to altruism proved surprisingly effective. Certainly the avail-able reservoir of unvarnished helpfulness had been underrated by the investigators. Such altruism was often reinforced by a mother's grati-tude to a hospital or a pediatrician, or by anticipation of help from

the Institute for Juvenile Research. In certain cases the prestige element of participating in research seemed quite strong. Some mothers
came out of a need to talk to professional people and clearly enjoyed
having someone listen to their problems. And, finally, there were a
few cases of overtly hostile or hopelessly haphazard mothers who, for
some mysterious reason, never failed to show up when requested.

All in all, it did not seem as if a specific kind of mother was
volunteering—some were rigid and striving, others distraught and
helpless, some were pleasant, others antagonistic, some were artificial,
others genuine. At no point could the investigators label a mother's
persona as being "typical" of one of the groups. Thus, at this impressionistic level, the sample did not seem biased in favor of a certain
kind of "cooperative" personality. The investigators were left with
the uneasy feeling that group differences, if they existed at all, had
to be discovered in the data themselves.

PROCEDURE

Structuring the Research. A special word should be said concerning
the technique for presenting the research to prospective subjects. The
social worker phoned the mother and immediately structured the project in terms of research on sick children. She then explained the
source for obtaining the mother's name and proceeded to describe the
experimental procedures in general terms. The mother was told both
she and the child would be seen by psychologists for some tests. She
was also advised to tell her child that he would be playing games, in
order to distinguish the tests from usual hospital procedures. Trans-
portation costs could be paid by the project. The worker emphasized
the voluntary nature of the participation, promising that it would be
interesting for the mother and fun for the child. However, she made
it clear that no extensive medical or psychological help could be expected. The worker then offered to answer questions which the mother
might have concerning the project.

If mothers in the Neurotic group said their children had emotional
problems, the worker answered that she was aware of this, but stressed
the importance of the child's sound physical health in the over-all
design of the project. With other mothers, mention of the length of
time the project had been in effect, the kinds of illnesses included,
and the confidentiality of the material proved to be reassuring.

Psychological Techniques. In the research proper, two sessions were devoted to giving the mother and child a series of psychological techniques. These will be described fully in subsequent chapters. Most of them were designed to yield information about the early or the contemporary mother-child relationship.

In the first session the mother told stories to describe a set of 20 pictures showing different aspects of infant care. She was subsequently asked to recall as many of them as she could and was also asked some general questions about the child and her understanding of his problem. The child was given a brief intellectual evaluation (the Stanford-Binet Vocabulary test, the Kent E-G-Y, and the Goodenough Draw-A-Man test), the Toy Choice technique, which was designed to evaluate his need for sensory stimulation, a series of ten pictures designed to stimulate fantasies about being mothered, and, at the end of the session, was offered a little present to see how he would respond.

In the second session the mother rated a number of items about the first year of her child's life. The child was given a multiple-choice questionnaire which tapped fairly obvious feelings and attitudes, the World Test, which was used to evaluate adjustment, and a series of techniques designed to elicit fantasies about the cause and nature of illness. Mother and child were observed through a one-way mirror while the child played with a toy, and, later, when the mother was alone, she was asked to check the responses she thought her child had given to the questionnaire.

There was a certain amount of attrition in the second session, so the groups consisted of 21 cases in the Psychosomatic and Neurotic groups and 20 in the Illness group. However, there was no significant change in age, intelligence, race, or socioeconomic status. The ratio of boys to girls did change to eight boys and thirteen girls in the Psychosomatic and Neurotic groups, and to seven boys and thirteen girls in the Illness group. Thus the predominance of girls was somewhat increased on the techniques used in the second session. The variety of diagnoses represented in the three groups did not change, nor was there a significant loss in a given diagnostic category.

Motivation of most children was high throughout, as they found the techniques interesting and enjoyed the individualized attention shown them. The mothers were not so enthusiastic but were generally cooperative.

Interviews. After the psychological data had been gathered, the mothers returned alone for a series of interviews with the social worker. The purpose of these interviews was to obtain information about the child's development, with particular emphasis on pregnancy and the first year of life. The interviews were semistructured in that the mother was given a fair amount of leeway in talking about herself or the child, but the social worker was sufficiently directive to make sure that a fairly detailed number of events were touched upon. The mother was usually seen for two or three sessions and the interviews were tape-recorded. The material obtained was richer and more revealing than a routine social history but naturally lacked the detail and the depth of material from intensive therapy.

Because of the investment of time required, there was considerable attrition in this phase of the research. The number of mothers in each group was as follows: sixteen in the Psychosomatic, fourteen in the Neurotic, and fifteen in the Illness group. However, these N's were quite satisfactory for the techniques used to analyze the interview material.

Data on the group are presented in Table 2.

Although it was never necessary to make statistical comparisons between the interview data and the psychological data, it is important to note that the attenuated group is quite similar to the total population.

The motivation of the mothers had to be high in order to see them through the series of interviews. Part of this cooperativeness was undoubtedly due to the skill of the social worker, who was able to establish an informal but interested relationship with the mother from the start. However, in the interviews themselves the mothers typically were least interested in talking about the first year of their child's life. Recent experiences or events closely related to a particular problem the child was presenting were both more compelling than a detailed exploration of infancy. As far as could be determined, there were no group differences in this matter.

The next chapter will be concerned with the specific findings about the three groups of mothers which were derived from this series of interviews.

Before proceeding, however, an important word about nomenclature. Throughout the book the three groups will be labeled Psychosomatic, Neurotic, and Illness. In discussing the mother or child these labels will be used as adjectives to designate the group to which they belong, such as "Illness mothers" or "Neurotic children." However, there are two possible sources of misunderstanding. The first is to regard the mother as having the group characteristic when all groups

Table 2

DESCRIPTION OF CHILDREN OF INTERVIEWED MOTHERS

	PSYCHOSOMATIC (n 16)	NEUROTIC (n 14)	ILLNESS (n 15)
AGE			
Mean	8–1	8–6	8–3
Range	5–11 11–7	6–4 10–10	6–0 10–11
SEX			
Male	6	8	6
Female	10	6	9
RACE			
White	14	12	12
Negro	2	2	3
INTELLIGENCE			
Mean	106.5	101.2	103.9
Range	86–133	77–122	85–131
SOCIOECONOMIC STATUS			
Middle	8	6	9
Low	8	8	6
FAMILY INTACTNESS			
Intact	14	13	13
Broken	2	1	2
DIAGNOSES			
	5 Asthma	7 Aggressive	4 Poliomyelitis
	5 Rheumatoid arthritis	5 Anxiety	3 Congenital cardiac malformation
	4 Ulcerative colitis	1 Delinquency	2 Legg-Perthes
	1 Ulcer	1 Withdrawn	2 Nephrosis
	1 Eczema	1 Sex problem	2 Sickle cell anemia
		1 Learning block	1 Hemophilia
			1 Bronchiectasis

are defined in terms of the children. Thus, "Neurotic mother" means a mother in the child-defined Neurotic group, rather than meaning that she herself has neurotic symptoms. However, there is an even more important type of misunderstanding. This is the tendency to think in terms of general personality descriptions rather than in terms of the variables being studied. Thus, in using "Psychosomatic mothers," it sounds as if a certain kind of personality is being described. Nothing could be further from the authors' intent. "Psychosomatic mothers" is really a shorthand way of saying, "attitudes toward child care found in mothers who have children with psychosomatic disorders." Such attitudes should not be confused with a general personality description, since theoretically they could be found in many different kinds of women. Nothing in the book justifies thinking in terms of a "psychosomatic personality," since the studies are concerned with a specific area—attitudes toward mothering and being mothered—and some very limited personality traits which accompany such attitudes.

4---How Mothers Perceive Their Children:
The Picture of the Past

Faulty caretaking in early infancy, according to the hypothesis of this research, sets the stage for later psychosomatic illness. To study the early patterns of mothering, there is no completely satisfactory substitute for direct observations of mother and infant as they participate together in daily caretaking routines. The practical considerations which made this approach impossible in the present research have been described elsewhere. The retrospective and reconstructive techniques which substitute here for direct observation are admittedly limited and imperfect. However, these methods do sample a variety of maternal attitudes, referring to both past and present situations; they permit specific predictions which follow from the major hypothesis; and they provide both direct and indirect approaches to the understanding of mother-child relationships.

Four methods seek to appraise the crucial first year of life as seen by the mothers. Three of these invite direct, undisguised recall of early events: (1) the interviews with the social workers; (2) the mothers' ratings of items describing the first year of their children's lives; (3) mothers' answers to two direct questions about the first year. The fourth, thematic storytelling approach, permits an indirect, concealed expression of maternal attitudes. These methods underlie the findings presented in this chapter and the next.

The hypothesized early mother-child relationship presumably persists, at least in broad outline, beyond infancy. Two additional methods evaluate the contemporary interaction between mother and child: (1) direct observation of mother-child pairs in a free situation; (2) maternal prediction of the child's responses to a personality questionnaire. Chapter 6 contains the description, derived from use of these techniques, of the mother-child relationship as it exists currently.

DIRECT RECALL OF THE FIRST YEAR OF LIFE

The Interview

The mothers who continued to cooperate in the project beyond an initial visit spent most of their subsequent time with the social worker. Their conversation with her ranged freely over many topics, from recalled events of their own childhood, their pregnancy, and the early months of their child's life, to current personal concerns and anxieties over the future. None but the most rigid or inhibited mother tried to restrict her comments to the details of child rearing in which the worker indicated she was particularly interested. Over the series of interviews, however, the worker returned again and again to the description of the child's early months, so that she eventually led the mother to talk about most of the major areas of infant development. With the mother's knowledge and permission, the interviews were recorded on tape as they progressed, and verbatim typescripts made from these recordings.

To quantify interview material and still preserve its characteristic flavor is always a difficult methodological problem. A sorting method, in which expert judges rated the interview content, constituted the technique here. Two of the investigators first prepared the interviews for judging by independently selecting those parts of the material which referred only to the first year of the child's life. At the same time, the two readers independently eliminated any content which might identify the groups to which the mothers belonged. These edited interviews, omitting identifying information and content referring to topics other than the child's first year of life, furnished the basis for study.

THE JUDGES' RATINGS

Thirty judges, either psychologists or social workers, read the edited interviews and characterized them in terms of 84 items. These items described, in short declarative sentences, the common events of pregnancy, childbirth, and infant rearing.

The items were constructed to be as objective and impersonal as possible, describing simple, realistic events and easily delineated attitudes. No effort was made to describe complex relationships or to tap inferred unconscious processes. Any research worker in the clinical field can appreciate the feelings of reluctance and sacrifice with which the project staff finally accepted this decision. The reasons, however, then seemed and still seem sound.

For one thing, the sorting technique was not conceived of as a method of evaluating maternal personality, but rather as a means to a much more limited and specific end—the description of the child's first year of life. Its purpose was simply that of quantifying, in a systematic way, the material obtained in an interview. For another thing, the interview itself remained on an informative rather than an interpretative level. Indeed, concern for the welfare of the mothers dictated an avoidance or even active discouragement of discussion of extremely personal material. Finally, as will be seen later, the design of this part of the study required the mothers to sort the same items as did the judges. In this situation, evaluative or highly personal items might be expected to evoke either disturbed or defensive responses, neither of which would constitute a fair test of the hypothesis.

Each item used was referable ultimately to the major hypothesis. Thus there are not only the common descriptions of infant feeding, sleeping, and toileting, but also descriptions of general activity level, sensory acuity, respiratory and skin conditions which might also correlate with maternal adequacy or inadequacy. Similarly, there are items which characterize the mother's physiological status during her pregnancy, but also some which describe her hopes and expectations for her child.

Each judge read and rated three sets of interviews, ordinarily representing at least two of the three groups of subjects. The assignment of cases was overlapping, so that two judges sorted each case, but the same pair did not sort together consistently. In line with the general principles of item selection, judges were instructed simply to characterize the first year of life in terms of the items provided.

On the basis of the judges' sorts, group differences emerge which provide the first picture of the past furnished by this study. For purposes of the present analysis, the items have been arranged in four large areas: (1) *Pregnancy:* "Mother availed herself of good professional service early in pregnancy." "Mother ate unusual amounts or was unusually selective in her diet during pregnancy." (2) *Child Training and Care:* "The baby was comfortable in relation to feeding."

"Mother seemed unusually disgusted by baby's stools or diaper changes." (3) *Physiological Status:* "Baby had excessive number of skin rashes." "Baby seemed to develop hunger at irregular times." "Constipation was unduly severe." and (4) *Maternal Attitude:* "Mother presented external appearance of good adjustment." "Mother seemed unusually fearful and agitated in relation to baby." In line with the hypothesis concerning motherliness, it was expected that the judges would characterize the Psychosomatic mothers in predominantly negative terms in the areas of Child Training and Care, and Maternal Attitude.

As expected from the hypothesis, the judges evaluated the Psychosomatic mothers negatively in the area of Child Training and Care. The picture represents a significant lack of positive attitudes toward infant care on the part of mothers of children with psychosomatic disorders. This is in sharp contrast to the mothers of chronically ill children, whom the judges characterized in terms of an abundance of positive attitudes toward child care. Mothers of neurotic youngsters fall between these two extremes. The three groups maintain the same relative order when specific training items, such as feeding and toileting, are considered separately. Again, to a significant degree the judges rarely characterize the Psychosomatic mothers in positive terms, but often see the chronically ill group in a positive light. It is a provocative finding that, particularly in the area of feeding, the Psychosomatic mothers seem to derive little satisfaction from their children.

The second prediction, that general Maternal Attitudes would be negative for the mothers of psychosomatically ill children, fares less well. Here it is the mothers of neurotic children whom the judges see as negative, while the Psychosomatic group seems to lack general attitudes of a negative sort. Comparatively few items define this area; they are confined largely to maternal control, neglect of child, and maternal nervousness. When these three groups of items—control, neglect, and nervousness—are studied separately, the Psychosomatic mothers still occupy a more favorable position than the hypothesis would predict. The judges do find the Psychosomatic mothers significantly more ambitious and controlling than the mothers of chronically ill children, but they see the mothers of neurotic children as equally ambitious and controlling. The other two areas yield no significant results. There seems little question that the Psychosomatic mothers do not maintain a negative over-all attitude toward their infants.

Two final groups of items reveal unexpected findings: *Pregnancy,* including anticipation of the child and expectations for him as well as the physiological events of pregnancy and birth; and the child's *Physiological Status* in the first year, including items relating to such processes as digestion, elimination, responsiveness and general activity level, and the mother's reactions to these processes. In the area of *Pregnancy,* the judges, to a highly significant extent, see the mothers of psychosomatically ill children in positive terms and the mothers of neurotic children in negative terms, with the mothers of chronically ill children falling between. Typically, the mothers of children with psychosomatic disorder welcomed their pregnancy, sought good medical care, suffered few physiological upsets, and anticipated the child's arrival with feelings of acceptance. The mothers of neurotic children, on the other hand, found their pregnancy unwelcome and anticipated their child's birth with some distaste or even dread.

Items describing total *Physiological Status* do not distinguish significantly among the three groups. This is true both when all the items in this category are included and when those dealing only with the infant's total physiological status exclusive of parental reactions to physiological processes are analyzed. Thus in the judges' opinion, the Psychosomatic mothers did not have to deal with unusually severe physical problems in their infants during the first year of life. At least in terms of physiological difficulties, the children who later developed psychosomatic illness occupied the same favorable position as did those in the other groups. The only group difference which emerged was when the items were subdivided into those pertaining to specific organ systems (e.g., respiration, digestion, elimination) and general responsiveness (e.g., activity level, sleep patterns). Even here it was not the Psychosomatic group which was different, but the Illness group which was rated negatively in regard to specific organ systems.

To reconstruct the first year of life for the psychosomatically ill children on the basis of expert judges' quantification of verbatim interview material is hazardous, but still, the significant findings here warrant a try. In contrast to the other two groups, the mothers of children with psychosomatic illness accepted their pregnancy, often with enthusiasm; their expectations were not unpleasant; they were, as nearly as can be determined, ready for a positive personal experience. Incidentally, the mothers' own sorts of the same items confirm in this aspect the judges' ratings, as the next section shows: the Psychosomatic mothers themselves painted a significantly less negative picture of their pregnancy than did the mothers in the other two groups.

But the realities of the first year of life did not confirm these anticipations for the Psychosomatic mothers. To be sure, the mothers' general over-all attitude was not extremely negative. It is from the specific areas of infant training and care—feeding and toileting, for example—that the positive attitudes disappear. The total situation, from pregnancy through the first year, seems to be one of unfulfilled anticipation.

Two questions immediately arise. The first and most pressing, of course, is the question of what might account for the gulf between expectation and reality in the mothers of psychosomatically ill children. There are a number of possible reasons.

High hopes are the more easily dashed by reality. Conceivably these women developed hopes about their unborn children or about themselves as mothers that were so high that no reality could meet them. No mother is perfectly loving and giving; no infant fits in detail any set of prenatal specifications. The pregnant woman who anticipates these proofs of perfection is inevitably disappointed. But the pregnant woman whose personal need system requires that she be the perfect mother of the exact infant of her pregnancy fantasies suffers more than disappointment. Indeed, her personal frustration may be great enough to distort permanently the relationship she develops with her child. Certainly if she tries to remake reluctant reality, to recast herself or her infant child in foreign molds, the consequence can be only caricature.

There are two independent lines of evidence indicating that the Psychosomatic mothers may have developed overly exact or pleasurable anticipations and then tried, after the child's birth, to confirm them. One line of evidence has already been reported: the judges saw the mothers of children with psychosomatic disorder as significantly ambitious and controlling in general attitude. This finding derives from a group of items such as the following:

"Mother had specific preference for sex of child."
"Mother had specific designs for the future of the child."
"Mother seemed unusually ambitious for the baby's training."

"Spoon and/or cup feeding were introduced unusually early."

"Bowel training was begun before the child was physiologically ready."

The items thus plainly define the combination of specific anticipation and subsequent control which we here hypothesize.

The social worker's summary descriptions of the mothers, based on the interviews but independent of the judges' sorts, constitute a second line of evidence. In all but two of the Psychosomatic cases, the worker described the mother as rigid, driving, perfectionistic, or ambitious. This description never occurred in the chronically ill group, although it characterized six of the sixteen mothers of neurotic children. Along the same lines, the worker described eleven of the mothers of psychosomatically ill children as demanding conformity of their offspring. Five mothers of chronically ill youngsters and six of the Neurotic group earned similar descriptions.

To say that the Psychosomatic mothers characteristically maintain unrealistically high or specific anticipations is, of course, only the beginning of an explanation. The crucial question is what the meaning of pregnancy and motherhood could be for these women, that they need so to overvalue or distort it. Here the evidence is entirely clinical.

Perhaps the most dramatic example of an unrealistically specific pattern of anticipation occurs in the interviews of Mrs. Parry.[1] This mother was, above all else, an angry woman. Her stiff, grim appearance, scattered but intellectualized discourses on child rearing, multiple complaints against schools, neighbors, and agencies, and outbreaks of stern moralizing testified to her difficulty in containing her anger. Burdened with many problems, she had little capacity to relate, either in the distant situation of the interview or the inevitable closeness of her own family life. With her own mother, however, she had developed a close identification. She fully expected her own maternal experiences to duplicate those of her mother, and she resented deeply what she saw as any departure from this duplication. Her mother had had six children, three boys and three girls, and Mrs. Parry stated bluntly that she wished and expected to duplicate that pattern.

She had the desired girl and boy when she became pregnant for the third time. But Tom's conception and birth destroyed her rigid expec-

---

[1] In this and all case examples in this book, names and personal details have been altered to preserve the anonymity of the subjects.

tation of family structure. "We wanted a curly-headed girl, just like Tom only we wanted a girl." Mrs. Parry was ambivalent and then openly rejecting of the newborn baby. Her reaction to the birth of a boy is best told in her own words: "I know what I did when they brought him to me . . . I didn't claim him . . . he didn't look like none of my children. I just laughed, I said, that's not my baby."

That Mrs. Parry's subsequent relation to her third child was characterized by ambivalence, with alternating staunch protectiveness and outbursts of angry punitiveness, should come as no surprise. To the frustration of unfulfilled anticipation which must have colored this early relationship were added other problems. The boy was restless, fretful, and colicky as a young infant, and continued to be a source of concern and exasperation. Here the mother's deeply rooted and rigid expectations were shaken at her son's birth.

There are in the group similar, if less dramatic, instances of expectations so rigid and detailed that no reality could meet them. One mother sat literally for hours bottle-feeding her infant son, forcing him to drink the last drop because she "thought he was supposed to." Another planned her child ("I thought it would be about time to have one") apparently as part of a larger life goal to be "less independent" than her own mother had been. Two others had such definite needs for a child of a particular sex that, like Mrs. Parry, when the "wrong" sex was born, they had difficulty in believing it. It must be such backgrounds of rigid expectation as these that are reflected in the quantitative findings that these mothers, in contrast to those in the other two groups, seem less negative about pregnancy, more negative toward child care, ambitious, striving, and demanding conformity of their children.

However, there is another factor to consider—that the anticipations during pregnancy were also frustrated by unusually difficult subsequent events arising in areas unrelated to infant care. Along this line, there is evidence that the first year of life often presented extreme difficulties to the Psychosomatic mothers. Some of these burdens seemed the result of a chance concomitance of misfortune: there was a piling up of problems over which the mother had little or no control. Other difficulties seemed largely of the mother's own making and often represented the persistence of old problems which were temporarily suspended during pregnancy, only to recur after the baby's birth. Whatever their source, however, these additional burdens during the first year contradicted the pleasurable anticipations of pregnancy.

Evidence on this point was evaluated by the social worker. Her summary statements indicate that eight of the sixteen mothers of Psychosomatic children had severe difficulties during the first year. Some mothers had to combine full-time employment with child care, some were alone with their children because of the husband's military service, some had acute marital difficulties during this period. Of the sixteen Neurotic mothers, eight fall into the same category; but it must be recalled that these mothers, unlike the Psychosomatic group, brought to their troublesome first years a pattern of troubled and negative anticipations. Of the fourteen mothers of chronically ill children, only two fall into the worker's "difficult first year" category.

Again, the flavor of some of these exceedingly difficult first years is communicated best by a clinical example: Mrs. Parks, a young and immature mother, had already found her marital situation unhappy before she conceived Polly. Indeed, she considered "dissolving" the marriage even while she was pregnant, although she realized this magical solution was impossible, and she abhorred the notion of divorce. But along with her early inability to handle the basic financial and sexual demands of marriage, she had a thread of strong maternal feeling and a genuine need for fulfillment through motherhood. She put it this way to the worker: "From the time that I was going to kindergarten, I was very sheltering toward very young children . . . and I . . . a little girl used to walk to school with me . . . oh maybe a block during my way to school, and I was just crazy about her and I couldn't wait for the day when I could have a baby girl for my own. . . ."

Other than her strong preference for a girl, Mrs. Parks seemed to have no rigid or detailed requirements for her baby. Even the marital discord seemed to subside during her pregnancy, with both parents at least calm in anticipation of the child. How much Polly's birth meant, and, more importantly, her ambivalent overvaluing of it, are suggested by the mother's account of her first view of her daughter: ". . . and it just came to me that that's something I've always wanted, and I was just hysterical when they told me I had one . . . I just cried and cried and cried and the baby cried and the nurses all cried [laughs] . . . it was real funny . . . but I mean. . . . It was just something that I was very happy about."

Polly proved easy to rear during her first year, but the marital friction resumed. Mrs. Parks went back to work, and Polly's care was shared by mother, father, and baby sitter. There were violent arguments, alternating with periods of cold remoteness, between the parents. The difficulties spiralled until the parents separated and, after a long period of litigation, were divorced.

Certainly the idyllic, if exaggerated, welcome given this little girl in the delivery room must soon have been submerged in the marital discord which followed. Mrs. Parks, spent by long daytime hours of working and long nighttime hours of quarreling, cannot have found in Polly the fulfillment of her schoolgirl dream of protecting motherhood. Yet here the contradiction between expectation and subsequent events seems to lie not so much in her rigid and detailed plans for the child as in the old frictions of a marital relationship which became impossible to maintain.

THE MOTHERS' RATINGS

Comparative freedom to talk in an interview invites from the mother elaborations, illustrations, and expressions of feeling which make for a rounded picture of the first year of life. Unwillingness or inability to give information becomes apparent as the worker returns again and again to certain topics which remain obscure. The mother's idiosyncratic means of expressing herself, her contradictions and hesitancies, give each interview its unique flavor. The very freedom of expression encouraged by the worker, however, makes the weighting of the various topics in importance troublesome. The question therefore arises as to how the mothers would themselves weight the various events of the child's first year if they were required to do so.

Consequently, a second approach to the direct recall of the first year was made. The mothers sorted the 84 items described above, now modified to first-person form, along the same scale as that used by the judges. Unlike the judges, however, the mothers sorted on the basis of their recall of the events of the first year, without direct reference to the interview material. They followed instructions simply to characterize the first year of their child's life in terms of this set of items.

A number of difficulties arose at once. Many mothers, unaccustomed to research technique and to the necessity for quantification of material, found this task extremely trying. Even the use of a graphic distribution chart, with spaces for each item and numerous guide cards, failed to eliminate confusion entirely. More than one mother reversed the ends of the scale, or lost sight of the sorting principle midway in the task. The notion of sacrificing one item to another, and of maintaining strict boundaries between sorting categories proved exasperating and occasionally altogether unacceptable. Motivation languished, and only the real devotion of these women to the larger project made the final results possible. Constant supervision by a staff member, who exercised great caution in avoiding suggestions of item placement, proved necessary.

Even more critical was a second problem which became apparent early in this part of the study. The original time schedule of project activities called for the mothers to sort after their interviews with the social worker were over. But this arrangement invited the interference of the interview situation with the mother's more quantitative evaluation of the first year. It was presumed that the interview, in its interpersonal aspects as well as in the content reviewed, might well affect the mother's later appraisal of the crucial early months of her child's life.

Only a separate methodological study could shed light on these two major difficulties. Consequently, a subgroup of mothers, representing all three diagnostic groups, was chosen from the original population to participate in a separate investigation. These mothers sorted at the time of their second clinic appointment, before the interviews began. They sorted again, under the same instructions, at the close of the interview series. A control group of mothers was chosen from the general clinic population as a basis for comparison. These mothers all had children within the age range used in the larger study, although their children did not necessarily suffer from the same sorts of disorders. The time interval between before- and after-sorts in the control group varied for the most part in accordance with that found in the experimental subgroup.

The mean before-after correlation for the subgroup of mothers from the larger project does not differ from that of the control group. Neither is there a significant relationship between before-after sorts and the time interval between sorts. Apparently, then, participation in a series of interviews concerning her child's development has no discernible effect upon the way the mother evaluates the common events of the first year of the child's life.

For purposes of comparison with the judges' sorts, it will be most useful to consider the results of the mothers' ratings in terms of the same four groups of items: *Pregnancy, Child Training and Care, Maternal Attitude,* and *Physiological Status.* Of the comparisons involved, only one achieves significance: the mothers of children with psychosomatic disorder rate themselves as significantly less negative than do mothers in the other two groups in the area of *Pregnancy*. This, it will be remembered, is in line with the judges' evaluation of these women, which was presented earlier. However, unlike the judges, the Psychosomatic mothers do not rate the items concerning Child Care and Training in more negative terms than do the mothers in the other two groups.

This failure of agreement between mother and judge on the larger groups of items brings into focus the whole question of mother-judge agreement. Arguing from the basic hypothesis in rather general terms, one might expect certain intergroup differences in degree of agreement between mother and judge. If, as has been hypothesized, the first year of life for the Psychosomatic group was a time of mutual frustration, then the mothers involved in such a turbulent relationship might well lack insight into its nature. Indeed, blindness to or lack of true maternal concern over what was going on in the child's early months are marks of the inadequate motherliness thought to be characteristic of mothers in the Psychosomatic group. In addition, these mothers, now sensing the shortcomings and difficulties of the first year, might understandably be unable to admit them, either to themselves or, at a more superficial level, to the project staff through their sorts. In either case, the expected finding here would be greater disagreement with the judges for the Psychosomatic than for the other two groups.

Correlations between mother and judge sorts on all cases provide the data for evaluating this expectation. Of the sixteen mothers of psychosomatically ill children who completed the sorts, ten show less agreement with the judges than do mothers in either of the other two groups. It is of some interest that, with one exception, these are also mothers upon whom the judges also agree poorly with one another. But, contrary to expectation, it is the remaining six mothers in the Psychosomatic group who furnish what is one of the most interesting findings of the entire study. These mothers achieve a high degree of agreement with the judges. Moreover, these are mothers upon whom the judges agree well with one another.

The temptation to speculate uncritically on the meaning of the emergence of a "High" and a "Low" group of mothers of psychosomatically ill children is strong. That there are two distinct groups of mothers separated by the validity of their sorts is unquestionable; the two groups do not overlap in mother-judge correlation. That they also represent two extremes of judge-judge agreement is likewise clear; only one reversal occurs in sixteen cases. At the most conservative level, the "High" group can be said to present a consistent picture to the judges and to themselves—at least to their public selves. The "Low" group can be said to present an inconsistent picture to the judges and to themselves. The "High" group, on this technique, is somehow more organized, more coherent; the "Low" group, conversely, is on this technique more scattered, more contradictory.

These descriptions raise at once the question of possible differences in intellectual or educational status between the two groups. Although there are no psychometric data on intelligence level, the two investigators who worked most closely with the mothers made rough evaluations of the mothers' intellectual status. On these evaluations there is no apparent difference between the groups. Data are available on educational level, as reported by the mothers themselves. Again there is no sharp difference between the "High" and "Low" groups.

It is more likely that the factors determining this group separation can emerge only after these two subgroups of Psychosomatic mothers have been compared on the many analytic techniques of this study. We may begin by examining the performance of the two groups on the four sorting areas defined earlier in this chapter.

The judges' sorts distinguish the "High" from the "Low" group reliably in only one area—*Pregnancy*. Here it becomes clear that it is the "High" mothers who are judged most positive in their statements about pregnancy. They are the ones who most welcomed their pregnancy, who looked forward most happily to their child's birth, who cared for themselves and the unborn infant with intelligent devotion. They are not distinguished from the "Low" group in the judges' ratings of Child Training and Care, Maternal Attitude, and the infant's Physiological Status.

In addition to this one statistically significant finding, however, there are individual items in the sort on which the "High" and "Low" mothers differ from one another. These are items placed by the judges in one of the two extreme positions on the scale, as being either highly characteristic or highly uncharacteristic of the case. Although no statistical analysis of these data is warranted, it is perhaps justifiable to look at the content of the items as a start toward further characterizing these mothers.

According to these extreme differentiating items, the "High" mothers planned for their pregnancy, while the "Low" mothers did not. The

"High" mothers held and fondled their babies during feeding, enjoyed playing with their babies, took care of their babies themselves, and were ambitious for the early training of their children. They did, however, appear to the judges nervous and worried about their babies; and their offspring, while described as not overly active but responsive, were seen by the judges as colicky and given to thumbsucking. The "Low" mothers were characterized as having a definite preference for the sex of the child, in sharp contrast to the "High" mothers, whose denial of such a preference seemed significant to the judges.

The faint outlines of a maternal portrait began to emerge from this initial examination. The "High" mothers, in contrast to the "Lows," seemed to be organized and planful in relation to their infants, and to show behavior which, at face value, could be taken to express high motherliness. Their infants, however, are not without some early problems, nor are the mothers themselves free of anxiety and worry.

It would be a mistake, however, to conclude that the "High" mothers are simply those who gave a "correct" picture to interviewer and judges. To the investigators who dealt with them, they seemed complex and sophisticated women, far from oversimplified or transparent in their attitudes. They spoke of negatives as well as positives in their descriptions of their children; they recounted what they could tolerate and what they could not tolerate in their relationships to their offspring. At this point, it is still an open question whether the "High" mothers represent a special subgroup of women who are particularly adequate in their handling of their infants, or whether their high level of organization and efficiency includes knowledge of good child-rearing practice which is attested to in word but perhaps not in deed. This question will recur in subsequent chapters.

DIRECT QUESTIONS TO THE MOTHER

A final approach to the direct recall of the first year of life may be mentioned briefly here for completeness only. Following the story-telling procedure described in the next chapter, the psychologist asked the mother three direct questions, two of which are relevant here: "Was there any way in which this child was different from other children when he was tiny?" and "What came easiest in rearing him? What was hardest?" While these questions often served to orient the mother to the interview with the social worker which followed immediately, the responses were too diverse to make significant statistical findings possible. A brief summary of the trend of the responses, however, may prove interesting.

That her child was "different" in any way from others was quickly denied by more mothers in the Psychosomatic group than in the other two groups, even though the phrasing of the question does not require that "different" be interpreted negatively. To the Psychosomatic mothers, however, the question clearly implied a criticism of the child, and these mothers responded with prompt denial. Apparently the Psychosomatic group had a stronger need than the other two groups to demonstrate that the child was perfectly "normal."

When all the responses are categorized grossly into those which describe "positive" behavior (developmentally precocious, pretty, healthy) and those which describe "negative" behavior (sick, fearful, slow), then a trend toward group differences appears. The mothers of the two ill groups, both psychosomatically and chronically ill, have a preponderance of negative over positive mentions, while the two categories are approximately equal for the Neurotic group. The same trend toward a group difference appears in the roughly rated maternal attitude toward the child expressed in the answers. The mothers of psychosomatically and chronically ill children revealed many more attitudes of dissatisfaction than satisfaction with their children as contrasted with the Neurotic group. As might be expected, the mothers of neurotic children showed a trend toward the mention of more psychological problems (anxiety, thumbsucking) than did the other two groups.

The range of responses to the second question—what came easiest and hardest in child rearing—is too wide to permit even this informal sort of appraisal.

The foregoing results provide beginning information concerning the nature of the first year of life for these mothers and their children. There is evidence that the psychosomatic pattern may be one of unfulfilled expectation, that negative attitudes toward the details of infant care counteract what may have been pleasurable anticipations. There is evidence also that these mothers of psychosomatically ill children met this discrepancy through ambitious striving for control and conformity in their children. In addition, many of these mothers were unusually burdened in the first year of the child's life. Even from this relatively straightforward approach to the problem through direct recall, however, it becomes apparent that there are many different patterns of unfulfilled expectation, many different problems presented by reality. The separation of the mothers of psychosomatically ill children into "High" and "Low" groups is only one expression of a lack of uniformity among the women in this study whose children developed psychosomatic disorder.

5---How Mothers Perceive Their Children: The Indirect Approach

The method of direct recall of early events has distinct limitations. No mother is without some feelings of inadequacy with respect to the details of her early relationship to her child and of his development. If the inadequacies are great, then direct efforts at reconstruction of this early period may invite defensiveness and evasiveness which could distort the picture beyond recognition. The appearance of instances of low mother-judge agreement in ratings, described in the previous chapter, is one example of the distortion which may occur. The definition of "High" and "Low" groups of mothers of psychosomatically ill children may prove to depend upon just such evasiveness and defensiveness. Certainly additional information, obtained through less direct techniques, must supplement that obtained from the interview.

But the hypothesis which guides this investigation limits the area over which the mother may freely wander in her talk. The focus of the study must remain the early events, primarily physiological, of maternal caretaking and infant response. Consequently, the technique used here shifts from a factual to a fantasy approach to the child's early life, while still requiring the mothers to focus attention on infants and mothers in a setting of physical care.

METHOD

Pictures. Twenty pictures related to pregnancy, delivery, and early child care constitute the stimulus material for this part of the study.

The pictures are all definite in outline; preliminary informal tryouts on a group of judges indicated that there was little difficulty in identifying roughly what was going on in the picture. The emotional tone of the situation is pleasant or bland, and there are no strongly negative mother-child interactions. While the children depicted range in age from newborn to toddler, they are all young enough to fall within the early developmental period considered crucial to the hypothesis. The pictures clearly represent a variety of early caretaking situations, including feeding, bathing, toileting, dressing, fondling, and playing, as well as certain events of pregnancy and childbirth. Indeed, they cover, as nearly as possible, the areas tapped by the sorting items described in the previous chapter. They differ from these items mainly in permitting the mothers to respond in third-person terms, and thus to increase, if they so need, the psychological distance between themselves and their own infants.

One further characteristic of the stimulus materials deserves mention. These pictures are reprints, minimally edited, of photographs taken from life and obtained from various sources. In every case, knowledge of the situation depicted is available. For example, Picture 1 actually shows a young woman who is pregnant; Picture 5 represents a woman who is a stranger to the particular infant; Picture 18 shows a mother reassuring her daughter, who has just had a toilet accident. This information regarding the actual events photographed makes possible a fairly detailed appraisal of the accuracy with which the mothers identify the events in the pictures.

Instructions. A psychologist presented the pictures to the mothers at the time of the first project visit. Scheduling this indirect procedure first raised some difficulties: the mothers were unacquainted with the psychologist and relatively unfamiliar with the project, so that their spontaneity may have been reduced. On the other hand, this scheduling eliminated the possibility of effects of the interview upon the story-telling and thus guaranteed the independence of the stories from the interview content.

After briefly reviewing the purpose of the study, the psychologist indicated that she was interested in information concerning pregnancy and child rearing. She presented the pictures as depicting "mothers, children, and pregnancy," and invited the mothers to make up a story about each picture, paraphrasing the usual TAT instructions. The psychologist transcribed the stories verbatim as the mother related them.

Immediately after the last story, the psychologist remarked that the mother had seen a great many pictures, and that she wondered how many she could now remember. The mother then described as many as possible of the pictures she had just seen. The recalled descriptions of the pictures were also recorded verbatim.

In general, the psychologist tried to maintain a detached attitude toward the mothers and discouraged the development of any close relationship. Two considerations dictated this approach. In the interest of simplicity in this multiple-technique approach, it was felt that the major personal relationship in the project should be reserved for mother and social worker. Indeed, the worker's use of the interview as her main investigative method guaranteed the establishment of some sort of close interpersonal relationship with the mothers. It was also hoped that a relatively objective, impersonal attitude on the part of the psychologist would enhance the mothers' freedom to respond to the pictures with a minimum of personal defensiveness.

Mothers' Approach. Acceptance of this unfamiliar task varied widely from mother to mother. At one extreme was the woman who gave brief, one-sentence descriptions of each picture, with a minimum of personal elaboration. At the other extreme was the mother for whom the pictures elicited highly personalized associations to the events of her own and her children's early lives. Some mothers spoke dispassionately and objectively; others permitted expressions of warmth or pleasure to creep into their responses; still others found the task so unpleasant as to call forth open feelings of anger toward the pictures, the psychologist, or the project. The very length of the task, requiring twenty separate but often redundant responses, dismayed many of the mothers.

One characteristic seemed typical of the majority of the mothers' productions. Regardless of explicit instructions to make up stories with beginnings and outcomes, the mothers in general seemed unable to construct "stories" in the TAT sense. In all probability this failure stemmed from the nature of the stimulus materials. The concreteness which adherence to the main hypothesis dictates invited description rather than narrative. Even the least inhibited and defensive mothers seemed to interpret the task as one of description; their freedom of response took the form of departing from the picture and discussing—often with detail and feeling—personal material recalled by the picture content.

Scoring.[1] The character of the pictures, the mothers' responses to them, and predictions from the guiding hypothesis, made possible the use of six different scoring scales for quantifying the mothers' productions. Two of these refer to more formal aspects of the task: (1) *the accuracy of identification of the situation depicted;* and (2) *the accuracy of immediate recall of the stimulus materials.*

(1) *Accuracy of identification* was determined by comparing the mothers' characterization of the pictures with the events known to be occurring when the original photographs were made. This scale locates the stories in one of three categories, High, Medium, and Low. The decision to include this variable in the research goes back to the concept of motherliness which is central to the study. Presumably the mother who is sensitive to her child's needs, who derives personal pleasure and satisfaction from smooth interrelationship with her infant, will be quick to comprehend the meaning of child and maternal behavior. Conversely, the mother who is insensitive to infant needs, who finds infant care frustrating or unsatisfying, should show her ineptness in a failure to appreciate what is going on in maternal and child behavior. Consequently, the original prediction here was that the mothers of children with psychosomatic disorder would score lower on this scale than the other two groups.

(2) *Accuracy of immediate recall* depends simply upon a description which is sufficiently accurate and complete to match the stimulus picture. Although special notice was given any major distortions or reversals of the stimulus picture, the prime comparisons were based upon a simple right-wrong dichotomy. Again the inclusion of this variable goes back to the hypothesized presence or absence of motherliness in the three groups studied. If the demands of the first year of life are unwelcome to the mother, if this is a time of conflict or dissatisfaction, then it is possible that the recall of pictures of this unhappy period would suffer distortion or decline with time. Some impressionistic evidence to this effect was also available from interviews with mothers of patients on the children's psychosomatic ward. The pictures of their children's early months which these mothers gave seemed so hazy and incomplete as to suggest the operation either of conflict and preoccupation at the time of the events or of ensuing repression. Consequently, the prediction here was that the mothers

----

[1] Rating scales and details of scoring are given in Part II.

of children with psychosomatic illness would recall fewer pictures than would the mothers in the other two groups.

(3) *Personal references.* The mothers' approach to the storytelling procedure, as the project went along, determined the development of the third scale for evaluating the productions. Many mothers, it will be recalled, used the stimulus material as a point of departure for what were essentially personal associations. These might be humorous anecdotes from their own or their offspring's childhood, or comparison, favorable or unfavorable, between the picture and their own experiences. While these comments were not, strictly speaking, part of the story constructed to the picture, they seemed worthy of inclusion in Scale 3. These personal references fall into one of three categories, Negative, Positive, or Neutral. Since a range of personal references was not foreseen in advance, but only developed as the study went on, there is no explicit prediction regarding its occurrence in the three groups. The meaning of these flights into personalized association remains for later discussion.

The last three scales derive directly and simply from the guiding hypothesis regarding the first year of life, and depend upon the major content of the mother's productions.

(4) *Attitude toward activities involved in child care.* According to the hypothesis, mothers of children with psychosomatic disorders should have a less positive, more negative, or ambivalent attitude toward child caretaking than the mothers in the other two groups.

(5) *Role assigned to the child.* Mothers in the psychosomatic groups should again assign a more negative or conflictual role to the child than mothers in the other two groups.

(6) *Role assigned to the mother.* The hypothesis dictates that mothers of children with psychosomatic illness should assign a less positive, more negative, or ambivalent role to the pictured mother than should mothers in the other two groups.

RESULTS

Six scales with multiple categories, of course, yield results which can easily become confusing in their detail. Since the scales all locate the stories within the categories of Positive, Ambivalent, Neutral, and Negative, however, it is simplest to introduce the results by characterizing the three groups generally in these terms.

The Psychosomatic mothers expressed many negative and neutral attitudes in their stories and relatively few positive ones. The pictures called up for them personal memories which were typically unpleasant; they cast child and mother in negative roles. Where their attitudes were not negative, they were likely to be neutral. Few positive feelings toward the situations represented emerged.

This paucity of positive attitudes toward child caretaking and the maternal role is a particularly striking finding. The stimulus pictures, it will be recalled, were for the most part pleasant or bland. Except for an occasional crying infant—certainly a commonplace rather than a traumatic event in any mother's life—there were no pictures which could objectively be considered negative. They depicted everyday happenings in the lives of mothers and their children. But, for the Psychosomatic mothers, these everyday events were simply not pleasant. The reader misses any thread of gaiety, spontaneity, or even casualness in the Psychosomatic stories. Certainly the flavor of early child rearing, as these mothers now recall it, was distasteful.

What this must have meant for the children of the Psychosomatic mothers can at this point only be guessed at. It is probably safe to say that for the Psychosomatic children, the early routines with their mothers were rather grim, unrewarding experiences. Maternal irritability and frustration may have been relieved occasionally by moments of impersonal, objective contact, but the spontaneous gestures of affection, the unexpected joke or the unanticipated gift, the "extras" that delight child and mother, were apparently missing.

The mothers of Neurotic children, on the other hand, expressed many positive and many negative feelings toward child caretaking in their stories. They had very few reactions which could be called neutral. There is a definiteness of emotional expression about the Neurotic stories which distinguishes them from those of the other two groups. The Neurotic child must have felt the impact of his mother's irritation, disappointment, and frustration in infancy, but he must have felt her pride, affection, and approval also. For him, few situations with his mother were neutral or unemotional; more than children in the other two groups, he was exposed to the extremes of both positive and negative maternal feelings.

The mothers of children with chronic illness told stories which were predominantly positive and neutral on the scales; the negative ratings are the most infrequent in this group. Even with the intervening history of chronic, severe illness in their children, these mothers reconstruct the early months in favorable terms. The Illness children, as they are described in these stories, spent their infancy in an atmosphere of pleasant, casual, maternal feeling. They apparently were exposed rarely to expression of anger, frustration, or irritability.

With this background, it is now possible to examine the results from the six scales in greater detail.

Formal aspects of the task

(1) *Accuracy of identification of stimulus situation.* Contrary to the hypothesis, the over-all comparison of the three groups on ratings on this first scale yields no intergroup difference. On mean ratings, the mothers of children with psychosomatic difficulties are most accurate in identification, the mothers of chronically ill next, and the mothers of neurotic children least accurate; but no intergroup difference achieves statistical significance.

The identification of individual pictures in terms of extreme scores, however, does yield significant results. Ten pictures achieve reasonably reliable intergroup differences. In five cases the mothers of psychosomatically ill children have significantly low accuracy scores; in the remaining five cases, the mothers of neurotic children are inaccurate in their picture identification. Moreover, on these ten pictures, the Psychosomatic and Neurotic groups are reversed: where the mothers of children with psychosomatic illness distort, the Neurotic group achieves significant accuracy, and vice versa.

The content of the particular pictures which distinguish between the Psychosomatic and Neurotic groups provides some leads as to the process underlying distortions of identification. All but one of the pictures misidentified by the Psychosomatic group depict individuals, either mother or child, alone. The exceptional picture here is the one involving a toilet accident—one which usually earns a negatively toned description in terms of accident from the open safety pin or of punishment by the mother for some misdemeanor. Similarly, all the pictures identified accurately by the Psychosomatic group show interactions, either positive or neutral, between child and parent. The situation is reversed for the Neurotic group, where the misidentifications occur typically in interaction pictures, and the accurate descriptions are those of single figures. It might be guessed that for mothers of children with psychosomatic illness, scenes of neutral or pleasant interaction somehow carry greater meaning than scenes lacking such interaction. Conversely, it might be hazarded that for the Neurotic group it is the solo scenes which carry the greater meaning. Whether this tentative finding is one facet of a more general attitude of maternal closeness in the Psychosomatic group and of maternal distance in the Neurotic group remains to be seen.

(2) *Accuracy of immediate recall of the stimulus pictures.* The three groups fall in the same order with regard to this scale as in the case of the preceding one: the mothers of children with psychosomatic illness recall the most pictures, the mothers of chronically ill next most, and the mothers of neurotic children the least. This intergroup comparison achieves statistical significance and, so far as the Psychosomatic group is concerned, it is contrary to prediction. Inspection of the frequencies involved, however, indicates that it is not the superiority of the Psychosomatic group which largely determines the overall difference, but rather the inferiority of the Neurotic group. Mothers of neurotic children made much poorer showings on the test of immediate recall than did mothers in the other two groups.

A number of different analyses, in terms of individual pictures, groups of pictures, and order of recall, failed to shed any additional light on this unpredicted finding. Informal appraisal of the length of the stories and number of pauses suggests that the simple variable of length of initial exposure time is not responsible for the group difference. The original reasoning behind the construction of this scale held that poor recall of pictures of the first year of life might follow from the operation of two factors. Maternal conflict and preoccupation during the child's infancy might have made this period initially too hazy for accurate recall, or the events of the first year might have been so frustrating and unpleasant that the mother would try to avoid being reminded of them. If this reasoning is valid, then it appears that the Neurotic mothers, more than those in the other two groups, were either remote from the events of the first year of their children's lives, or employed avoidance techniques extensively, in order to protect themselves from facing their negative feelings. As will be seen later, this protective non-involvement in potentially disturbing situations is characteristic both of the neurotic child's handling of thematic material about being mothered and of the interaction of the mothers and children in the Neurotic group.

It is on the scale of accuracy of immediate recall that the only significant difference between "High" and "Low" Psychosomatic mothers in the storytelling technique occurs. While the Psychosomatic mothers as a total group are superior in recall, within this group the

"High" mothers are significantly more accurate than the "Low" mothers. This finding fits in with the impression, reported earlier, that the "High" mothers are more organized and more planful than the "Low" group. Perhaps, at a superficial level, it reflects also their apparent desire to be seen in a good light by the experimenter.

(3) *Personal references.* There is a statistically significant intergroup difference in total number of personal references made by the mothers in the course of their storytelling. The mothers of children with psychosomatic disorder make fewer personal references than do mothers of neurotic children. The greatest number of such references occurs in the productions of the mothers of chronically ill children. Breakdown of the personal references into those which are positive, negative, and neutral also achieves statistical significance. The mothers of children with psychosomatic illness have fewer positive and more negative personal references than do the other two groups. The mothers of chronically ill children make relatively the most positive references and the fewest negative ones, with the Neurotic group falling between the other two groups. It is striking, however, that, within each of the three groups, the negative personal references outnumber the positive ones.

The interpretation of these findings rests largely upon the definition of personal reference which underlies this scale. For many mothers, the stimulus pictures provided a springboard to informal chatting with the examiner about personal matters. To the extent that these excursions into informal conversation are stimulated by the pictures, they must represent some sort of associative phenomenon. They must reflect also one aspect of a general freedom to communicate with the examiner, or a flexibility great enough to permit the inclusion of matters other than the task at hand in the discussion.

Such an interpretation would shed further light on the characteristics of the Psychosomatic mothers in particular. These women, in contrast to the women in the other two groups, make few personal associations to the pictures of child rearing. They appear wary or self-protective—"cagey," we have often claimed—in their communication with the examiner. Or, put in another way, their attitude toward this situation is too inflexible to allow them to go beyond the strict boundaries of the stimulus materials in dealing with the task. Conceivably, the background of this sort of approach to the storytelling task could lie in two different maternal characteristics. Perhaps the mothers of psychosomatically ill children do not make personal references easily because they cannot do so. A real inability to associate personally to pictures of mother-child situations may exist, perhaps because the early months of child rearing were too frustrating and unhappy to provide material for casual conversation later. On the other hand, perhaps the meagerness of personal references reflects only resistance or defensiveness at the level of social interaction with the psychologist.

These two hypothetical antecedents are not mutually exclusive, of course. To argue for one at the expense of the other would be unwarranted by the data. However, some evidence does point toward the interpretation of personal references at the level of association rather than the level of acceptable interpersonal communication. It would seem that, if a mother were simply defensive about discussing her maternal role with the examiner, she would, if she could, inhibit those personal associations which had a negative flavor. But this is not the case: mothers in all groups give more negative than positive personal references to the pictures. In view of this finding, it is tempting to accept the explanation that the group differences obtained reflect the operation of earlier and more pervasive background factors than the social structure of the immediate storytelling situation.

The findings which distinguish the Psychosomatic group now take on more meaning. Positive incidents and anecdotes from their own experience simply do not occur frequently to these women when they view the pictures. Put in more general terms, mother-child situations call up pleasant personal associations much less frequently for these mothers than for those in the other two groups. It would seem justifiable to suggest that the original mother-child situation for the Psychosomatic group must have been distasteful, unrewarding, or conflictual.

(4) *Attitude toward activities involved in child care* produced no intergroup differences in positive, negative, or ambivalent attitudes; the prediction that the mothers of children with psychosomatic illness see child care activities in a negative light goes unconfirmed. In part, this finding is due to the brevity and meagerness of the mothers' productions, a shortcoming which underlies all the analyses of the storytelling data. Another factor may also contribute here. Child caretaking, of course, always involves mother and child together; only the eleven pictures which show such interpersonal activities enter into this analysis. It is possible that the restriction of the pictures to those of mother-child interaction has correspondingly constricted the range of response and the possibility of group differentiation. That the mothers

of psychosomatically ill children do react selectively to pictures of interaction has already been shown; these mothers identify such pictures with greater accuracy than they do pictures of single persons. The factor of closeness, suggested earlier, may be sufficiently strong to mask other elements in these abbreviated responses.

The one category in the scale which distinguishes among the three groups is that of neutral feeling. The mothers of neurotic children have significantly fewer neutral stories than do the other two groups. This finding receives further support from one additional analysis. When all feelingful stories, either positive or negative, are combined, another significant result emerges: the mothers of neurotic children have significantly more of such ratings on child care activities than do the mothers of the other two groups. Apparently mothers of neurotic children express more feeling, either positive or negative, about child caretaking than do the other two groups.

(5) *Role assigned to the child* yields significant intergroup differences throughout, but the relationship of findings to original prediction is not simple. The mothers of psychosomatically ill children cast the child in a negative role. So also, however, do the mothers of neurotic children. It is the infrequent occurrence of negative ratings in the chronically ill group which makes the difference. The Psychosomatic and Neurotic groups are distinguishable at this point only in terms of the additional category of ambivalence. The mothers of neurotic children admit an appreciable ambivalence into their descriptions of the child's role, while the mothers of psychosomatically ill children are significantly low in the frequency of such ratings. However, it is the mothers of chronically ill children who cast the child most often in a role judged ambivalent.

A return to the original content of the stories for further analysis of the negative ratings might make possible greater understanding of what is going on. Accordingly, the content of the negative productions has been regrouped into smaller categories. The effect of this procedure, while it provides leads for study at some future date, is so to attenuate the frequencies in the subcategories as to prevent the obtaining of statistically significant results. The following picture, therefore, is offered only in a suggestive way and must be viewed with great caution.

About a third of the negative stories cast the child in the role of positive frustrater. The three groups are practically identical in this subcategory. Apparently if mothers take a negative view of the child at all, they do so in large part by way of the conformity aspects of behavior. The major part of the intergroup difference is accounted for by stories where the child is anxious, unhappy, or insecure: the mothers of children with chronic illness do not see the children as suffering in this emotional way as frequently as do the Psychosomatic and Neurotic mothers. Moreover, the mothers of chronically ill children see fewer children with specific objects of anxiety (worry over sibling, fear of falling) than do the other two groups. The mothers of psychosomatically ill and neurotic children remain closely similar to one another in their "psychological" appraisal of the child's role. They remain similar also in their tendency to interpret the child's role as that of someone who is sick, hurt, or uncomfortable. Indeed, they find the child ill more often than do the mothers of the chronically ill children. This is particularly interesting in view of the absence of serious physical illness in the neurotic children and the judges' estimate of no significant physiological upsets in the first year of life for either the neurotic or the psychosomatically ill children.

At only one point does the consistent similarity between the Psychosomatic and Neurotic groups begin to break: more often than mothers in either of the other groups, the mothers of neurotic children see the child as bewildered or unhappy because he does not comprehend an adult situation—either the mother's behavior or an argument or discussion between adults at a distance. Speculation on the relation between this finding and a generally distant attitude of mother toward neurotic child is tempting but unjustified in view of the small number of cases.

The other categories of this fifth scale yield results which are more straightforward. The responses of mothers of children with psychosomatic illness are distinguished by a paucity of positive ratings; less often than the other two groups do they cast the child in such positive roles as sources of pride or pleasure. As in the preceding scale, the Neurotic group has few stories which contain only unemotional descriptions of the child's role; in occurrence of either positive or negative expressions of feeling the Neurotic mothers rank highest.

To relate these diverse findings to the main hypothesis is not easy. That the Psychosomatic group casts the child in a negative role and cannot see him in a satisfying one is clear. So also is the relative lack of ambivalence about the child's role and the relatively strong tendency to avoid expressions of feeling. This picture is not inconsistent with the hypothesized early mother-infant relationship, which was conflictual and unhappy. The Neurotic group differs from this largely in its greater freedom of emotional expression; its equally high negative ratings are accompanied by high positive ones and by relatively high ambivalence. This would not be inconsistent with an early mother-infant relationship which provided some satisfaction as well as some frustrations. The Illness group differs from both in its significant lack of negatives and abundance of positives. Its high frequency in the ambivalence category, however, testifies that even in the presumed benign mother-child relationship here, conflicts and frustrations were present.

(6) *Role assigned to the mother* yields significant intergroup differences throughout, but again the results are complex in their relationship to the hypothesis. As predicted, the mothers of psychosomatically ill children view the mother in a negative light, but so also do the mothers in the Neurotic group. Once again it is the infrequent occurrence of negative stories in the Illness group that makes the difference. There is a tendency, not as marked as on the preceding scale, for the mothers of children with psychosomatic disorder to have few positive stories and for the Neurotic group to have many. The mothers of neurotic children maintain their previously noted ability to express feeling: they are low in their frequency of stories containing only unemotional descriptions of the mother's role.

Again, a further breakdown of the negative category is necessary to the understanding of the difference between the Psychosomatic and the Neurotic groups. The category in which the mother's situation is described alone, without reference to the child, as dejected, unhappy, worried about things other than the child, makes the crucial difference; and here the difference attains a statistically significant level. Much more frequently than mothers in the other two groups, the mothers of the neurotic children see the mother in negative terms without relating her to her child: she is concerned over financial matters, or her health, or her marital situation, or some other adult problem. It might be suggested at this point that the Neurotic group's significantly low score on immediate recall of the pictures, reported earlier, could be related to this same preoccupation over matters other than mothers and their children. The mothers of psychosomatically ill children see the pictured mother in negative terms, but they do not separate the child from this maternal role; the mothers of neurotic children also find the pictured mother's role frustrating, but they tend to separate the child from the mother's situation. Apparently the mother of the neurotic child can conceive of sources of adult anxiety other than those bound up in her child, while the mother of the psychosomatically ill child cannot. Again the impact of closeness in the psychosomatic mother-child relationship and distance in the neurotic relationship is felt.

The special position of the ambivalence category on this scale deserves mention. On the previous scale, it will be recalled, the Psychosomatic group showed little ambivalence in its characterization of the child's role: the child was seen in largely negative terms. On the present scale, the Psychosomatic group is the highest of the three in ambivalence. Although the mothers of psychosomatically ill children still find the maternal role a negative one, their attitude here is less clearcut and they admit a significant number of instances of ambivalence.

6 --- Mother - Child Interaction:
The Contemporary Picture

No study of human personality can successfully restrict itself to the past. The continuity of behavior is too compelling a fact to be ignored. Sooner or later the present to which the past has led must come into focus; eventually the question, "What are things like today?" must find an answer. To this universal interest in contemporary behavior the present investigation offers no exception. This chapter, therefore, seeks to describe the contemporary interaction between the mothers and the children of the study.

Observed Interaction. A number of considerations determined the decision to observe the current behavior of mother and child. Chief among them was sheer curiosity. Informal observation of project mothers and children on their way to the appointment, in the waiting room, and in the pediatrics clinic often provided definite impressions of the mother-child relationship, impressions that were tantalizing in their incompleteness. A mother sat silently on one bench, ignoring magazines, intent on her own preoccupations; her son sat silently on another bench, fingering a piece of woolen blanket. Another mother laughingly excused the violent battles waged in the hall by her twin daughters while their sister, our subject, stood watching in frightened fascination. One mother lost the thread of her talk each time she heard her son in the hall; the nine-year-old boy interrupted the interview repeatedly to enter and lean against his mother. Another mother was so disturbed by the sound of fire engines in the street outside that she had to leave the interview room and check on the whereabouts of her son, in apparent preparation for rescuing him in flight from the building. Such glimpses of the contemporary picture could not easily be ignored.

The general hypothesis underlying the research, of course, also supported a study of current behavior. To be sure, the particular antecedents of psychosomatic disorder presumably occurred during the first year of life. The activities of physical caretaking which are crucial to the hypothesis do not persist through the school years. But the more general factor of adequate or inadequate mothering is, in a sense, timeless. Insofar as motherliness develops into a particular pattern in the service of deep personal need, it should persist at least as long as the need persists. The ambitious mother who needs to mold her child into the form of her unrealized pregnancy fantasies, for example, may continue her efforts all her life. The strict four-hour schedules of infancy may give way to planned nursery school at three, enforced ballet lessons at five, and organized dancing parties at twelve, but the strong thread of maternal control remains unchanged. The mother who wanted a girl but had a son may stop dressing the boy in ruffled clothes after infancy but persist in feminization through the encouragement of passivity, say, for years afterward. Patterns of mothering are presumably persistent; and predictions made about them should hold, in some basic way, over a long span of years.

The obverse of this argument is so commonplace today as almost to need no mention. The early relationship which a child develops with his mother is presumably the crucial one; its emphasis colors or distorts his subsequent interactions with other persons. If the pattern of mothering persists in time, so also does the pattern of being mothered.

Granting the relative permanence of these aspects of maternal and child behavior, then, certain predictions about the contemporary situation of mother and psychosomatically ill child follow. The interrelationship between these two should continue to be the close but uncomfortable and mutually frustrating one postulated for the first year of the child's life. Inadequate mothering should still characterize the relationship, although inadequate handling of caretaking routines should give way to other forms of maternal incompetence. If the picture of compensation for unfulfilled anticipation, presented earlier, is an accurate one, then a typical maternal approach to a psychosomatically ill child should be one of control and domination. Confirmation of these predictions would add to the certainty with which the basic hypothesis regarding the first year of life could be accepted.

The *interaction* between mother and child, it will be noted, is the significant element in these predictions. Many different patterns of personal need, many different structures of personality variables, we have said, must underlie the behavior of the mothers and children of this study. To examine the personality characteristics of mother and child separately, therefore, would contribute relatively little to the understanding of the main problem. The focus must be on the mutual interrelationship between mother and child. Consequently, direct observation of mother and child together in a relatively free situation constitutes the method in this part of the study.

The mother-child interaction took place on their second visit to the laboratory. The experimenter took the child to a small room containing a table and two chairs, facing a one-way mirror. Over in the corner was a third chair holding popular adult magazines of recent date. The child waited in the room while the experimenter interrupted the mother's interview with the social worker. He instructed the mother to take a toy in to her child and then to do whatever she liked as her child played. The mother knew she was being observed; the child did not. The toy was a box of stone blocks of various sizes and shapes, and an instruction booklet with pictures of possible constructions. The mother was left free to present the task to the child in any way she chose, and to enter into the child's activity as much or as little as she wished. The pair remained uninterrupted for ten minutes.

For all its brevity, this ten-minute interval yielded a complex and highly significant sample of behavior. The mothers responded to the interruption of their interview with the worker in a variety of ways: some were relieved, others angry, still others resigned to one more meaningless event in the jumble that made up "research." The combination of freedom implied in the instructions with knowledge that they were being observed raised the general level of tension for most mothers. Embarrassed glances at the mirror or steadfast ignoring of it, parrying of children's questions about the interview, firm attempts to keep the child working on the blocks, all attested to the pressures which the mothers felt. Interpretation of this situation for the mothers, therefore, must take into account both the mother's reaction to the fact of being observed and her abiding attitudes toward her child.

The use of a ten-minute observation period raises serious problems of validity. Whether the behavior viewed through the one-way mirror is congruent with that which went on at home, on the street, or in the waiting room is, of course, open to serious question. The mothers' comments to the social worker upon their return to the interview did add information which helped define the validity of the situation. One mother, for example, returned in a highly distraught state, complaining that she saw herself doing all the "wrong" things with her child, but that she could not modify her behavior toward him, even though she knew others were watching. Such dramatic testimonials to the validity of the behavior samples are rare, but a number of mothers spoke, in one way or another, of the inevitability of the reactions which the experimental situation evoked. It is still safest, however, to take the observed behavior as a relatively independent sample, without attempting to generalize systematically to other situations.

The children, for their part, accepted the procedure with somewhat greater ease than did their mothers. They had just completed the World Test, under very free instructions, and their shift to an interpersonal relationship with their own mothers often carried with it a dramatic shift of attitude. Some who seemed inhibited in the previous technique surprised the observers with enthusiastic outbursts to their mothers. Some who seemed placid and conforming with the experimenter berated their mothers angrily in the interpersonal situation. Others became quieter and more constricted with their mothers. Free of any awareness that they were being observed, the children were probably under less extraneous pressure than were the mothers. Consequently, specifying the mother as the single differentiating element for the child in this situation is probably justified.

The block game to which the child's attention was directed during the interaction served many functions. In a general way, it became a relatively objective, bland focus for maternal and child response, alleviating in some instances feelings which might otherwise have become uncomfortably strong. It permitted the mother to retire to a corner, if she needed to, without feeling that she had completely deserted her child. And it allowed the child to ignore his mother in favor of the blocks, without necessarily feeling guilt or remorse. The game pointed up the dependence of child upon mother, as the child asked for help in building, proceeded alone, or rejected offers of maternal assistance. It made possible mother-child competition, since certain particularly desirable or necessary blocks were limited in number.

Even some peripheral and unforeseen aspects of the building game proved useful. The level of constructiveness at which the child built, for example, sometimes furnished a clue to the degree of disturbance or comfort he felt with his mother. The character of the buildings constructed sometimes seemed significant, as when one child spent considerable time working on a tomb. The instructions about the blocks were written in three languages; the mother's handling of the child's questions about these unfamiliar languages also provided unexpected clues to underlying attitudes. While many mothers admitted calmly that they could not interpret the printing literally, some grew defensive, some became angry at the experimenter, the instruction booklet, or the child, some paraphrased the foreign words with greater confidence than accuracy.

The ten-minute period, then, proved to be a complex, three-way situation involving mother, child, and task. Knowledge that she was under observation undoubtedly raised the mother's level of tension and imposed some constraints upon her behavior. Lack of this knowledge on the part of the child left him relatively free to respond to the task and to his mother without much editing. The task itself served almost as a projective stimulus, fulfilling whatever function the needs of mother and child dictated.

Three psychologists observed the interaction from the other side of the one-way mirror and took running notes on the behavior of mother and child. Immediately after the observation period, each psychologist rated the interaction between mother and child on 35 different variables, each describing one aspect of the interaction relevant to the main hypothesis. These scales focus on three observable general characteristics of the interaction situation: (1) the *atmosphere* of interaction, including such variables as positive closeness, empathy, comfort, negative interaction; (2) the *techniques* of interaction, such as domination, competition, victimization, and encapsulation; and (3) individual *personality* characteristics, such as anxiety, helplessness, and narcissism. The judges attempted to characterize through their ratings the interaction rather than the two individuals being watched; and they described only the ten-minute period observed, without trying to generalize to other situations or to general personality patterns.

Although considerable preliminary attention had been given to the definition of the scaled variables and a pilot study had been carried out, there still remained areas of disagreement among the judges. Statistically speaking, the interjudge unreliability occurred exclusively on the *personality* variables: the three judges were unable to achieve significant agreement in their ratings of overt and covert anxiety, or in their ratings of maternal and child helplessness in dealing with the interaction. This difficulty is not surprising in view of the inferential nature of these traits by contrast to such other variables as anger, irritability, closeness, or distance.

From those judges' ratings which are reliable, there emerge three rather distinct pictures of mother-child interaction, corresponding to the three subgroups of the study. Statistically speaking again, these pictures are differentiated from one another at a high level of probability.

Interaction Between Mother and Psychosomatically Ill Child. These mother-child pairs interact within an atmosphere which is preponderantly negative. There is very little closeness of a positive sort between mother and child; the judges see the interaction as uncomfortable for both participants. The discomfort is shown not only in ratings of the general atmosphere but in the rated reactions of mother and child. Thus the mothers earn high ratings in irritability and anger, and the children rate high in anger. The mother's empathy for her child is significantly low. This uncomfortable, negative relationship, of course, is the one which follows from the hypothesis of mutual mother-child frustration in the first year of life.

The techniques of interaction which mother and psychosomatically ill child employ also fit those predicted by the general hypothesis of the research. Domination and competition are the typical Psychosomatic techniques of handling the interaction. Furthermore, it is more likely to be the mother than the child in each pair who dominates and competes. The judges see the child with psychosomatic disorder as victimized to a significant degree by his mother. The most telling characteristic of this group of differentiating variables is not so much its negative flavor as its quality of mutual entanglement. Mother and child seem literally trapped in a negative situation. The mother cannot relinquish the techniques of competition and domination which keep her continually reacting to the child, nor can the child find relief in independent or encapsulated task-oriented activity. This unrelieved mutual frustration in a setting of closeness is the sort of mother-child relationship predicted by the hypothesis and supported in a fragmentary way by the interview and storytelling results presented earlier.

One last finding for the Psychosomatic group approaches statistical significance closely enough for inclusion here: mother narcissism. This is the one personality variable on which the judges achieved agreement; they found the mothers of children with psychosomatic disorder significantly high in narcissism, or more simply, much more self-centered than the mothers of the other two groups. It might be suggested, on the basis of this finding, that the power tactics of domination and competition employed by these mothers are used in the service of some deeper maternal need. Possibly more than in the other groups, the psychosomatically ill child is an extension of the mother's self, still not differentiated from the mother in any realistic sense. If this is true, then domination, manipulation, and control of the child must represent self-aggrandizement of the mother, both through the exercise of power per se and through the resultant achievements of the child. The mother's knowledge that she was being observed probably contributed here also. Her greater observed narcissism may stem in part from a greater sensitivity to the opinions of the observers, and the understandable desire to make a good impression may be seen by the judges as the mother's attention to herself rather than to the child or to the task.

The characteristic flavor of the interaction in the Psychosomatic group can best be communicated through an illustration, based on the running accounts made by the judges:

Mother and child stand together, Mary talking and the mother looking at first cold and distant. As Mary starts playing with the blocks, mother hits her by accident and says "Sorry," but in a sarcastic tone. Mary says, "I will make this city." The mother replies, "You will make whatever city you want, puss," in an irritated way. The girl demands that they "make this city together," and at each step asks, "Is that right?" and otherwise pesters and makes demands on her mother. The mother attempts to help by entering in, selects a block, is rejected by the child, becomes confused, and finally says, "I'm not sure." Finally she does find an appropriate block, and says, "Sometimes your mother is right," to which Mary answers, "Sometimes." The mother comes back and imitates the child's way of saying "Sometimes" in a mocking tone. Mary says, "I like all the games," and the mother replies cynically, "Okay, what do you want me to do about it?" As the experimenter enters, mother is trying to praise the child's efforts, but in a bored, brusque manner.

Interaction Between Mother and Neurotic Child. The general atmosphere within which mother and neurotic child interact in this brief observation is similar to that described for the Psychosomatic group. Mother and child are uncomfortable with one another to a marked degree; the mothers are typically irritable and angry, as are the mothers of psychosomatically ill children. The neurotic children also show some anger toward their mothers, although the judges do not consider these reactions as extreme as those in the Psychosomatic group. There is little positive closeness between mother and child, and mother empathy is at its lowest point. If only the over-all quality of the interaction were considered, then it would be difficult, if not impossible, to distinguish between the Psychosomatic and Neurotic groups. Both develop negative, uncomfortable mother-child relationships in which outbursts of anger and irritability are prominent.

The techniques of handling the interaction, however, differentiate clearly between the Psychosomatic and Neurotic groups. The domination, competition, and victimization with which the mothers of children with psychosomatic disorder dealt with their offspring are absent from the Neurotic group. In their place a set of techniques which increase the distance between mother and child emerge as characteristic of the neurotic interaction. To a highly significant degree, for example, the neurotic child is rated as independent of the mother. He is task-oriented more than mother-oriented; he can devote himself to the block game without asking for maternal support or entering into power struggles with the mother.

In the same way, the neurotic child achieves significantly high ratings on encapsulation; he can use his independence of the mother in a self-protective manner, becoming almost oblivious of the human environment as he works on the task. That the neurotic child can maintain this relatively distant position reveals a good deal about his mother as well as himself, of course. Unlike the mother of psychosomatically ill children, the mother of the neurotic child can tolerate some distance from her child. Indeed, she seems to welcome and even foster a certain degree of remoteness in the situation; for many of the mothers of neurotic children, the magazines on the chair in the far corner were an obvious refuge from an otherwise unpleasantly close association with their offspring.

The major difference between the psychosomatic and the neurotic interactions now becomes clear. The mutual entanglement of mother and psychosomatically ill child, negative but still unbreakable, contrasts sharply with the distance, negative but at least protective, which mother and neurotic child can maintain from one another. Nowhere in the study does the lack of real differentiation between mother and psychosomatically ill child come out more clearly than in this contrast. It is tempting to relate this finding to the respective antecedents of psychosomatic and neurotic disorder, which psychoanalytic theory in general and our hypothesis in particular would dictate. Certainly the mutual entanglement of the Psychosomatic mother-child pair is consistent with an antecedent disturbance in interpersonal relationship occurring very early in the life history—in the early months of infancy, as the guiding hypothesis of the study puts it. The ability of the Neurotic children and mothers to free themselves from one another, on the other hand, suggests that the interpersonal relationship here had progressed beyond the infantile period before the crucial disturbance developed.

Again the peculiar quality of the Neurotic interaction is best communicated through an illustration:

The mother enters, smiles, proffers the box, and says, "A surprise, hm?" The mother then immediately goes to the corner, picks up a magazine, and sits down, apparently reading. Sandra starts building a wall, then animatedly tells about the techniques preceding this interaction. The mother says "Mm" and continues reading, changing her facial expression very little. Sandra makes more and more complex buildings, calling her mother's attention to these constructions. Mother tries to smile, but often does so inappropriately, as if her real attention were elsewhere. As Sandra goes on building, she asks for reactions less and less frequently, and the mother lapses into lethargy, seeming tired and worn out. As the experimenter enters, Sandra is building by herself and her mother, standing over in the corner, is leafing through another magazine.

Interaction Between Mother and Chronically Ill Child. A catalogue of positive qualities describes the rated interaction between mother and chronically ill child. The general atmosphere is one of positive closeness; the direction of interaction is typically positive, and the mother achieves significantly high ratings on empathy. The over-all ease of the relationship emerges not only in high ratings on the comfort variable, but in the relative absence of signs of anger or irritability on the part of either mother or child. There seems to be little question that the mother and her chronically ill child find pleasure in being with one another in this situation and that they can participate together without overt signs of tension or distress.

It is unfortunate for our understanding of the details of this relatively wholesome relationship that the Illness group is distinguished from the other two almost exclusively by default. While this result is again the consequence of the dependence of the rating scales upon the underlying hypothesis, it leaves unanswered many questions about the nature of the mother-child interaction. It can be said, for example, that the mother of the chronically ill child does not dominate or victimize her child, or compete with him, or enter into other forms of power struggle with him. But what positive techniques of interaction contribute to her positive interrelationship with him cannot be specified on the basis of these results.

Two ratings, however, do shed some light on the quality of the Illness situation: child independence and child encapsulation. On the former scale, the Illness group rates so high as to be practically indistinguishable from the Neurotic group. On the latter scale, the Illness group also resembles the Neurotic, achieving significantly higher ratings in encapsulation than the Psychosomatic group. If these two variables do express some form of distance between mother and child, then the Illness group, like the Neurotic, has achieved a higher level of mother-child differentiation than has the Psychosomatic group. Unlike the neurotic children, however, the children with chronic illness maintain their distance from their mothers within an atmosphere of ease and comfort. There would seem to be a strong possibility that the distancing technique in the Illness group is less a self-protective measure than a sign of greater maturity.

The following illustration includes many of the elements typical of the interaction between mother and chronically ill child:

Mother introduces the game by saying "I've got something for you— wonder what it is" in a very animated tone. Joan opens the box and says, "Oh, you make houses and things." Joan chooses a picture and starts building, while the mother makes suggestions, says "Mm," moves the box closer to Joan, or encourages her by smiles and jokes. Mother often repeats or reflects Joan's comments: "That was easy"; "You like this kind." Joan builds competently, completes one construction, and starts another during the ten-minute period. Mother tells a story about Joan's brother, and both laugh together. Mother puts the picture in better position for Joan to see. Joan is carefully matching blocks to pictures, with the mother occasionally handing her some blocks, when the experimenter enters.

"High" and "Low" Mothers of Psychosomatically Ill Children. An earlier chapter, it will be recalled, presented evidence in favor of dividing the mothers of psychosomatically ill children into two groups: those whose ratings of their children's first year agreed closely with the judges' ("High"), and those whose ratings deviated widely from the judges' ("Low"). Subsequently there have been hints that these two groups differ from one another in other respects also. The "High" mothers, for example, seem more organized, more planful, perhaps more evasive and self-protective, than the "Low" mothers. Analysis of the interaction ratings for these two groups separately provides still more information about the characteristics of these two subgroups of mothers of psychosomatic children. While this analysis does not basically alter the picture of the total Psychosomatic group already given, it does suggest that the typical traits of the mothers of the

psychosomatically ill children receive different emphases from different women.

Neither the "High" nor the "Low" mother develops a comfortable interrelationship with her child during the ten-minute observation period. Ratings of discomfort for both subgroups resemble those of the Neurotic group and are significantly higher than those of the Illness group. Tension and distress between mother and child form a backdrop against which the different reactions of the "High" and "Low" groups can be projected.

The mothers of the "Low" group—those who disagreed with the judges and upon whom the judges also disagreed—provide a rather extreme picture of negative interaction. They fall below all the other groups in positive closeness and empathy; they exceed all the other groups in domination, maternal competition, mother anger, and mother irritability. More than any other group, the children of "Low" mothers are seen as victimized by their mothers—as dependent upon their mothers in passive but negative ways. The "Low" group seems to have as a prototype a domineering, controlling mother of a helpless, victimized child. This would be the extreme—almost the caricature—of the postulated close but mutually frustrating relationship of psychosomatic illness were it not for the defenseless position of the child in these ratings. The child of the "Low" mother seems, from these ratings, so passive and colorless as to be almost the innocent object of an unjust and unreasonable attack. An illustration of an interaction in the Low group will make the picture clear:

Mother enters, opens the box, takes out the pictures. Roberta ruffles through the box, handling a few blocks. The mother begins arranging blocks on the table; her daughter ignores her and builds a high tower. As Roberta drops a block and dives under the table for it, her mother moves into her play space and goes on building. The mother asks Roberta for a particular block the girl was using, takes it from her, and goes on building. She pushes Roberta's hand away as the child tries to help with the mother's construction. The mother asks the child what she is trying to build, then selects a picture for the girl to follow, and disarranges the child's building, actually knocking over some of the parts. As Roberta tries to start another construction, the mother enters in again, and takes over. Roberta begins hitting the instruction booklet hard, and then throwing the blocks back into the box angrily. As the experimenter enters, Roberta is tossing blocks into the box while the mother, now quizzing the girl on her plans, is rebuilding Roberta's latest endeavor.

The situation among the "High" mothers—those who agreed with the judges in sorting and upon whom the judges also agreed—is dramatically different. The mothers win distinctly high ratings in empathy and relatively high scores in positive closeness. Toward their children they express neither anger nor irritability to a significant degree, nor do they typically dominate or compete with their offspring. In the picture of self-control and social acceptability they present in the interaction they are the organized, self-protective mothers which the earlier techniques made them out to be. Indeed, it might be fairer to say that they resemble the benign mothers of the Illness group, were it not for the high general discomfort rating and, more importantly, the behavior which their children show toward them in the interaction.

The children of the "High" mothers demonstrate emphatically the emotional responses which are so surprisingly absent from their mothers' behavior. The children are the ones who dominate in this situation; they are the ones who compete for blocks, for attention, for power. They show more overt anger toward their mothers than any other group, and they approach the Neurotic and Illness groups in their rated independence. In the "High" mother-child interaction, the child seems to have the upper hand, while the mother is the well-meaning, innocent victim. The following illustration is typical:

Mother opens the box, takes out the pictures. Elsie is sitting at the table, mother remains standing over her. There is some initial discussion about the size of the blocks; Elsie insists some are the wrong size, and the mother repeatedly selects other blocks for her, which are quickly rejected. Elsie becomes hostile, puts all the blocks back in the box, and says with confidence, "I'll soon find out!" She shows her ease by humming happily in the situation, while the mother becomes silent. Each suggestion by the mother is rejected with increasing impatience and exasperation. The mother retreats to the other side of the chair, watching carefully but remaining quiet. Elsie, comparing blocks, says "Lookit here!" and then holds the block so close to the mother's face that she cannot see it. As the mother tries again to help, Elsie raps her hands loudly on the table and goes on to something else. She seems to ask for help only to reject it, to lead her mother forward only to push her away. As the experimenter enters, the mother is again trying to help, but she is unable to manage the situation. Elsie, on the other hand, is confidently building, with an occasional complacent "How's that?" in aside to her mother.

The two versions of uncomfortable, mutually frustrating relationship represented by the "High" and "Low" groups deserve some attempt at interpretation. Both, of course, represent forms of inadequate mothering: it is no more effective, from the point of view of emotional maturing, to invite or tolerate uncontrolled attack from one's child than it is to initiate an angry attack upon him. But the antecedents of the interaction in the "High" group seem at once more obscure and more interesting than those of the "Low" group. If the ten-minute observation period represents a segment of a lifelong development between mother and child, then the question arises as to how the apparently empathetic and beneficent mother earned at length the role of innocent victim of her child's aggression.

The origin of such a relationship must lie in mutual interplay of maternal and child need. Short of the unlikely occurrence of genetically determined cantankerousness in the child, there is no other alternative. A number of possibilities arise, none of them completely verifiable by the data, but all of them worthy of record for the help they may give some later investigations. Perhaps the most obvious would assign central importance to maternal guilt feelings stemming from the earlier suggested operation of unfulfilled pregnancy anticipations. The mother who openly recognizes her infant as a personal disappointment may be prevented by her consequent guilt from behaving consistently toward her child. She may well find the handling of the child's angry and hostile feelings her major problem and adopt an unduly permissive attitude out of her own guilty need. The somewhat masochistic flavor of the victimized mother's attitude would support such an interpretation.

The hypothesis that maternal guilt feelings are pivotal in the establishment of the "High" mother-child interrelationship is attractive for several reasons. The "High" mothers, it will be recalled, appear more highly organized, more consistent, in their personality structure than the "Low" mothers. Within such a high degree of intrapersonal organization, the techniques of inhibition, self-appraisal, and self-control must certainly have developed; and these are the roots from which guilty attitudes spring. The very organization of these personalities favors the development of guilt. This fact, still speaking hypothetically, could well have important consequences for the child of a "High" mother. For one thing, it gives him license for the free expression of hostility; he has learned that his mother does not crumble under open assault. For another thing, it provides him with a vulnerable target for his negative feelings—his mother's guilty reaction. If this line of reasoning is valid, then one would expect uninhibited negative behavior from the child.

An alternative but not altogether independent line of reasoning is also possible. The frustrated mother's angry feelings, suppressed in the observed interaction and conceivably also in other life situations, may find their outlet in the child's behavior. The acting out of maternal need by a child with whom the mother is closely identified is by no means unknown in the literature of child pathology. Indeed, the satisfaction given the mother by such emotional expression in the child would serve to reinforce the domineering and competitive attitudes which here seem so deep-seated a part of the "High" child's behavior.

Certain situational factors might also have been important in determining the behavior of mother and child. The "High" mothers, it will be recalled, seemed to be planful, organized, self-protective women who were highly sensitive to matters of social acceptability. In the interaction situation they knew they were being observed, and this might have been an important factor in prompting their positive, accepting, empathetic attitudes. It is equally important to understand the situation in regard to the child. As it happened, the observed children of "High" mothers were girls, and they all found the techniques stimulating and the exclusive attention of the psychologist flattering. If the mother entered the situation with a feeling of having to maintain an acceptable social facade, her daughter entered with the feeling of ruling the roost. For the child so quickly to sense her advantage strongly implies that a competitive struggle for power is an important dimension of the mother-child relationship; in fact, the "High" Psychosomatic mother described in Chapter 10 constantly referred to the "battle of wills" between her daughter and herself. It is also congruent with the image of the "High" mother to assume that this battle takes place at a refined and intellectual level rather than at the level of direct emotional outbursts. If this speculation is valid, then the observed interaction offered a glimpse into the jockeying for advantage which constantly goes on between mother and child.

Whatever the ultimate explanation of the "High" and "Low" groups' behavior, one fact deserves re-emphasis. Both these groups represent mother-child interactions which are close, uncomfortable, and mutually frustrating. Both represent relationships which are so interdependent, so undifferentiated, as to be of very early origin in the life history of the child. Both could result from a failure in the realization of early maternal anticipations and hopes for the child. The differences between the groups stem from the particular patterns of maternal need and satisfaction—patterns which would never, in real life, be identical from one woman to another.

One further informal finding remains for consideration. If the entire

Psychosomatic group is considered again for a moment in comparison with the Neurotic group in the interaction, a final point of contrast becomes apparent. In the Psychosomatic group there is considerable overt expression of emotion, either by mother or child, or by both. The ratings of domination and competition depend upon overt behavior, verbal or nonverbal, displayed by mother and child. The mother interrupts or ridicules the child; the child accuses the mother of taking the desired blocks; the mother compares the child's building unfavorably with her own. In the Neurotic group, on the other hand, the overt statement of these attitudes is absent; instead there are the distancing techniques, expressed in their most extreme form by a silence in which the child works away at the table and the mother reads quietly in the corner.

This tendency for the Psychosomatic group to become openly involved emotionally and for the Neurotic group to forego such expression contradicts the findings from the mothers' stories reported in the previous chapter. There, it will be recalled, it was the mothers of psychosomatically ill children who made the most neutral, descriptive stories, and the mothers of neurotic children who expressed the most feeling, either positive or negative. On the level of simple observation, it would appear that the realistic interaction of a mother and her own psychosomatically ill child calls forth definite expressions of feeling which the mother can omit when she is dealing only with picture materials. There is something compelling about the situation which leads the mother of the psychosomatic child to demonstrate that her relationship with her child is far from a neutral, unemotional one. Again this informal finding is consistent with the mutual closeness of mother and child which is hypothesized for the Psychosomatic group.

Questionnaire. Another approach to the problem of understanding the contemporary mother-child relationship utilizes the accuracy of a mother's prediction of her child's response to a multiple-choice questionnaire about himself. The rationale underlying such a technique is that accuracy of prediction is one index of understanding or empathy. In a close, positive relationship one would expect the mother to be cognizant of her child's feelings about himself, his family, and his peers; by the same token, a mother's imperviousness to her child's individuality is one of the hallmarks of a disturbed relationship.

In constructing the questionnaire, the primary goal was to stay within the bounds of everyday experiences and reactions. No effort was made to get at deeper levels of personality or to tease out covert feelings. The 25 items represent the type of material which might be obtained from asking the child how many friends does he have, does his mother become angry when he plays hard and gets dirty, would he like to have a little brother or sister. The fact that the items are multiple-choice stems only from the necessity for objectivity.

Although the purpose of the questionnaire was to obtain a measure of the mother's cognizance of her child's surface behavior and feelings, the investigators were well aware of the fascinating issues which such a limited approach side-steps. The whole area of what particular feelings and attitudes the mother has knowledge of, the depth of these feelings (situational reactions, underlying attitudes, unconscious motivations), the use she makes of this knowledge, and, finally, what kinds of awareness are characteristic of good and bad mothers, is well worth intensive exploration. However, it lies beyond the scope of the present investigation.

There was another reason for keeping the questionnaire at the level of everyday reactions. The task of having the mother predict her child's response is quite a complicated one even at this level. The mother is not really predicting how her child actually feels or behaves, but what her child will tell a comparative stranger, the investigator, about his (the child's) feelings and behavior. This means she must take into account the strength and nature of his social defenses. Some of the mothers were consciously aware of this and would remark, "He really thinks X but will probably tell you Y." Now, the situation would be a good deal more complicated if an attempt had been made to get at levels of feeling, say by the use of doll-play situations. Although such material stimulates fantasy, children differ widely in their responsiveness to it: some go off into fantasy play easily, some become defensively constricted, some persist in maintaining a factual set. This means the mother not only would have to predict content but also accurately evaluate the interplay of defense and revelation. Also, the chances that prediction of the child's responses would set off defensive maneuvers on the mother's part is greatly increased. In view of such complexities, the investigators decided to adopt the simpler approach described above.

One final point about the items on the questionnaire remains. Care was taken to avoid including a choice which would be more socially acceptable than the others. This is because children this age have a strong tendency to give "good" answers when questioned directly about themselves.

The administration of the questionnaire was quite simple. The investigator told the child he would like to know how he felt about some things, and proceeded to read the items and check off the child's choices. Later, the mother was given a questionnaire sheet and asked to answer them the way she thought her child had. The mother's score was the number of Agreements, i.e., the number of times she correctly predicted the choice her child made.

The prediction was that the Psychosomatic mothers, because of their disturbed relationship with their children, would have the least number of Agreements. The results, although not achieving too high a level of statistical significance, were in the opposite direction—the Psychosomatic mothers had the greatest number of Agreements. Moreover, there was a tendency for the "High" mothers to be more accurate than the "Low."

At this point two interpretations were possible. The first was to regard the results as unexpected evidence of understanding and empathy in the Psychosomatic mothers; the other was to re-examine the nature and rationale of the questionnaire itself in light of data from the other techniques. The investigators chose the second alternative. Not only was the weight of evidence from both mother and child strongly against an appreciable amount of empathy in the Psychosomatic group, but the questionnaire results could be reinterpreted without doing violence to the technique.

The crux of this reinterpretation lies in the psychological processes which one infers from accuracy of prediction. Many psychologists using this kind of technique have assumed it tapped something akin to empathy; however, this has been established more by fiat than by convincing experimental evidence. In fact, a recent analysis of such techniques [1] reveals that accuracy of prediction may result from a number of factors, none of which could be labeled empathy. For the present study it is sufficient to point out that understanding in its most positive connotation has two components: an intellectual awareness of the child's personality and a sympathetic emotional bond with the child. Now the Psychosomatic mothers, especially the "High" ones, have a good deal of the former quality but are deficient in the latter. The case of Mrs. Fenster described in Chapter 10 nicely illustrates this. Also, evidence in the two preceding chapters points to the fact

----

[1] Lee J. Cronbach, "Processes affecting scores in 'Understanding of Others' and 'Assumed Similarity,'" *Psych. Bull.*, 52, No. 3 (1955), 117-93.

that the Psychosomatic mother can be extremely shrewd and knowledgeable.

Thus, the questionnaire shows a somewhat heightened intellectual awareness in the Psychosomatic mothers of the child's everyday reactions and attitudes, but it says nothing about the affective concomitants of this awareness: it might be accompanied by sympathetic understanding, it might be cold and objective, it might be used in the service of destructive hostility. The results can be accounted for in terms of the previous findings of the Psychosomatic mother's over-investment in her child without having to modify the fact that this is accompanied by a lack of motherliness.

The contemporary interrelationship between mother and child now takes on added meaning. The Psychosomatic interaction is the close, negative one predicted by the hypothesis, but the closeness may include a large share of intellectual awareness on the mother's part without corresponding emotional empathy. The Psychosomatic child's contemporary role may be that of passive victim or aggressive opponent, depending upon the special quality of the mother's personality. The question of how the children view their mothers, a matter thus far only speculated upon, now becomes crucial. The following chapter deals with this central problem.

7---Children's Attitudes Toward Mothering

In the preceding chapters attention has been focused on the mother's feelings about taking care of her child. The child's attitude toward being mothered is the other side of the interaction coin. It is this area which will be explored now.

The guiding theoretical notions continue to be derived from the main hypothesis concerning the lack of "motherliness" in the mothers of children with psychosomatic disorders, and the close, mutually frustrating relation between mother and child. Because this relationship is one of contaminated intimacy, it was hypothesized that the child would have highly ambivalent attitudes toward being mothered. On the one hand there would be deep longings for the tenderness and protection he has never received; on the other hand there would be strong negative feelings of rage, fear, and mistrust.

It is obvious that, when dealing with children, the retrospective approach has little meaning. The investigators had neither the time nor the ingenuity necessary for lifting infantile amnesia. Instead, the task was one of devising techniques which would be sensitive enough to reveal the children's contemporary attitudes toward being mothered. Having done this, one would have to assume that such attitudes have their roots in the past and reflect certain abiding characteristics of the mother-child relationship.

One further point should be made in this connection. The picture of the mother to be presented here derives solely from the ideas and feelings expressed by the child on one particular psychological technique. "The mother" in this chapter is really "the mother as the child sees her." Whether such a picture corresponds to reality and how such a picture complements or conflicts with findings obtained from the mother herself is of no immediate concern. Such problems will be dealt with subsequently.

APPROACH TO THE PROBLEM

A thematic projective technique seemed the most suitable one for eliciting attitudes toward being mothered. Under the protective guise of "telling a story" a child can often express feelings which he might hesitate to state directly. Also, thematic material can reflect attitudes which are not readily available to the child's consciousness either because of their threatening nature or because they were formed before verbal communication was established and have therefore received little intellectual articulation.

The thematic technique which was devised consists of ten pictures. The first five are photographs of realistic mother-child interactions: a mother buttoning a little girl's jumper, another mother holding a sobbing boy in her arms, a child in a crib looking at a mother standing in the doorway, a mother and child looking at a present, and, in the final picture, a mother and boy looking at a turkey which is being roasted. In all the pictures the factor of closeness is underlined both by the physical proximity of the figures and by the obvious mutuality of activity or interest. The atmosphere and the expression of the figures range from clearly positive to ambiguous. No clearly negative situation or expression is depicted. However, in each picture there is always at least one important element of ambiguity (e.g., a child's expression or the fact that a mother's face is not shown) so that negative interpretations can be given.

The first five pictures, then, show close, generally positive kinds of mother-child interactions and will be referred to as the Realistic pictures. Such pictures seemed most suited to stimulate the ambivalence about intimacy hypothesized in the Psychosomatic group.

The next five pictures are drawings of witches and children in different fairy tale settings. Because the witch is such a very common symbol for the hostile, frightening elements of a mother's personality, these pictures allow the child to express the intensity of his concern about the mother's malevolence. Pictures from well-known fairy tales were avoided for the obvious reason that they would probably elicit stereotyped stories.

The choice of witches rather than realistically negative mother-child situations was an outcome of observations of the ward children. These children seemed quite preoccupied with witch fantasies and through them clearly communicated their feelings about the destructive power of the mother. The symbolic disguise allowed them to express attitudes which might be vehemently denied if translated into terms of realistic relationships. Thus the chance of stimulating the expression of negative feelings and the opportunities for gaining insights into the nature of such feelings seemed better via a series of Witch pictures.

The entire set of ten pictures was presented to the child with the usual instructions for thematic projective techniques. He was told that this was a "storytelling game." He was going to be shown some pictures and he should make up a story about each one. The story should identify the people in the picture, tell what is happening to them and how they feel about it, and what will happen later on. The child almost never spontaneously included the element of feeling in the original story, so a special inquiry had to be made at the end. He was specifically asked how the mother felt and how the child felt from the way each looked in the picture and why they felt that way. Thus, both the thematic material and the inquiry could be analyzed in terms of reflecting positive, negative, or neutral feelings about the relationship. For the Witch pictures the child was required only to tell a story and the content could be analyzed for the amount and kind of traumatic material introduced.

PREDICTIONS

A number of predictions were made which derived from the hypothesized lack of "motherliness" in the Psychosomatic mothers. These predictions stressed the neutral and negative reactions to mothering rather than the child's unsatisfied longings for closeness.[1] Specifically, it was predicted that, on the Realistic pictures, the Psychosomatic children would have fewer positive and more neutral themes and perceptions of feeling than would the two control groups. The decrease in positive thematic content would reflect these children's dwindling expectations of love or happiness or help in situations of close contact with the mother. The increased neutral content would reflect either an attempt to inhibit negative feelings or a sense of

---

[1] Another technique was designed specifically to get at this aspect of the ambivalence. Unfortunately it yielded no significant findings. (See the discussion of Toy Choice in Part II.)

emptiness and isolation. Predicting results about negative thematic material was not such a simple matter. This was because of the investigators' suspicion that Psychosomatic children might be too clever and guarded to produce large quantities of negative material in response to the Realistic pictures. If this suspicion were justified, however, there would still be the possibility of a qualitative difference in the negative material. Thus, an either-or prediction was made. Specifically, it was predicted that there might either be an increase in negative content or a different kind of negative content in the Psychosomatic group (e.g., the Psychosomatic mothers might be seen as self-centered, while the Neurotic mothers might be more directly competitive and angry). Finally it was predicted that the Witch pictures would elicit more traumatic material from the Psychosomatic group and that oral themes such as eating-up and poison would be more prominent. This latter point derives from the common equating of food with love; love contaminated with negative feelings then becomes symbolized by aggressive, destructive oral activities.

Although the data were analyzed in terms of these predictions, the investigators felt free to embrace any unexpected insights which the material might contain. This was fortunate since two of the most revealing characteristics of the stories—the so-called Mixed Themes and Unspecified Mothers—were totally unforeseen.

SCORING

A more detailed description of the scoring system will be helpful in defining the dimensions of the thematic material as well as in giving a clearer picture of the nature of the stories themselves.

Mother-child interaction

1. Positive Content. Here the relationship is one of love, sympathy, caretaking, defending, mutual sharing, or enjoyment of activities.

Example: "This picture is a mother putting her little baby to bed and she went out of the room and she came back to see if he is all right and he was. He was sort of kneeling in his crib. So she was happy and went out again."

2. Neutral Content. Mere description of the picture, absence of relationship or interaction, mother and child described separately, are all scored as Neutral.

Example: "The boy is in bed. The boy is crying. The mother is walking into the bedroom. The mother has a lamp. The mother has a doll. The mother has a dress. The mother has earrings. The mother and baby has hair. There we are."

3. Negative Content. Since the specific kind of negative relationship is important, a number of categories were empirically differentiated. The most important are the following: the *overtly angry* mother (mad, hollering, punishing); the *mildly angry* mother (irritated or mildly punishing by sending child to bed); the *depriving* mother who clearly and irrevocably refuses to give to the child; the *delaying* mother who says, "Wait" to a child's request either without reason or with a realistic explanation; the *controlling* mother who manipulates or moralizes or traps the child. Also scored but infrequently met were the competitive, self-centered, burdened, or impatient mothers. Sometimes it was the child who was pictured as being overtly or mildly angry, or as being surreptitious by acting in an underhanded, deceptive, or sneaky manner. All such content was scored as Negative.

Example: "Well the mother is coming in to see if her little daughter is sleeping and the little girl is sitting up in bed and she is looking at her mother and the mother feels mad because her little girl didn't go to bed and the little girl doesn't want to go to bed. So she sits up in bed."

4. Mixed Themes. This category had to be added since some stories combined both Positive and Negative content. It will be discussed in detail later.

5. Deviant Interpretations. Originally this category was designed to catch serious misinterpretations or distortions of the picture. Examples would be seeing the mother as sitting in mid-air, saying she had a black face, or saying that buildings in the background were crumbling. Such interpretations proved to be extremely rare. More important here were the so-called Unspecified Mothers, i.e., the mother was entirely omitted from the story, or was referred to vaguely as "she" or "a lady," or both mother and child were indiscriminately referred to as "they." This category came as a surprise since the pictures were selected on the basis of the clarity of the mother figure and her close interaction with the child.

Perception of Feeling in Mother and Child

These data were obtained from the inquiry concerning the way the mother and child felt in the picture. Positive, negative, and neutral feelings were scored following the same general criteria listed above.

A more specific breakdown was made in terms of whether the mother's feelings related directly to the child (e.g., happy because her little girl got a present) or to other people or events (e.g., happy she was going shopping). Similarly, the child's feelings were scored in terms of relating directly to the mother (e.g., unhappy because mother left) or to other people and events (e.g., disappointed because he doesn't like turkey). It was hoped that this finer differentiation would give more specific information about the direction of feeling either toward or away from the mother-child interaction.

The Neutral feeling category was eliminated because it contained too few cases to warrant analysis.

Traumatic Themes on Witch Pictures

There were four criteria for judging a story as traumatic: (1) Destructive oral themes such as poison, biting, eating-up, exploding food; (2) Excessive violence, such as exaggerated killing, bloody struggles, burning to death; (3) Negatively toned elaborations of the witch, such as spooky, terrible, evil, cruel, mean, and ugly; (4) Stories ending with the child being killed, indicating a lack of mastery of the fantasied situation.

Example: "The little girl is washing her hair and there is a witch in her house and she does not know it. Finally she turns around and sees the witch. The witch says, 'I'm going to eat you up.' The little girl says, 'Why are you going to eat me up?' 'Because I want to eat you up.' And the little girl calls her mother but the witch flew away. The mother said 'What is it?' The girl said, 'I just saw a witch right in the house.' 'Don't be afraid. Come in the living room and watch TV.' Then the girl went to bed and the witch was in her bedroom. When she was asleep the witch ate her up for supper. The mother found she wasn't in bed in the morning. She saw blood and cried because the little girl was dead."

RESULTS

In discussing the results, the three groups will first be described and compared with each other in regard to their depiction of the mother-child relationship. As will be seen, there is a certain amount of uniqueness but also a good deal of commonality among the groups. In the next section, the Mixed Themes will be discussed, since these proved to be the ones which most clearly differentiate the Psychosomatic group from the control groups. Finally, the Deviant Interpretations will be discussed briefly for the light they throw on the children's attitudes.

An overview of all the experimental results reveals a striking finding when the Psychosomatic group is compared with the Neurotic and Illness groups. On none of the 22 categories does the score of the Psychosomatic group represent the extreme of positive feeling either toward the mother-child relationship or toward the mother herself; in 17 of the categories the Psychosomatic group shows the most extreme negative feeling. Clearly, then, the Psychosomatic children showed least responsiveness to the positive elements in the pictures and the greatest responsiveness to the negative ones.

For the sake of simplicity, further intergroup comparisons will be suspended for a while, and the results for each group will be evaluated in detail.

The Psychosomatic Group

The first notable finding in regard to content and perceptions of feeling on the Realistic pictures is that the lack of positive thematic material is more striking and statistically more stable than the presence of strong negative material. This finding is in keeping with the prediction and deserves elaboration in greater detail.

In the original hypothesis it was stated that there was a lack of maternal feeling in the mothers of the Psychosomatic children. Thus, the absence of a positive quality, motherliness, was thought to be as significant as the different kinds of bad mothering which might be found. This was indirectly but dramatically illustrated on the ward when a boy reacted with complete incredulity to such small acts as a nurse running his bath water just because she thought he would be pleased, or when a girl could hardly believe that a candy-machine man had given her a box of gum for no other reason than he had taken a liking to her. It should be remembered that the children's routine needs were being met all along, and often met with understanding and warmth, but the children usually took this for granted. It was the "irrational" and spontaneous gesture which transcended routine and bypassed the question of merit and deserts which seemed never to have existed for them. The stories reflect a similar quality—a real inability to feel that being with their mother could be an intrinsically happy experience. This lack of positiveness has a further implication. The total emotional impact of a mother on a child is never in terms of the quantity and quality of her negative behavior but of the balance of positives and negatives in the total situation. This would imply that the negative features of the relationship would have more damaging consequences to the Psychosomatic children because of the lack of compensating rewards.

Although the Realistic pictures elicited negative thematic material, group differences here are not as sizable or as stable as with positive thema. From the quantitative point of view there is no evidence for a significantly greater amount of negative feeling than one would find in a group of neurotic children, although there is more than in non-psychosomatically ill children. Thus the caution about predicting quantitative differences seems justified. Certain significant qualitative differences were found, however. There were fewer mildly angry mothers in this group and an increased number of controlling mother-surreptitious child combinations. This latter finding will become more meaningful when the Mixed Themes are discussed.

The largest number of Deviant Interpretations are to be found in the Psychosomatic group. Many of these interpretations took the form of omitting the mother from the story or identifying her as some other female figure. A common clinical interpretation of such inaccuracies is that they represent a defense against unconscious negative feelings, such as anger or fear, which are directed toward the mother. By not identifying her, the child protects himself against the arousal of such anxiety-producing ideas. Thus the present results can be taken as evidence of the strength of the underlying negative feelings in the Psychosomatic children.

Further evidence for the strength of the negative feelings in this group comes from the Witch pictures. The stories here are saturated with traumatic material and represent the extreme as far as themes of poison and eating-up, blood and violence, destruction and general ghoulishness are concerned. Contrary to predictions, however, there was not a significant increase in oral trauma as compared with the other groups.

The Illness Group

The Illness group will be discussed next because the results, while conceptually confusing, are statistically more clear-cut than those of the Neurotic group.

The striking finding about this group is that all of the thematic material on the Realistic pictures indicates a greater amount of positive feeling toward the mother and fewer negative attitudes than are found in the other groups. This is consistently true for all the realistic content and perception of feeling categories. Taken by itself this would suggest a very healthy kind of mother-child interaction, with an abundance of love, sharing, and help, and a minimum of anger, antagonism, and manipulation. Such a relationship seems ideal indeed.

It is surprising to find, therefore, that on the Deviant Interpretations and the Witch pictures the Illness group loses its favored position. The traumatic content of the Witch stories does not reach the heights achieved by the Psychosomatic children nor, as will be seen later, are their Deviant Interpretations as extreme; yet there is definitely more disturbance here than is found in the Neurotic group. Such an incongruous finding requires an explanation.

The findings about the Witch pictures will be discussed first. As was pointed out earlier, the Realistic and the Witch pictures differ in their psychological distance from the mother, one tapping attitudes close to conscious awareness and the other more akin to irrational fears. In the healthy latency child such frightening, irrational fantasies are pushed further and further from consciousness by the accumulation of satisfying new experiences and by an increasingly realistic orientation toward life. In the Illness group this process does not seem to be taking place—realistic, positive feelings and fearful fantasies exist side by side.

There are two possible explanations for this strange juxtaposition. In the Illness group it was assumed that the illness struck at random as far as mother-child relationships were concerned. Therefore, what looks like incongruity might be characteristic of the attitude of any random sample of latency children. However, such an explanation does not seem plausible. It not only goes against the widely held idea that latency is a period of realism and stability, but it also does not agree with the finding that the Neurotic children, who are known to be disturbed, have fewer traumatic witch fantasies.

One is therefore forced to speculate about the possible effects of illness itself on the children's fantasies. Such speculation naturally applies to the Psychosomatic children as well as the ones in the Illness group.

When a child is suffering intensely or when he has an anomaly which endangers his life, it is quite possible that he will be strongly sensitized to the potentially dangerous, frightening, destructive aspects of his environment. To complicate matters, the child's intellectual grasp of the nature of the disease process is feeble and, at a very basic level, the distress of illness must therefore constitute incomprehensible suffering. Thus, as so often happens with children, fantasy becomes the arena for the struggle to master the unknown terror.

The child's illness also has significant interpersonal repercussions, both increasing the tensions within the family group and fostering special anxieties, guilts, and resentments in the mother. Thus a mother who is under added strain must care for a child highly sensitized to destruction. Since evidence from other parts of this study indicates that the mothers of the Illness children were good mothers in many respects, it is reasonable to assume that they were quite adequate in caring for their sick children. In all probability it was the hypersensitivity of the child which nurtured the witch fantasies. The mother's overt irritability or distress, which would seem justified to an adult observer or would be ignored by a healthy child, might become disproportionately threatening to the ill child. In addition, the child's natural sensitivity to covert moods may be heightened and make him especially responsive to underlying resentments in the mother. The irrational association of early childhood might also play an important part, with the mother becoming intimately connected with the pain and discomfort of illness, the anxiety of separation during hospitalization, and the medication or restrictions she must administer for the child's health and survival.

Finally, the realistic limitations imposed by illness may make it more difficult for the child to overcome his frightening fantasies. In the healthy latency child a host of new experiences divert him from his earlier concentration on the family circle. With new horizons opening up, the old attachments, antagonisms, and emotional entanglements at home need not be so intensely experienced. In the case of the ill child these horizons are often more limited for realistic reasons. This means that the protection and care of home still loom large for him, and, in a similar manner, the perpetuation of irrational fantasies is more likely.

This speculation can best be summarized in the following manner: Every child splits the mother image into a good mother who loves and rewards, and a bad mother who threatens and punishes; prolonged illness serves to fixate the image of the bad mother.

All this speculation implies that a certain amount of traumatic fantasy is to be expected of ill children even with adequate mothering. More important for the present study is the probability that some of the distortions of the mother image seen in the Psychosomatic children might be due to the effect of illness rather than to unusually destructive attitudes on the part of the mother. A good example of this is the failure to find the predicted increase in traumatic oral themes in the Psychosomatic group. On an *a priori* basis, such themes were thought to epitomize, as no other theme could, the Psychosomatic child's attitude toward receiving affection. In reality, the evidence indicates that such fantasies are probably common in many illnesses. One could even question how much such responses symbolize interpersonal relationships and how much they reflect a realistic experience of having to take disagreeable medicine or having to eat while in a state of physical distress.

But more generally, the results show that more attention must be paid to the psychology of illness per se. Almost no psychosomatic theory clearly differentiates the psychological problems inherent in any illness from those which antedate and contribute to the original physiological breakdown. Until the former can be identified and allowances made for it, psychosomatic hypotheses are open to a serious source of error.

This topic of fantasies common to any severe illness will again be discussed in Chapter 9. As will be seen, there is evidence that both the Psychosomatic and Illness groups share the belief that illness is caused by aggressive acts or by transgressions.

The Neurotic Group

The Neurotic group occupies a kind of middle ground on the realistic themes and perceptions. Closeness with the mother is not as positive an experience as it is for the Illness children, but it is not as barren as the Psychosomatic group pictures it. Similarly with the negative material—at times the feelings expressed are more intense even than those found in the Psychosomatic group, but at other times they are notably absent. Like the Illness children, neurotics are more apt to see the mother as depriving or delaying gratification than controlling and moralizing. The interesting twist is the significant decrease in the kind of traumatic Witch theme and Deviant Interpretations of the pictures, which were so prominent in both illness groups. This indicates a relative freedom from the intense anxieties which underlie such fantasies and a concomitant ability to evaluate situations with a minimum of distortion.

Thus the Neurotic group, while never feeling as consistently or intensely positive and negative about being mothered, are also freer from the irrational fear of intimacy found in the Illness group. Such tepid conclusions are more or less in keeping with the theory that basic doubts about being loved by the mother do not constitute the pivotal problem in neurotic children.

Yet this is not the whole story, as there is one more factor which must be included. A number of Neurotic children seemed to be reluctant to get involved in the task of telling stories. This characteristic was first apparent when the Deviant themes were being analyzed. Taking a cue from them, all the data were examined for evidence of resistance to the task. Such signs as refusals to tell stories, expressions of impatience or irritation, dismay over the number of cards, concern over how many pictures remained, were tabulated. The results show that the Neurotic group displayed a significantly greater amount of this kind of behavior (ten subjects as compared with three in each of the Illness groups). Thus Neurotic children were trying, as much as was socially permissible, to escape the situation. The need to use this defense indicates that the pictures were more disturbing than the scoring summaries might imply. The lack of consistently strong positive and negative feelings and the decrease in traumatic Witch themes might well represent a defensive maneuver aimed at keeping all feelings under control.

This finding throws a somewhat different light on the results. On the credit side it indicates defenses stable enough to protect the child from the feelings and fantasies so disruptive to the Illness groups. On the other hand, it suggests that the results should not be interpreted as proving either that the Neurotic children have no problems in the areas tapped by the pictures or that they have mastered such problems successfully. It seems more probable that they are seeking the safety of non-involvement; they are trying to solve the problem by not facing it. Such protective unresponsiveness is reminiscent of the defensive encapsulation revealed in the observed interaction. A healthier group of children might not have to resort to such a maneuver.

MIXED THEMES

In the discussion so far, the Psychosomatic group has differed from one or the other group but not from both. However, the Mixed Themes from the Realistic pictures contain attitudes toward mothering which significantly separate the Psychosomatic children from those in the Neurotic and Illness groups. Because of this, such themes deserve to be examined in detail.

Mixed Themes are those in which both positive and negative elements are included in the same story. At first glance this category might appear to reflect the hypothesized ambivalence of the child—his longing for tenderness and his rage over not receiving it. However, examination of the stories themselves would not justify such an interpretation. Their general form is more one of hostile dependency, with the child unable to get along with the mother but unable to do without her. Clinically speaking, they should be classified as a special kind of Negative content.

More important than the problem of classification are the insights such stories furnish into the nature of the mother-child interaction. However, before describing this interaction, it is important to stress the fact that the findings here are much more tenuous than the ones previously discussed and should best be regarded as hunches to be evaluated by further research.

Two different patterns of interaction emerged from the Mixed Themes and were labeled Manipulative relationships and Inconsistent relationships.

Manipulative Relationships

The outstanding feature of the Manipulative relationship is the duplicity of the mother. Her primary goal is one of maintaining a facade of perfection. It is not so much love as the show of love that counts, not so much closeness as doing the right thing for all the world to see. These are the quotation-mark mothers: they "love," "understand," "give," "help," the child just as they should and they know all the right answers. Yet the subtle, crucial components of feeling are lacking. This adroitness at form and absence of substance is a new variation of the previously discussed absence of genuinely positive feeling in the Psychosomatic group. Although the following story is not a Mixed Theme, it is an excellent example of the facade of perfection.

Well, this little boy, he lived in a house and at his house he had some swings and every day after breakfast he used to go out and swing on them. And one day he invited his friend over to swing and there was only one swing so he said, "You can swing first because you are my guest." And his mother was sitting nearby and she said to herself, "I am proud I have a little boy who knows how to share" and after he swang and afterwards the friend and himself went inside. There was only one toy horse. So the little boy said that he would let his friend ride the toy horse while he had the gun. And his mother said that they should put the things away and just then the little boy's mother called him—the one from next door—and had him come home for supper. So the little boy picked the toys up and said, "Mother, I have picked them up." And just then his mother called him to dinner and she said to his father and himself, "I saw my little boy playing today and he knows how to share his things." And they lived happy ever after.

An important consequence of the mother's need for observable perfection is that her giving to the child is always conditional—he must behave in keeping with the facade. The perfect mother must have the perfectly behaved child. This is the essential ingredient of the mother-child interaction. A few examples will illustrate this conditional giving, as well as the emphasis on good behavior and propriety.

Well, this little girl went to the store with her mother and bought a new dress because she was going to the party. And her mother is putting on her dress and the little girl likes it very much—it is really a skirt. And they went to the party and they had a nice time and she was playing around and then she spilled something on the dress. And her mother is taking it off of her and putting something dry on. And she says, "If you are going to drop anything—if you are going to"—she was a very careless little girl—"If you are going to ruin all your dresses I am not going to buy any more." And—she didn't do anything more on her dress.

Thus the child is in the frustrating situation of having a mother who does the right things (buys pretty dresses, takes care of injuries) but always with strings attached (good behavior on the part of the child). Instead of giving, the mother bargains.

On his part the child is not aware of the negative feelings behind the mother's facade. Although the mother gives, her irritability can be quite close to the surface at times. Or, again, her control can become so obvious that the child gets almost nothing out of the bargain.

Well—the boy asked her [sic] mother if he could go out and play and the mother says, "After you eat." So he hurried up and ate. And she said he should make his bed and straighten up his room. That is what he didn't like. So he snuck out and went to the back yard to play. He called his boy friend over to play. And they were on the swing and he was on the swing and he happened to fall off—the boy accidentally shoved him, pushed him too fast. His mother came running in the yard and asked him what happened. He said he fell off the swing. She said, "Did you make your bed?" Now the little boy was really stuck and didn't know what to say. He said, "I did," and the mother said, "No you did not because I was just up there." And she said, "That will teach you a lesson for not obeying me. First comes work and then comes play." And from that point on the little boy always obeyed his mother and then went out to play.

Furthermore, there is evidence that the child resents the mother's manipulation. The stories are full of negative feelings, ranging from mild unhappiness through "accidental," mischievous, or petulant behavior. (The Witch stories also furnish evidence of strongly negative attitudes.) Direct anger or defiance is never present; since the mother is always right, rage is never justified. Instead, the children tend to become sneaky and underhanded. Remember that, in scoring different kinds of Negative content in other stories, there was a significantly greater number of controlling mother-surreptitious child interactions in the Psychosomatic group. This pattern is exactly the same one which comes up again in the Mixed Themes, except that in this case the mother gives something in return for good behavior.

The crucial point is that, in each story, the child is ultimately condemned and the mother's values are upheld. Rebellion is never condoned. Many stories end on a moral note such as the child learning a lesson. Such an ending, while obviously hollow to the reader, should not be dismissed as mere verbalism. It shows that the children are patterning themselves after the mother. In some cases this is accompanied by snobbishness and a readiness to judge others as inferior; in other cases it is expressed in an excessive niceness and self-control. Regardless of the individual variations, however, the mother's system of values is taken over by the child.

In sum, the children in the Mixed Themes are pictured not only as being manipulated by their mothers for ulterior reasons, but also as identifying with her system of values. Thus they are trapped between a sense of outrage at being given conditional love and a self-censoring demon working for the preservation of the facade of perfection.

Inconsistent Relationships

One of the outstanding features of the Manipulative mother is the highly integrated nature of her control. When one turns to the Inconsistent mothers the opposite quality is equally striking.

This boy is crying. He feels sad. He just fell in a puddle and he don't like it and he hurted himself—his noggin. Mother comes up. "What happened?" "I fell in a puddle of water and hurted my knee." "Come on in and I will bandage it up." And they went in. Then he had to go to bed. They put some iodine and bandage on it. And then the mother said, "How do you feel now?" "OK." "Do you want to get up?" "No, I want to stay in bed so I won't have to go to school." "Oh you! Now you have to stay in bed a week!" "I have to figure out how to get out of this." "Oh no. If you get out I will spank." "Ha ha! You can't get me." "Oh can't I? How does this feel?" Bang, bang. "That is only a sample. I am not going to let you up. You can't play with your girl friends or your boy friends. If you sneak out you will have to stay home two weeks. But if you stay home one week you can go out." "Hooray!" "If you are good you can get something to eat." "Is that good?" "Yes."

Here there is no facade to give a consistent structure and organization to the relationship. Instead there is a senseless alternation of highly charged positive and negative feelings. The example is a particularly lush one since the story gets completely out of hand. In a more controlled child the theme was expressed in the following manner. "Is that a play pen or a bed. A play pen. No, no; it is a crib. And the mother is coming in and she sees that the baby is still up and she is supposed to be sleeping. So she gives her a bottle to drink the milk and she will turn the light out again and she will make her go to bed again. The baby looks like she is crying. The mother looks like she is hollering at the baby."

However, the essential feature of all the themes is the inability of the mother figure to relate in a consistent manner. Whereas the Manipulative mothers are highly purposeful, the actions of the Inconsistent mothers lack continuity and are abrupt and unpredictable. The picture which emerges from the stories is of a mother who is confused and conflicted about herself and her role, and who communicates this confusion to the child.

Unlike the Manipulative mothers, Inconsistent mothers are pictured as being much more open and aboveboard about the way they feel. One does not have to look behind a facade to detect what is going on. Ordinarily such overtness might be helpful in defining the mother's personality for the child. Even if she were hostile, he would know where he stands and could defend himself accordingly. In this case, however, the advantages of overtness are constantly being nullified by the shifting, unpredictable nature of the mother's activities. Thus giving is followed by irritation, indulgence by deprivation, caretaking gestures by selfishness.

The tenor of some stories indicates that the mother and child have little to do with one another, but when they do get together, it is on the basis of mutual inconsistency. However, the more impressive cases are those in which there is a mutual entanglement, with both mother and child reacting in such a way as to perpetuate turmoil and confusion. The mother is either unable to cope with the child or descends to the level of childishness herself. The control she should exercise is nowhere to be found. Thus both mother and child are inseparably attached to one another and irresistibly driven to anger, annoyance, and irritation.

A word should be said about the relation of the Manipulative and Inconsistent themes. Most of the stories fall into these two groups, but there are some cases which have elements of both. Although the number of stories is too small to permit a definitive statement, there does seem to be continuity from one group to the other instead of two pure types. The progression goes from the chaotic kind of hostile dependency in the Inconsistent stories, to a less dramatic alternation of giving and deprivation, to stories in which the mother gives but covertly feels angry about it, and finally to the establishment of the duplicity of surface perfection and underlying irritation found in the Manipulative stories. Such a finding might be an artifact of the test or of the scoring system. However, it is also possible that this continuity reflects a psychological continuum. The common denominator in all the stories is the mother's inability to relate directly to her child. Some mothers are pictured as being more skillful in managing this ambivalence (possibly they are, in reality, better integrated women) while others are seen as helpless to control their feelings and are buffeted about. This matter will be discussed in greater detail when the psychological findings from both the mothers and the children are integrated.

One final point. The stories with Manipulative mothers are much more coherent and usually richer than those with Inconsistent mothers. This might lead one to think that the children telling the former are psychologically healthier and, conversely, such a relationship is not as damaging as an Inconsistent one. There is no evidence to confirm such an inference. The Witch themes are equally traumatic in both groups and the World Test (a personality assessment technique to be described later) shows the same degree of psychological disturbance. Thus the spurious consistency of the Manipulative mother has as many negative effects on the child as the uncontrolled overtness of the Inconsistent mother.

UNSPECIFIED MOTHERS

Unspecified Mother stories deserve special examination because of the different kinds of interpretative distortions involved. The total number of such stories is rather small, but the fact that the pictures were chosen so as to minimize ambiguity and prevent distortion, adds to their importance. The stories fell into three categories: (1) *Omitted mothers,* in which the subject did not include the mother in the original story and, in extreme cases, continued to block even when asked specifically about the mother figure in the picture; (2) *Identity stories* in which both mother and child were called "they" or "we" and given identical roles in the story; (3) *Surrogate stories* in which the mother figure was called "she" or identified as another female and, at times, given a maternal function. This last category represents the smallest amount of blocking to the mother figure, and the first represents the greatest.

The two illness groups had the greatest number of such stories but the Psychosomatic group had more Omitted and Identity themes. Not only was the female figure differentiated more frequently in the Illness group but in a few cases she was also given a maternal role. One would therefore infer that underlying attitudes toward the mother were less disturbing in this group than they were in the Psychosomatic group. The Neurotic group had very few Unspecified Mother stories and these were in the general context of a brief, superficially pleasant touch-and-go approach to the entire series of pictures. This defensive non-involvement is very much in keeping with the Neurotic group's general attitude toward the task of telling stories.

Two findings are of interest in the Psychosomatic group. The fact that the blocking here is more severe than it is with any of the other groups fits in with the previous evidence of a more disturbed mother-child relationship. Second, the increased number of Identity stories is significant in light of the hypothesis that the mother-child relationship is a pathologically close one. Such stories in no way imply a healthy sharing or enjoyment of participation in similar activities. The merging of two identities into one, and the use of "we" both reflect a more infantile stage of development. What is represented is a basic lack of differentiation of mother and child rather than the mutuality which can develop between two well-established identities.

Thus, the Unspecified Mother stories disclosed little that was new but served to underline some of the previous findings—the severely disturbed, pathologically close relationship in the Psychosomatic group, the less disturbed but still disruptive elements in the Illness group, and the defensive non-involvement of the Neurotic children.

8---*Personality Characteristics of Psychosomatic Children*

One of the goals of clinical research is that of relating historical antecedents to contemporary character structure in order to achieve a comprehensive understanding of personality. Although this research project focused primarily upon reconstruction of the historical past, the question of the nature of the children's present personality was a continually tantalizing one. It seemed presumptuous to think in terms of the ultimate question—Just what are children with psychosomatic disorders like?—since the project concentrated on the circumscribed area of the mother-child relationship. Certainly a host of other formative influences as well as many significant facets of personality have been neglected. Yet it was possible to explore a limited number of areas systematically, so that some light can be shed on the contemporary personality picture.

The specific areas studied were the child's emotional responsiveness, the extent of his psychological disturbance, and his attitude toward receiving.

EMOTIONAL RESPONSIVENESS

Although the children on the psychosomatic ward had quite different personalities, many of them shared a peculiar kind of emotional distance. Their therapists would complain of the difficulty in developing either a positive or negative transference relationship; the nurses and teacher, speaking more directly, described the children as "hard to get close to." From all evidence, the children were as unresponsive to each other as they were to adults.

This was something beyond the expected debilitation of illness. Rather it seemed a basic affective vacuousness. Because these were youngsters, one was constantly anticipating expressions of affection or rage or fear, and finding instead a bland response. This does not mean that the children were totally affectless. Outbursts of anger, moments of high excitement, dramatic demands for attention, all occurred from time to time. However, these were present more or less as special events. It was the main current of the children's emotional life which lacked vitality.

Yet the children were not withdrawn in the usual sense of the term. Intellectually they were alert and perceptive. They had many techniques for playing up to ward personnel or capturing the attention of adults. For example, a very bright nine-year-old was master of the technique of remembering the special interests of a number of adults both on the ward and in the general hospital. Because of this he could immediately hit upon a topic which would intrigue the adult into a conversation. Significantly enough, he often could not sustain the relationship and his contacts, though highly individualized, were typically quite brief. Also his ability to turn this technique on and off indicated that he used it primarily to satisfy his own needs and that his intellectual acuity did not result from a great emotional investment in others. Further evidence that the children were not withdrawn is the fact that their understanding of social interactions was especially keen. Even the most inhibited child on the ward could come forth with a drily humorous remark epitomizing a social situation. The children's techniques for manipulation and control of one another were additional evidence of their perceptiveness; e.g., one boy organized the other children into a club, got himself appointed treasurer, and, by playing on the psychological vulnerabilities of the members, proceeded to extort money and presents from them. He was also a perfect Iago, subtly inciting the others to aggressive or sexual acting out, and then striking a pose of mildly righteous condemnation when the nurses arrived. All such activity indicates a high level of social awareness in the children, as well as good reality contact.

Putting these two characteristics together, one sees an unusual combination of affective emptiness with intellectual alertness in the ward children. Such a finding merited more systematic investigation.

The Rorschach was the research technique of choice since it is sensitive both to emotional responsiveness and intellectual activity. Because the research schedule was too tight to permit systematic administration of this technique, and because a number of records had previously been accumulated, a somewhat different population was used. There were still three groups (Psychosomatic, Neurotic, and Illness), but only six boys and six girls per group. The age range was from 5-9 to 16-1, with a mean age of 9-7. Intelligence was average or above, and the groups were equated for race, socioeconomic status, and family intactness. The general principles used in defining the experimental and control groups were the same as those described in Chapter 3.

In order to obtain specific Rorschach criteria of unresponsiveness, five clinical psychologists with considerable experience interpreting children's records were given a written description of the personality characteristics described above.[1] They were then asked to list five scoring categories and five qualitative signs which they considered to be particularly sensitive indices in the Rorschach of the type of emotional emptiness which had been observed. When three of the five judges listed the same category or sign, it was included as a criterion.

The final list of criteria was as follows:

Formal Signs. (1) Low Sum C (weighted color response); (2) No Y or decreased Y (shading response); (3) High F% (form element); (4) Low M (human movement response); (5) Decreased H (human response), and Hd (human details) greater than H.

Qualitative Signs. (1) Dehumanized humans; humans not interacting; few ordinary humans; humans set at a distance; (2) Limited fantasy; less animation; (3) Impersonal content; increased inanimate content such as water, clouds, landscape.

Analysis of the Rorschach records revealed a significant increase in F% in the Psychosomatic group, with a corresponding significant decrease in Y. There was only a trend for Sum C to decrease in the Psychosomatic group, but there were significantly fewer C responses, and significantly fewer violent C responses (i.e., blood, fire, and explosion responses). Interestingly enough, the greatest differences were always between the two illness groups, with the Neurotic group falling between them. Although there was no significant decrease in Human

----

[1] The authors are grateful to Drs. Joan Swift, Rae Sternberg, Marion Wieman, and Alan Rosenwald for their expert help.

responses in the Psychosomatic group, there was a tendency for these children to see proportionately more Hd's than H's. There was no significant difference in the M responses or in any of the three qualitative signs.

The large number of negative findings means that a Rorschach expert would not characterize these children with psychosomatic disorders as empty and emotionally lifeless. Their fantasy life is as rich, their concern about interpersonal relations as great, their symbolic expression of conflict as varied, their intellect as alert, as one would find in neurotic or severely ill, non-psychosomatic children. However, it should be noted that these are all ideational, imaginative, and fantasy dimensions of personality; they all take place, so to speak, "in the head." What is striking in the Rorschach records is the absence of expressiveness. There is little direct access to showing joy or hate or fear, little spontaneity of action. On the contrary, the children tend to be overcontrolled, colorless, and bland. What they lack is the capacity to react intensely and express directly what they feel.

To summarize the Rorschach picture, the Psychosomatic group is characterized by overcontrol, introversion, and emotional distance. The children are at home in the realm of ideation rather than in the realm of action. Their social awareness is intact but their capacity for direct social participation is limited. Generally they live more within themselves and to themselves.

How does such a Rorschach picture compare with the ward observations described at the beginning of this section? It is tempting to say that the two are identical, but such a conclusion seems somewhat wishful. The two descriptions have a good deal in common, but the clinical picture seems more dramatic and extreme than the Rorschach findings. For example, one can see why a standoffish child would be difficult to relate to, but one would also wonder why the ideational and imaginative liveliness revealed in the Rorschach would not serve as an important bond between him and the sympathetic adults on the ward. This element of disparity might be due to a number of causes: the ward population was small and consequently might be biased; the Rorschach might have been insensitively used or invalid as a measuring device; or the ward behavior might reflect not only the lack of expressiveness described here, but also a number of other factors such as the difficulty in receiving and the mistrustfulness, which will be dealt with in a later section. Whatever the reasons for disparity, it seems most appropriate to conclude that there is a large area of congruence between the clinical observations and Rorschach findings, although the former picture is more extreme than the latter.

It is interesting to speculate about the reasons for the Psychosomatic child's sacrifice of overt expression of feeling and retreat into control and covertness. To begin with, it does not seem to be the kind of total inhibition found in the severely traumatized child or the washed-out blandness of the neglected child. Rather, one is struck by the imbalance of personality structure, certain characteristics developing normally while others are markedly impaired. Instead of being totally rejected or neglected, then, these are children in whom certain positive traits have been stimulated while others have atrophied.

Is it possible to be more specific about this imbalance? When one thinks of C and Y on the Rorschach one somehow thinks of bodily activity. Color and shading, in contrast with movement and vista, have the connotation of directly observable acting out of feeling. By contrast, self-control means that dramatic forms of bodily expression are inhibited, while fantasy implies that activity is removed from the realm of action to the realm of ideas. It is possible then that these are children in whom overt acting out has not been tolerated, but who have been rewarded for self-control and stimulated intellectually. Such a child might be quite acceptable to a rigid, ambitious, intellectual mother. Viewed in this light, the children's unresponsiveness would be the product of a more or less familiar pattern of neurotic mother-child interaction.

Yet the problem is more complex than this. To regard these children merely as neurotically inhibited would be to ignore the fact that they are also desperately ill physically. This means that the body is not only the vehicle for acting out feelings, but it is the source of anxiety and pain. In non-psychosomatically ill children there is evidence for a considerable amount of overtness of behavior; with them moodiness, anger, affection, find ready expression. Why does not illness have the same liberating effect on the experimental group? One possible explanation is that illness plays a significant but quite different role in the two groups. To understand this role and how it relates to emotional responsiveness, it will be helpful to return to the main hypothesis of the research.

According to most developmental theories, emotional expressiveness in the latency child represents a refinement of the global, undifferentiated reactivity of the infant. In order for a latency child to have normal emotional responsiveness, certain physiological and psychological developments must have taken place. On the physiological side, the massive, erratic, and extreme reactivity of the infant must be integrated into a smoothly functioning organism which is both differentiated and coordinated. Psychologically, the child must discriminate people and events in his environment and master some of the refinements of symbolic activity. Finally, these two functions must be integrated. Thus, a three-year-old being angry at his father represents quite a developmental achievement: it means he has learned to differentiate his father as an individual, that his physiological apparatus is responding in an adequately dramatic fashion, and that the ideational and visceral components are well integrated.

In the case of Psychosomatic children, integration of the erratic physiological responses during infancy has not taken place because of faulty mothering. As was mentioned in Chapter 2, it is a matter of conjecture as to exactly how this disarticulation eventuates in a psychosomatic symptom. Regardless of the process, however, the essential factor is that the physiological responses remain extreme and erratic; in short, they are "out of control." Because of this, the further step of integrating them with the higher symbolic processes is inadequately accomplished. To return to the example of the three-year-old, in the case of a Psychosomatic child, his incipient feelings of strong anger toward his father would stimulate such abortive physiological responses as severe cramps or joint pains or panicky gasping for breath; this not only prevents the emotional response from being carried out but diverts the child's attention from his father to himself. In this manner the child is prevented from investing feeling in people or events. The physiological concomitants of strong anger or fear or joy or love are short-circuited into extreme, primitive reactivity. The enforced self-concentration which accompanies this pattern might well be the basis of the narcissism which some observers say is characteristic of children with psychosomatic disorders. It should also be noted, however, that the psychological processes may develop normally and produce the adequate intellectual evaluations of reality which these Psychosomatic children evidenced.

There is one final complication which is relevant here. Once the physiological concomitants of emotion have been short-circuited into primitive reactivity, it would seem reasonable to assume that the child would try to defend himself against exposure to this painful experience. As with any traumatizing situation, it would soon happen that even the innocuous beginnings of physiological reaction would call forth defensive maneuvers. Thus, it is possible to imagine the Psychosomatic child using such mechanisms as repression or denial in order to avoid arousing strong feeling. This is very much like Grinker's description of the ego which is burdened with the task of protecting the body from breakdown under stress. The important point here is that such defensive maneuvers would be another factor contributing to the lack of emotional responsiveness in Psychosomatic children.

The above theoretical considerations have interesting implications in regard to the difference between neurotic inhibition and "psychosomatic" unresponsiveness. Theoretically the neurotic child has developed differentiated reactions (e.g., organized aggressive or sexual impulses) to specific individuals (e.g., parents). He has been punished for such reactions and consequently repressed them. In children with psychosomatic diseases no such refinement has taken place. This means impulses are relatively undifferentiated and unmodified by intellectual or symbolic processes, and in this sense, certain aspects of the child's personality remain at a primitive level of development. Subsequent defenses try to prevent physiological primitivization when the individual is under unusual stress.

A further implication is that children with psychosomatic disorders should be more difficult to treat psychotherapeutically. To begin with, their physiological disarticulation has prevented the integration of intellectual and symbolic processes with emotional impulses. Since the main tools of therapy are intellectual and symbolic ones, such emotions should be much more difficult to reach. In the second place, a potentially more catastrophic reaction is being defended against than is the case with neurotic children. The neurotic child is anxious because of some discrete, differentiated impulse while the child with a psychosomatic illness fears a return of the overwhelming trauma of infancy.

SEVERITY OF DISTURBANCE

According to psychoanalytic theory, the earlier a trauma, the more actual or potential damage to personality development. If this is true, it should follow that children with psychosomatic disorders should be more disturbed than neurotic children, since their difficulties stem from the earliest mother-infant interaction.

To test this hypothesis, the World Test was given to the original group of children and the results were used to measure severity of disturbance. This test consists of 200 miniature toys representing, among other things, people, animals, buildings, vehicles, and trees. The child is told to make anything he wants and is left free to construct whatever he wishes. Later he is asked about what he has made and about the activities represented in his World.

In the World Test there are three general indices of psychological disturbances. The first is the construction of *Empty Worlds,* which are characterized by the use of very few pieces or the absence of humans. Next there are *Aggressive Worlds,* which include violent themes such as fighting, accidents, fire, or wild animals biting. Finally there are *Distorted Worlds.* These are divided into three different categories—*Closed Worlds* in which the major part of the construction is enclosed by fences, walls, or shrubs; *Rigid Worlds,* which have unnatural alignments of pieces into rows or exaggerated symmetry in their arrangement; and *Disorganized Worlds,* in which pieces are placed chaotically or bizarrely, or are used in a highly undifferentiated manner. The Distorted Worlds are of most interest here because both clinical judgment and empirical evidence indicate that they represent the greatest amount of psychological disturbance. Empty Worlds and Aggressive Worlds might represent neurotic inhibition or impulsivity; the Distorted Worlds, however, reflect the kind of faulty reality contact and primitivization which are associated with deep pathology.

Results of statistical analyses show a strong tendency for the Psychosomatic group to have a greater total number of signs of disturbance. More important is the significant increase in Distorted Worlds as compared with both control groups. The Psychosomatic and Neurotic groups have more Aggressive Worlds than do the Illness group, and there is a strong tendency for both illness groups to have more Empty Worlds than are found in the Neurotic group.

Thus, the World Test data do indicate more signs of disturbance in the children with psychosomatic disorder, and more pathological kinds of disturbances.

Another approach to the problem was via the Rorschach protocols. Theoretically the content of Rorschach responses can furnish symbolic clues to areas of psychological stress. If the children with psychosomatic disorders had a very disturbed infantile period, residuals of this disturbance should be reflected in the content of their Rorschach responses. Three categories of responses were used as signs of early trauma: (1) *Oral trauma.* This represents a combination of orality with aggressivity or destructiveness, such as biting, cannibalism, spitting, bloodsucking; (2) *Depression*. This includes references to death, debilitation, and decay, as well as intensely dark percepts such as "midnight" or "the inside of the heart"; (3) *Suspiciousness*. This category includes masks, hidden people, pretense, emphasis on eyes, watching or stalking animals, and manipulatory instruments, all of which symbolize mistrustfulness. Criteria for the three categories were made quite rigorous in order to conform to clinical standards of judging a response as indicative of deep disturbance. An effort was made to exclude all signs of neurotic hostility as well as the more phobic kinds of anxiety, since these theoretically do not originate in the earliest stages of personality development.

Statistical analysis of the results shows there is a definite tendency for the Psychosomatic group to have more symbols of early trauma than the other groups. Although the results are in the predicted direction, they do not meet the more rigorous criteria of significance.

In summary, then, evidence from the World Test, and to some extent from the Rorschach, indicates greater psychological disturbance in the Psychosomatic group than one would find in neurotic children or children with non-psychosomatic illnesses. However, a word of caution should be added. The findings definitely do not constitute evidence that the Psychosomatic group is as deeply disturbed as psychoanalytic theory implies. Whether the extent of pathology represented here is equal to that found in severely disturbed or schizophrenic children can be determined only by further research.

ATTITUDE TOWARD RECEIVING

Some of the most striking observations of the children on the ward concerned their attitude toward receiving, whether this involved tangibles such as presents and food, or intangibles such as affection and attention. Their behavior seemed to represent a fusion of insatiable longings to be given to and chronic dissatisfaction with what was given. Thus there would be demandingness with little evidence that their needs could ever be fulfilled.

There were many expressions of this difficulty and many fascinating variations. However, only a few can be mentioned briefly. One ten-year-old boy would go into dark, brooding rages in his therapy hour before he could bring himself to ask for a special present; when it was brought to him, however, there was not a flicker of responsiveness to it. Another therapist's desk drawer was filled with presents her patient had requested but could never accept. This inability to enjoy being given to was also apparent in group behavior. It was noted that, after a special outing such as a picnic or a trip to the zoo, there was none of the residual excitement, discussion, and reliving of the experience which is so characteristic of children; instead the event seemed to vanish and routine living took over as if nothing had happened. Another expression of insatiability and discontent was the children's inability to share an adult's attention; a child would often have to have exclusive attention or he would become resentful and withdraw. It was as if he felt there was never enough affection to go around, and what was given to others necessarily deprived him. Certain children had set up strong defenses against demandingness; however, in therapy they clearly expressed the fear that their need to be given to would become overwhelmingly intense if it were ever permitted expression. One boy even went a step further by stating, "If I wouldn't be so greedy I wouldn't be so sick," thus building the psychosomatic bridge between greed and illness. Finally, the children's mistrust of the giver was seen in their belief that the show of affection concealed destructive intent. This was epitomized by a boy's spontaneous remark when a very decorative candy house was presented to the ward at Christmas time; he immediately asked, "Is there a witch inside?"

Unfortunately the fascination of such observations far outstripped the authors' ingenuity in designing procedures to investigate them experimentally. Although two techniques were devised, they are rather peripheral. They are presented here as limited studies which make no claim of going to the heart of the matter.

The first technique consisted of systematically observing and recording the child's response to being offered a gift. Before the first session the experimenter had put a small gold box containing ten pieces of hard candy inside a cabinet in the playroom. At the end of the session, after the subject had finished with the Witch pictures, he was complimented on his storytelling ability and informed that the experimenter had a present for him. He was told the location of the little gold box which contained the gift. After that the examiner kept a running account of the child's behavior. He spoke only to answer questions briefly and to encourage the child once to take all the candy he wanted.

It was predicted that the children with psychosomatic disorders would show more behavioral signs of difficulty in accepting the present. Specifically, there would be more rejection of the candy, more hesitation while taking it, and less positive responsiveness of delight or appreciation. These predictions were borne out to a highly significant extent, with the Psychosomatic group being quite different from the two control groups.

The specific kinds of behavior indicative of difficulty over receiving were varied. The clearest examples were excessive inhibition, delay, hesitation, extraneous activities, and signs of general discomfort. Some children could not allow themselves to take any candy before obtaining additional permission from the examiner, while others took only a few pieces even after being encouraged. Certain subjects were not inhibited in their actions but failed to show any sign of affect—no change of expression, no communication except perhaps a perfunctory "Thank you."

Many other types of behavior were observed but did not differentiate the groups. These are described in detail in Part II. However, the category of Dependency deserves brief mention. Here the child either pestered the examiner with questions and demands or constantly looked to the examiner for permission or reassurance. This was the only category in which the child made persistent attempts to draw the observer into the situation. There was a definite though not statistically significant tendency for the Psychosomatic children to behave in this manner. Such a finding, while of little value in itself, is interesting since it is on the same continuum of Negative Closeness as was observed in the mother-child interaction. The children were using, with the examiner, the same techniques which were so dramatically displayed with their mothers.

The second procedure focused on the element of mistrust which was so prominent in certain children's difficulty in receiving. In order to obtain evidence of this, both the content of the Rorschach responses and the thematic elaborations of the World Test were examined for symbolic expressions of lack of trust, sneakiness and slyness, hidden or evil intent. The Rorschach responses indicative of mistrustfulness were described in the previous section of this chapter—masks, hidden people, pretense ("two tigers pretending they are girls"), emphasis on eyes, stalking or watching animals, and manipulatory instruments. In the World Test, themes of hiding, secretiveness, spying, and disguise were regarded as the relevant ones. In each technique there were significantly more of such symbols and themes in the Psychosomatic group, and fewest in the Illness group.

In summary, the two techniques, while limited in scope, did furnish

evidence that children with psychosomatic disorders have more difficulty in accepting presents and are more mistrustful than the children
in the other two groups.

Turning to more speculative matters, one wonders what kinds of
experiences could produce this intense longing which is so resistant
to fulfillment. As with the lack of emotional responsiveness discussed
in the first section, such a pattern does not seem to be the end product
of simple neglect or deprivation. For one thing, the ward children
have not given up the desire for affection and settled for shallow contact, an adjustment often seen in minimally satisfied children. Nor is
their insatiability the kind which implies they were starved for affection. Rather, nothing they get is ever satisfying—they want this and
they want that, but they feel they never get what they really need.

It seems more meaningful to infer that these children have been
greatly stimulated by their mothers but have never received the kind
of love they crave. The mother might focus a good deal of attention
on the child and have a large emotional investment in him, but be
incapable of giving him basic maternal affection. A few examples of
this overstimulating but unsatisfying interaction might be helpful.
The mother of a six-year-old girl was always bringing her daughter
more expensive presents than were requested. If the child had her
heart set on an ordinary doll, her mother would bring a very elaborate,
showy one. Thus the child was continually in the dilemma of not
knowing whether to feel excited and superior and grateful or to feel
enraged at not getting her real heart's desire. Another mother was
physically overstimulating to her ten-year-old boy, sleeping with him,
bathing him, and especially delighting in washing his hair. All this
seemed sheer self-indulgence on her part and she did everything she
could to perpetuate his dependence upon her. Thus the boy was over-
stimulated erotically while his basic assertive urges were undermined.
In some cases the stimulation was intellectual rather than physical,
with the mother priding herself on her own intellectual understanding
and pushing the child to similar achievements. The lapses in empathetic understanding in such cases were striking. For example, one
adolescent girl liked any dress material except plaid, which she pub-
licly announced she hated. When she requested a new dress from
home for a very special occasion her mother promptly sent her a plaid
one.

It should always be kept in mind that the glaring inconsistencies in
behavior were not seen as such by the mothers of the ward children.

Hostility or rejection or insensitivity to the child's needs would be vehemently denied. Since the mothers themselves were so mistaken about the appropriateness of what they gave, the child was constantly being asked to believe that he was receiving true understanding and warmth. This is exactly what is so confusing to the child—what is basically self-indulgence or guilty overcompensation or distant intellectualism is offered as maternal love. Thus emotional deprivation takes place under the guise of fulfillment. It is the combination of intimacy without genuine love which seems the most logical antecedent of the children's observed behavior. Such a relationship might well produce the insatiability, dissatisfaction, and mistrust which are so characteristic.

Parenthetically it should be remarked that there is a tremendous amount of hostility implicit in such an interaction, whether it be in the mother, in the child, or in both. The mother's giving often contains unconscious hostile elements while the child is enraged by the frustrations intrinsic in the relationship. This contamination of closeness with rage was most succinctly expressed in some of the ward children's fantasies about poisoned food. However, it seemed that the children's rage was often the result of being deprived and deceived. Thus, while it was an extremely important variable in the total pathology of the child, it did not seem to be the basic cause of pathology. That is why the primary focus of therapy was the satisfaction of basic, often infantile, needs for affection, rather than the release of pent-up rage.

9---Children's Fantasies Concerning Etiology of Physical Illness

At times it is necessary to underscore the obvious. To isolate a cluster of diseases from the gamut of illnesses and label them "psychosomatic" is a complex and difficult undertaking; to disregard the psychological concomitants of illness per se in this process is to invite erroneous conclusions. This point has to be made because of the current lack of rapprochement between the psychosomatic and somatopsychic approaches. Some of the most fruitful psychosomatic theories have come from investigators who often fail to compare their findings with research on non-psychosomatic illness. On the other hand, somatopsychic studies tend to be piecemeal, or to lack either the depth or the scope of psychosomatic theories. There are hopeful signs that the disjointed character of this development is being remedied. However, the present situation is still unsatisfactory enough to warrant a testimonial in favor of a comprehensive and unified approach to the problem of illness.

Ideally this problem should be attacked head on. The present project was not designed for this purpose and relevant findings have come about obliquely by way of the Illness control group. Such findings were always regarded as important by-products and were discussed in detail. However, it was also possible to branch out from the strict confines of the main hypothesis and explore certain facets of illness directly.

One of the most intriguing areas of exploration was the child's fantasies about the cause of his illness. As was pointed out in Chapter 7, a realistic explanation of illness can probably be only dimly grasped by the child. One might expect that he would parrot such explanations but that his innermost answer to the question, "Why am I sick?" would tap highly personalized ideas and motives. The combination of vividly experienced discomfort and tenuous intellectual comprehension would seem to be highly conducive to fantasy.

It was further speculated that there might be a difference in the content of the fantasies of Psychosomatic and Illness children. According to psychosomatic theory, vulnerability to physiological breakdown is predicated upon a period of intense emotional stress. This gives the disease a different psychological status from that of a non-psychosomatic disorder which might or might not have such a dramatic antecedent. It implies that the children with psychosomatic illnesses should be more sensitized to the relation between severe interpersonal conflict and disturbed physiological functioning because of the consistent association of the two. By contrast, the assumption regarding non-psychosomatic illness is that it strikes at random with respect to interpersonal difficulties, and therefore is not as consistently linked with psychological stress. On the basis of these considerations it was hypothesized that the Psychosomatic children would focus more upon negatively toned interpersonal situations in their fantasies as to the cause of illness than would the Illness children.

The problem of devising techniques was even more difficult here than in the other parts of the research since precedents were almost nonexistent. It was decided to use a number of approaches, each of which had a certain face validity. Four techniques were finally devised in the hopes that at least one would be successful in eliciting the child's fantasied reasons for illness.

(1) The Garner Illness Fantasy Technique (GIFT) consists of twelve stick-figure drawings depicting a child, either alone or with a parent, in various emotionally pleasant or unpleasant situations; e.g., the child is having fun playing ball with his father, he is being scolded by an angry mother, he accidentally breaks his mother's best vase. As each of the drawings is shown to the subject, the depicted situation is described explicitly. When all the pictures are before the subject, he is told that, subsequently, the stick-figure child became sick, and he is to choose the three causal situations. After each choice he is asked, "And why did that make him sick?" The subject's choices and reasons are recorded.

This technique was designed in such a way that the pictures could be analyzed for the following psychological dimensions: (a) Emotions involved—whether the situation involves pleasure, anxiety, guilt, depression, love; (b) Interpersonal element—whether the child is alone or with a parent, and the particular parent involved; (c) Responsibility—whether the child provokes a negative response or is an innocent victim of negative action; (d) Punishment—whether transgression is detected or not.

(2) A doll representing the sick child depicted in GIFT is presented, and the subject is asked to pretend to be the doctor examining the child. In this context he is encouraged to fantasy freely as to the nature and origin of the illness.

(3) A drawn outline of a child is presented and the subject is encouraged to draw the insides of its body and the sickness. Again the subject is encouraged to fantasy freely about the illness and the events leading up to it.

(4) The child is asked about his own illness and its causes. An attempt is always made to get beyond the level of clichés and parroted medical explanation so that the child can express his more personalized thinking about etiology.

The purpose of this multitechnique approach was to give the child a variety of outlets for his fantasies. It was expected that different children would find different techniques more congenial for expressing their ideas, some blossoming under the spell of drawing, others needing the stimulation of pictures, and still others being most articulate about their own personal experiences with sickness. It was never expected that one technique would be "deeper" than another or get nearer the "real" fantasy level.

Looked at from this point of view, the techniques were reasonably successful. Almost all the children were intrigued into revealing personalized material somewhere along the line. A few surprises turned up in GIFT, however. The purpose of this technique was to present the child with a variety of situations with affective implications which might be relevant to fantasies concerning illness. Theoretically the specific situations chosen by a given child would be the ones which resonated to his particular fantasies about etiology. The actual results were quite different. If the pictures resonated to anything at all, it was probably to the preconceived notions of the investigators; the children showed absolutely no difference in their choice. However, the technique was salvaged by the responses to the question, "How did that [situation] make him sick?" It was here that the child was given the freedom to express his own ideas and produced a number of revealing fantasies.

The techniques were first analyzed in terms of the hypothesized increase in interpersonal fantasies in the Psychosomatic group. The over-all results were not striking. On GIFT there was a strong tendency for both illness groups to have more interpersonal fantasies than the Neurotic children. For example, a stick figure became sick "because she would be afraid to face her mother and father after that" or "because he got mad at his mother." In the other three techniques, however, the sheer number of interpersonal situations did not discriminate any of the groups.

More significant were the kinds of interpersonal situations which were fantasied by the groups on the non-GIFT techniques. Examination of the data revealed three distinct categories. First there were "pure" interpersonal situations involving well-defined interactions with parents, other adults, or peers. For example, a child got sick because her parents failed to warn her of some danger, or because she gulped forbidden food so her parents would not see. Next there were situations in which God was responsible for the illness, either as a punishment or as a sign of a specially chosen destiny. This category was considered as interpersonal because children so often personify God. Finally there were situations involving contagion which were defined in terms of a general statement that a person gets sick from being with others who are sick.

Analysis of the data revealed marked group differences in regard to the three categories. The Psychosomatic children had a predominance of "pure" interpersonal situations, the Neurotic children emphasized contagion, while the Illness group had more references to God. Thus, the Psychosomatic child's fantasies focus more directly upon interpersonal elements, the Neurotic child is more generalized, while the Illness child tends to displace the reason for illness onto a supernatural source.

GIFT proved its worth by revealing something quite unexpected about the children's fantasies. It was noticed that some children viewed illness as a direct consequence of negative emotions while others viewed it at the result of the outward expression of negative feelings. These categories were arbitrarily labeled Primary and Secondary expression of affect. In the Primary cases the child answered the question, "Why did that make him sick?" by referring to a negative emotional state. For example, the stick figure could be angry, frightened, lonely, uneasy, guilty, etc., and such feelings were the direct cause of illness. In the Secondary category it was the overt expression of the emotion and not the affective state itself which produced illness. For example, yelling (not anger) made the boy sick, or stamping his foot (not anger) made him hurt his foot. The most frequent reason in this category was crying. Often it was just the act of crying itself which was responsible for producing the sickness, although some children blamed the consequences of crying such as sore eyes or headaches. There were a few borderline cases in which crying was seen as an expression of an emotional state such as loneliness. While such cases have both Primary and Secondary features, it was decided to score them as Primary because of the emphasis on the affective component. Analysis of the results showed a significant increase in Primary reasons and a significant decrease in Secondary reasons in the Psychosomatic group; this situation was reversed for both control groups.

Summarizing the findings up to this point, it can be seen that the Psychosomatic children's fantasies about causes of illness are related more directly and specifically to interpersonal situations and are more intimately associated with negative feelings. It would probably smack of confabulation to merge these two findings and claim proof of the hypothesis that these children's fantasies focus on negative feelings about interpersonal relations. The present results, while not exactly hitting the mark, come very close, and certainly are of interest in themselves.

The unexpected finding about Primary affect is of special interest in light of the lack of emotional reactivity in the Psychosomatic children discussed in Chapter 8. If all sorts of negative emotions—anger, fear, loneliness—are seen as causing sickness, then this is another powerful reason for avoiding the expression of such emotions. Thus, negative feelings become dangerous not only because of their interpersonal implications but because of their potential destructiveness to physiological integrity as well.

At a more speculative level one might say that the Psychosomatic children are essentially correct in their fantasies. If the reasoning in previous chapters is valid, then early traumatization prevents the healthy integration of physiological activities. Subsequently the physiological components of emotional behavior cannot be kept within the bounds of normal fluctuation but become pathological in their activity.

Thus the same stimulus which produces a strong emotional response would also set off pathological physiological reactions. In a very literal sense, then, strong negative feelings cause illness.

It might also be added that this is one of the things which makes therapy so complicated. A Psychosomatic child who tells his therapist, "You make me sick" is not only using a cliché to communicate his anger, but is also expressing a literal truth. One of the principal difficulties in doing therapy is the ever-present danger that the arousal of strong feeling will produce an exacerbation of the disease.

There is one more finding which is noteworthy. The situations depicted in GIFT were designed to include a fairly large number of acts of aggression or transgression. For example, the mother could be fussing at the child or the child could be taking money from his father's wallet. The child could either be the source or the recipient of aggressive activity and could transgress unintentionally or purposefully. Such situations were included because it was believed that the Psychosomatic children might have a stronger tendency to fantasy that their illness was caused by activity which represents a dramatic departure from pleasant, socially acceptable behavior.

Analysis of the results, however, revealed that both illness groups had a significantly larger number of such reasons than the Neurotic children. This means that a child who has been chronically ill, regardless of the role of emotional factors, will tend to attribute the etiology of illness to aggression or transgression more than a physically healthy, neurotic child will. Whether this is because such children regard their sickness as punishment, or whether it is an irrational equating of the pain of illness with the painful psychological consequences of socially unacceptable behavior, is a matter of conjecture. However, the important point is that such fantasies are not unique to the Psychosomatic children, but seem to be a concomitant of any severe illness. In this sense, the finding here resembles that concerning the traumatic Witch fantasies described in Chapter 7. Thus it seems that two of the concomitants of any severe illness in children are exaggerated fantasies of the malevolence of the mother and a tendency to attribute illness to aggression or transgression. Such findings are certainly important in developing a general theory of the psychology of illness.

Pertinent data about etiology of illness were also obtained from the mothers. One of the questions they were asked was, "How do you understand your child's present illness [or "trouble" in the case of the Neurotic group]?" The question was designed to be exploratory rather than being geared to a particular hypothesis, and the responses were recorded and later classified.

A number of relevant findings came to light. To begin with, the largest number of responses were those classified as Psychological. They included the mother blaming herself, her husband, or other relatives, the mother blaming the child or playmates, trauma such as being scared by a dog, and such psychologizing as references to "complexes." To a highly significant extent, Psychosomatic and Neurotic mothers had a large number of such reasons, while the Illness mothers had comparatively few. Such a finding is even more impressive when one remembers that the Psychosomatic mothers were talking about reasons for physical illness while the Neurotic mothers were giving reasons for psychological problems.

The Illness mothers, in contrast to the other groups, tended to describe the illness in response to the question, indicating that they focused on understanding the process itself rather than the cause of the disease. These mothers also had more references to God, God's will, or fatalistic concepts such as "it was meant to be." This fits nicely with a similar finding about the Illness children.

Although other categories of reasons were devised, they were either not significant or did not contribute to further understanding of the problem.

The finding that Psychosomatic mothers give psychological reasons for illness has important implications in regard to the interpretation of their children's fantasies. One might well argue that it precludes the need for any deep or speculative interpretation. To begin with, the physicians who cooperated in referring children for the research were probably attuned to thinking in terms of psychosomatic causation. More likely than not they would stress emotional etiology when talking to the mothers. The mother would pick up the idea and, consciously or unconsciously, communicate it to the child. This line of communication from physician to mother to child would account for the mother's psychological reasons and the child's fantasies of Primary affect.

This simple explanation, while completely plausible, does not fit the evidence at hand.

In the first place, not all referring physicians regarded the child's disease as psychosomatic and not all Psychosomatic mothers were told about emotional etiology. Added to this is the fact that most pediatricians are far too busy to explore this matter in detail with the mother. Thus, uniformity of information cannot be assumed. Even more important are the data indicating that there is no one-to-one relation between a mother's being told of emotional etiology and her acceptance of this information. It was found, for example, that five of the eleven mothers giving non-psychological reasons had been told about the possibility of emotional etiology. In addition, a closer examination of the responses of the mothers who did give psychological reasons revealed varying degrees of acceptance of the idea. Some seized upon it with intellectual avidity, others quoted the physician but said they disbelieved him, and some rejected the idea angrily. Thus, the mother's reaction to the information and the use she makes of it seem to be a function of her own needs and defenses.

There is even more impressive evidence against a simple communication of explanations from mother to child. If this kind of communication took place, one would expect a significant relationship between mothers who gave psychological reasons for illness and children who fantasied in terms of direct interpersonal relations and Primary expression of affect. However, statistical analysis of the data failed to yield any evidence of such a relationship.

There is an important caution which must be added at this point. Many of the data on information given to the Psychosomatic mothers were obtained after the fact. This is because their psychological reasons as well as the children's Primary affect responses were not foreseen. Thus the evidence suffers the usual limitations of post hoc treatment. Certainly data on the kind and extent of information should have been systematically gathered beforehand, and the mother's use of this information in relation to her child should have been more thoroughly investigated. The Illness group should also have been systematically studied in terms of the information they received about the emotional effects of severe illness and their communication of this knowledge to their children. In light of the haziness of post hoc data, the above conclusions should be regarded as tentative.

With this caution in mind, the present results can be summarized as follows: a Psychosomatic mother's response to information about emotional etiology of illness is a function of her own personality dynamics. Reactions range from complete repression to avid championing of the idea. Her acceptance might play a role but is certainly not the decisive factor in regard to her child's fantasies. Rather, the

Psychosomatic child sees illness as resulting from interpersonal interactions and negative emotional states and such fantasies are not dependent on the mother's beliefs. It was speculated that these fantasies reflect the child's own concern that the expression of negative feelings not only threatens interpersonal relation but destroys physiological integration as well.

10---Four Portraits

Any discussion which remains at the level of delineating group characteristics inevitably lacks the type of finely wrought understanding of individuals which is the hallmark of the single case study. No matter how clearly the typical behavior of the group emerges, each individual in it departs to a greater or lesser degree from the composite picture, elaborating, supplementing, modifying it in subtle ways until the "typical" is transformed into the "individual."

In the present study, it is a practical impossibility to portray each mother and her relation to her child; instead, four cases have been selected for detailed examination. The particular cases chosen illustrate rather vividly some of the distinctive group characteristics which have been discussed in the preceding chapters; however, the detailed descriptive material will also serve to put such characteristics into the context of the unique personalities of the individuals involved.

Data from all the research techniques were evaluated in order to evolve the pictures of the mothers and their relationships with their children although, as will be apparent, most extensive use was made of the case history material. In order to disguise the material sufficiently, names have been changed and many specific details altered, so that the portraits presented do not accurately or recognizably represent any given individual.

Mrs. Fenster: A "High" Psychosomatic Mother

Mrs. Fenster is a tall, blonde, youthful-looking woman of 35. She is meticulous and tasteful in her dress and make-up. In her social manner, she is alert, smiling, and sweet. Long an ugly duckling overshadowed by a beautiful sister, she was forced to rely on intellectual achievement to gain recognition when she was a child. In her teens, however, she made a determined effort to overcome her awkward, dumpy unattractiveness and its attendant self-consciousness and shame. Aided by medical science, diet, beauticians, voice training, and her own will power, she succeeded.

What Mrs. Fenster is completely oblivious of, but what is almost pathetically obvious to others, is her artificiality. The investigators described her as appearing glossy, too sweet, melodramatic; in the Interaction she was seen as "glittering and false," "arty," "very much on display," speaking "like a Hollywood script—perfect diction but false and feelingless." Even the typist who transcribed the interview was impressed with how unreal she sounded, in that what she said was "too good to be true." Yet there is no duplicity about Mrs. Fenster; what to others is patent self-dramatization is, to her, the genuine drama of her life.

In spite of her changed appearance, her intellectual drive has continued unabated. She has succeeded in evolving an intellectual outlook which has the same flawless but false quality which characterizes her social facade. In this she is very much like the quotation-mark mothers described in Chapter 7, who always say the "right things" and know all the "right answers." Here is a sampling of her opinions: in regard to propping the bottle while feeding Darlene, "Never, never. I don't believe in it. I believe a child needs that warmth"; about dressing up an infant, "I never was the kind of mother that insisted on frills. I felt every baby is so pretty unto itself"; on handling sibling rivalry, "We used every trick in the book. . . . We had—I had a closet full of gifts wrapped so that if anybody came without a gift for Darlene and one for the baby, I had one for Darlene"; on calming Darlene's fear of the dark, "I explain to her that I too was afraid. And that other people are afraid. I show her that it is nothing physically and there is nothing there. And explain to her that it's nothing wrong in being frightened and that we all need someone to comfort us sometimes."

In all this incessant intellectual flow there is almost no real understanding or genuine feeling. Only in talking of her unhappiness as a child was there a glimmer of deeply felt emotion. Again it should be stressed that such talk is not a thin veneer to cover contrary feelings. Intellectualizing might have been such a defensive maneuver long ago, but now it has permeated her entire personality. Such total imperviousness gives her a kind of strength in that she seems invulnerable to contradictions from without or to doubts from within.

One final point about Mrs. Fenster is that she is quite a demanding, domineering individual. It is not that she is overtly aggressive but rather she has a strong need to monopolize a situation. In a certain sense, being on display is also being on trial; the attention or admiration given others threatens her own self-esteem. Her early relationship with her sister seems an important dynamic factor here.

Mrs. Fenster has many techniques for alleviating her feelings of inferiority. It is characteristic of her that she blames others, particularly her husband or his family, when things go badly. However, doctors, nurses, and teachers come in for a fair share of censure. When she admits to mistakes it is primarily to ennoble herself through such admissions. "It is this deficiency in myself where I try too hard to please . . . I waited on my husband hand and foot and I did the same for Darlene. If I have a difficulty it is the fact that when I love, I love too much and I just lavish it on a person." A final element in this display of superiority is her emphasis on status. She refers to herself as belonging to "the high I.Q. set" in college, and states that Darlene receives "reflected glory" from her being a committeewoman. She characterizes doctors as being eminent or well known.

Just as Mrs. Fenster puts herself on display for the world to admire, she puts Darlene on display also. In doing so, she weaves a saccharine web around her daughter. When Darlene was born "everyone was crazy about her. She was thoroughly adorable." In toilet training, "She was so easy to manage. I never forced her. She forced me (at seven months of age)." At school, "Everyone is crazy—the children are crazy about her and she gets invited to 15 parties a year—in her room alone." When she was hospitalized, "Everyone on the floor was looking forward to a visit from Darlene—every child on the floor would ask the nurse when is Darlene coming." As a daughter, "She gives me strength I never knew I had." The model mother must have a model child.

Yet this is only half the story. The other half consists of negative feelings. These come out bit by bit, in the interview, and each one is sugar-coated; it is only when the pieces are put together that the comprehensiveness of Mrs. Fenster's hostility can be grasped. To begin with, the pregnancy itself was highly saturated with competitive feelings toward her sister. Although Mrs. Fenster never said so directly, she did state they were both pregnant at the same time. "In fact, if I had had my original child, ah—they would have been born practically together." However, she miscarried and, although the doctor strongly advised her to wait, she states with pride that she was pregnant with Darlene soon afterward. She says she never felt better in her life, in spite of a period of depression in the seventh or eighth months. Although she thought the "whole world had been given us because—we wanted a baby so badly," she frankly states she would have preferred a boy, and her first impression of Darlene was in terms of her being ". . . a mess. I can remember looking at her and crying bitterly and saying, 'On top of being a girl, you have to be so homely.' And then feeling so ashamed that I remember saying to her, 'Don't worry honey; if nobody else loves you, I will.'" Although Darlene was "loving and adorable," she was "sensitive" and would cry at loud noises; she was "a terrible eater from the day she was born," and she was "terribly constipated." Always an active baby, later she was "into everything. You couldn't leave her for a minute. I left the house in the morning in self-defense." She was "overly attached" to her mother and was "exhausting to take care of." When she became sick and Mrs. Fenster had to "work my fool head off cooking and tempting her with this bland diet" she became "an obnoxious character." At school "she is very bossy." Finally, "She is by nature very dominating and insists on getting the center of the stage. This can be very wearing in any family."

Clearly what this adds up to is a negative attitude toward the child at every stage of development. Only once did Mrs. Fenster admit to her own inadequacy when she said frankly that bathing the infant terrified her.

To understand Mrs. Fenster thoroughly it is important to realize that she was unaware of any contradiction in what she was saying about her daughter. The good and bad pictures of Darlene do not represent cyclic swings of feeling from love to hate. A few examples will illustrate this point. "She was sensitive, she was constipated and she was a feeding problem . . . and she was overly attached to me. Other than that she was perfectly normal and healthy." "She seems very well adjusted. The teachers say she gets along beautifully. The only thing the teachers all say that they have never seen such tension and such worry in a child." "I don't have to tell you I love her madly. She drives me to distraction." "She was thoroughly adorable but completely exhausting to take care of." Mrs. Fenster was even unaware of factual contradictions, such as saying the infant was breast-fed and denying this a few sentences later.

Elaborating this picture with some speculation, the following interpretation can be made. Mrs. Fenster's effort to be the Model Mother is primarily an extension of her desire to display herself as the Model Woman. She wants her child to be a showpiece—the prettiest, smartest, most popular of all little girls. There is little evidence of warmth or enjoyment of the child for her own sake, or of any ability to tolerate deviations from this ideal. On the contrary, she lives in a constant state of irritation at the child's failure to perform as she should. On rare occasions this erupts into overt anger, as when she struck Darlene after she persistently refused to eat. Typically, however, her anger remains at the level of chronic aggravation. Thus the child at one and the same time is stimulated by the myth of perfection and undermined by incessant faultfinding.

Although there might be many others, two sources of the mother's irritation can be inferred. The first is the fact that no child could measure up to Mrs. Fenster's idealized picture. A baby is not consistently adorable; development is never perfectly normal. Such facts of life are basic blows to Mrs. Fenster's narcissism and she responds with keen resentment. Another source of hostility is somewhat more subtle. Mrs. Fenster states that Darlene's illness started because she was so jealous of the attention her baby sister was getting. Later she also said that, when Darlene was particularly happy because she was the teacher's pet at school, Mrs. Fenster herself developed what she thought was the same illness. Thus the disease is equated with jealousy. One can speculate that this mother who needs so desperately to absorb all the attention into herself is extremely jealous when too much is diverted to her daughter. As long as she can feel Darlene's triumphs serve to enhance the image of the Good Mother she is pleased, but once she senses Darlene is attracting attention in her own right or getting a great deal of admiration for herself, she must undermine her. The old threat of a more attractive competitor has not diminished.

It is clear that Mrs. Fenster's need for perfection prevents her from being a warm mother. There is equally persuasive evidence of a pathological closeness between mother and child. Mrs. Fenster's complaint that Darlene is overly attached to her was touched upon briefly. The nature and extent of this attachment can be seen by the following remarks. When Darlene was an infant, "She would not let anyone else [but Mrs. Fenster] near her. With other children they become frightened of strangers at 13 months or so. Darlene was frightened of strangers at 3 days." "She was always mine exclusively, but believe me I made no attempt to make her so . . . and I think that is why it is always so hard for her to adjust because she does not want to share the one she loves." "She would have nothing to do with anyone but me." Before she was a year old Mrs. Fenster describes taking her out in the buggy. "She'd fall asleep and she'd sleep as long as I walked, but if I dared to stop and have lunch with the women, Darlene was up and screaming. You couldn't stop. You had to keep going. Some children you can leave them outside of the store and go in and shop. And they cry once, they cry twice and that's all. Darlene never gives up. I had to take her with or else what went on was simply terrible." This same pattern was repeated when Mr. and Mrs. Fenster would go out together in the evening and, to this day, Darlene allows them one night out but protests if this limit is exceeded. Finally, there is the fact that Mrs. Fenster fed Darlene until she was six years old.

This last fact warrants further discussion. It will be recalled that Darlene was quite a feeding problem, and the one thing which infuriated Mrs. Fenster above all else was the fact that her daughter would not eat. Yet she persisted in trying to feed her for a six-year period. The only reason she stopped then was that Darlene decided to feed herself. What was happening before then was what Mrs. Fenster aptly calls the "battle of wills" between herself and her daughter. Darlene stubbornly resisted her mother's incessant pressure to eat, and Mrs. Fenster could never completely "break her will" or leave her be. Both seemed irresistibly drawn to an antagonistic relationship.

One gets the impression from the interview material that Darlene realized her power to upset her mother quite early. It is possible that this was a significant component of her initial resistance to being fed. More direct evidence of her retaliatory control over her mother was seen by the time she was two. The family went to California and the plan was for Mr. Fenster to take over the care of the baby so his wife would have some time to shop and enjoy herself. Darlene, however, "would not take one step without me," not even to go to the beach, which she dearly loved. Or, when the family went to a restaurant, "She would have to go to the restroom three, four times a meal" and the mother could never tell her to wait. Certainly the expected negativism of a two-year-old would give Darlene ample opportunity to realize how she could tyrannize her mother. The persistence of this pattern was quite evident in the observed Interaction, in which Darlene was depreciating of her mother and negativistic in response to suggestions.

Thus the close, mutually frustrating relationship can be well documented. The mother sees the "battle of wills" as starting almost at earliest infancy since she attributes most of the difficulties in child care to Darlene's willful opposition. On her part, Darlene very early learned that her stubbornness was upsetting to her mother and that it could be used for retaliation and control. In all this time Mrs. Fenster has been able neither to resist nor resolve this critical problem.

At a speculative level it is easy to understand why Mrs. Fenster was so possessive and demanding. This is part of her controlling, narcissistic orientation. What is more difficult to understand is why she did not engulf her daughter more successfully, and why Darlene did not become a frightened, withdrawn, pathetic little girl. Unfortunately there is no evidence on this point. There might be some guilt or some empathy with her daughter's distress which counteracted Mrs. Fenster's demandingness, or there might be some basic temperamental factor which predisposed Darlene to fight and resist rather than withdraw. If this matter can be settled at all, it will have to be on the basis of data outside the limits of the present study. There is the intriguing possibility, however, that the child's ability to resist being overwhelmed might be one of the decisive factors in preventing a more pathological emotional disturbance in the form of a severe alienation from reality.

As for Darlene herself, her attitudes about being mothered are aptly described in the discussion of the manipulative, deceptive mother figures which appeared in the Mixed Themes; such fantasies clearly mirror the reality of Mrs. Fenster's facade of perfection with underlying hostility. The psychological techniques also reveal the extent to which Darlene has identified with her mother: just as Mrs. Fenster was an incessant talker in the interview, Darlene pushed herself to tell the longest stories, build the most complex World, evolve the most elaborate fantasies about illness. She also showed the demandingness and need to monopolize attention which is so typical of Mrs. Fenster. Darlene has her mother's facile intellect and her stories were particularly rich, well organized, and full of perceptive details. Yet two of the five Realistic stories were pleasant vignettes which had almost nothing to do with the picture; when forced to deal with the stimulus, she produced brief, somewhat deviant themes. This leads one to suspect that, like her mother, she is upset by real feeling and is beginning to spin saccharine webs of her own.

One final point: the psychological techniques clearly show that Mrs. Fenster knows her daughter well. True to her classification as a "High" Psychosomatic mother, she can describe Darlene with unerring accuracy—the exhibitionism, the demandingness, the excitability, the willfulness are all there. What Mrs. Fenster fails to grasp is her role in fostering such characteristics. When one adds to this the infrequent evidence of tenderness or affection or delight in relation to her daughter, it becomes clear that motherliness has been replaced by narcissism.

Mrs. Merrill: A "Low" Psychosomatic Mother

Mrs. Merrill is a distraught woman. She lives in a state of turmoil, constantly buffeted about by feelings beyond her control. She is a voluble talker who rarely stays on the track and often ends up in a jumble of loosely associated ideas. Insightful evaluations and naïve notions come forth indiscriminately. Her emotional life is intense and equally haphazard, with anger, guilt, sentimentality, anxiety, pity, succeeding one another pell-mell.

Yet this intellectual and emotional chaos does not represent a process of disintegration under the impact of overwhelming trauma; rather, it has been Mrs. Merrill's pattern for years. She is a woman who lives a life of crisis. This clearly has been true since Archie's birth, and in all probability it was true before that time. Because she appears to be on the verge of going to pieces at any minute and yet has actually not become significantly more disorganized over a period of years, it is best to think of her as a character disorder. And because her principal problems are ones of faulty self-control and diffuse identity, she can most aptly be described as having an ego defect.

Examples of her lack of stability can be found on every page of her recorded interview material. At one point she was asked if her husband were easily upset by Archie's behavior. She denied this and immediately went on to talk of the deliberate manner in which Mr. Merrill speaks, alternating between complaining about how aggravating it was and searching for an explanation of it in terms of a childhood accident or a family trait. She started to use an incident at supper to illustrate her point but got sidetracked into talking of her husband's dietary habits and how she has to force him to eat. This, in turn, called forth a description of her own food preferences, and she was finally interrupted by the social worker in the middle of her description of a lunch of fruit salad and cottage cheese. This was only one of the many instances in which the worker had to bring Mrs. Merrill back to the main topic. Otherwise her chain thinking, her inner distractibility, her incessant asides and irrelevances, would have defeated the purpose of the interview. A particularly important aspect of this distractibility was the fact that one person often reminded her of another, and she might begin talking of Archie, for example, but end up discussing her father, her husband, her mother, or herself. This inability to deal with others or herself as distinct individuals is one indication of her weak sense of identity.

There is no doubt that Mrs. Merrill has some awareness of the chaotic nature of her thoughts and feelings and her inability to manage most aspects of life effectively. In the interview there are many implicit and explicit cries for help. "Well, it is very bad at times. . . . Yes. . . . But then on the other hand, I really don't care . . . actually . . . because when no one comes to my rescue . . . so if I don't make the hurdle it is just not made. But that is why I am so anxious to work with you people and see if I could ever find out an inkle [sic] . . . get a little help as to what to do. What is it that I am doing so wrong all the time that this picture can't shake itself?" Yet, when the worker recommended that she contact the clinic at the Institute for Juvenile Research, she replied, "Could I do what they would find? Would I want to do what they would find? That is another thing." In reality Mrs. Merrill has sought professional help often and has consistently been dissatisfied or has angrily rejected advice. True to her demanding, restless nature, she is constantly latching on to others and then feeling that what she gets is never really helpful.

According to Mrs. Merrill's interview material she was not always this distraught. Her early childhood in a small Canadian town seems to have been pleasant. She also describes a comparatively happy time when she was in her twenties and unmarried. Her parents were both alive and all of her siblings were married. "All the others, younger and old, got married. All had families. I got my satisfaction from them. I raised their kids. When I wanted to, I worked; if I didn't want to, I stayed home, played with the kids, raised the kids, took them home with me. I was their sitter and everything. I, I had my life sort of in theirs. I didn't want to get married." Her jobs had a similar quality of irresponsible, vicarious living—in one she did volunteer canvassing and loved to visit "those wonderful homes"; in another she worked at a school for crippled children and "loved the kids." Although she stressed her great freedom in all this, there is some doubt as to her real independence. Her definition of independence is: "My mother and father let me do whatever I wanted, always." In reality, she was being guided by a sister in her choice of jobs and was under her mother's thumb to the extent that she had to give up her volunteer work when her mother objected to it. Thus, this happy time seems to be one in which she could enjoy peripheral caretaking activities with children while having no real responsibility for their welfare and could feel independent while remaining within the protective framework of an intact family structure.

When Archie came along, all this changed. Her marriage is summarily dismissed—"I didn't want to get married"—and there is no evidence that she ever expected to give or receive love. Somehow she got married and somehow she stayed married. It is the birth of her son which is the pivotal event. For one thing, it meant the end of her freedom, and this she resents. However, the burden of responsibilities is only a minor complaint. Archie's entire existence is associated, in her mind, with a continuous series of disasters.

Before chronicling these misfortunes, it is important to point out that the list represents a mixture of realistic and unrealistic items. Certainly the deaths and illnesses Mrs. Merrill has had to cope with would try a much stronger individual; on the other hand, she is continually driven to anticipate disaster and thereby manufactures a crisis when none really exists. It is also important to realize that Mrs. Merrill gives many positive descriptions of Archie. He is called "a doll," "adorable," "a charmer," and is seen as friendly, very bright, and mechanically adept. There is no reason to question the genuineness of these positive feelings; it is just that she cannot sustain them. No sooner do they appear then she is enmeshed in reactions of anger or guilt or anxious concern. In spite of these frequent glimmers of affection, Archie usually means distress or disaster.

The pregnancy itself was stamped by tragedy, since Mrs. Merrill's mother died during that time. At first she said the death was due to the same illness Archie had, but later she corrected this. Archie's birth is also associated affectively, if not temporally, with the death of the sister who gave her so much guidance in her work, and the loss of the protection of her family. "So she [the sister] died, and her death and my mother's death was in a couple of years of each other, throw us all for a loop. So that broke up the family. Well, then Archie came into the picture."

After his birth she seemed driven to become pregnant again, in spite of the fact that her husband was jobless, their apartment was small and overcrowded, there was little money, and her doctor had strongly advised against it. She says that she wanted children because, at 36, she was "no spring chicken," and this might well be one factor. Yet, the unrealistic components in the pregnancy indicate other factors were also at work. One of these might have been an irrational attempt to deny the death of her mother and the disintegration of the family. Evidence for this comes from Mrs. Merrill's frequent identification of Archie with her mother, not only in terms of a common disease, but also in terms of positive qualities which they shared. However, like everything about Mrs. Merrill, her motives here were mixed. In spite of the depressive response to her mother's death there is no evidence of a strong positive attachment. Rather she says that it was only after her mother was gone that she realized how little she had been appreciated. Such a statement suggests there might have been a good deal of unconscious hostility during her lifetime which was transformed into guilt and depression. Thus having more children would not only deny the loss of a mother but her symbolic restitution could help protect Mrs. Merrill from her guilt.

The reason it is necessary to postulate rather complex dynamics is that this is not a case of unambivalent longing to have children. Her frequent miscarriages and her carelessness about herself which resulted in a severe injury during pregnancy both indicate important unconscious destructive components directed both toward the baby and toward herself. As will be seen later, there is ample evidence that this is not an isolated pattern, and that much of her caretaking of Archie is marked by a conscious overconcern for his welfare and an unconscious destructiveness.

There are undoubtedly many other factors contributing to Mrs. Merrill's overinvestment in pregnancy but these lie beyond the scope of the present study. Clear evidence of the importance of this matter, however, comes from her response to an operation which made further childbearing impossible, "So that . . . that really throwed me again. So then from then on I must have watched Archie like . . . something, and I think that was the beginning when Archie started"—i.e., the beginning of the real troubles with Archie. He was three at the time, and not even his frequent illnesses were as disturbing to his mother as was the thought that he would be the only child.

Returning to the time of Archie's birth, it is clear that he not only came into the world during a period of psychological distress for his mother, but he brought with him realistic burdens in the form of innumerable illnesses. He was a colicky baby, he suffered from severe infections and stomach disorders, and he had allergic reactions to food. By the time he was six months old, he had been hospitalized many times. In addition, there were the usual accidents and diseases of childhood. As can happen with such children, trouble is compounded by the fact that medication for one illness can itself precipitate another illness.

There are also many borderline cases in which it is impossible to tell if an actual illness exists or whether it was manufactured by Mrs. Merrill's overconcern. For example, in trying to find a reason for Archie's lack of achievement in school, Mrs. Merrill first blamed his vision, then his hearing, and finally his teeth. In each case she succeeded in finding a doctor who succeeded in finding something wrong in the appropriate area, but in all probability the defects would have gone unnoticed had Archie gotten good grades.

The basic difficulty, however, lies in the fact that these trials came to a woman incapable of meeting them constructively. Mrs. Merrill's total view of life is that tragedy is lurking everywhere, ready to strike without warning the people who least deserve it. Because she is incapable of moderation, every hint of trouble becomes an omen of disaster. The following incident aptly illustrated this point.

He was due for a party; he hasn't had a party in quite some time—ah—and I heard everybody had the measles . . . it was going around like wildfire. Well I had taken Archie down a couple days before . . . the party was going to be on a Saturday . . . but I took him down a couple days before to the doctor—ah—and I told him . . . Doctor, tha . . . he's been complaining . . . that it hurts. And the doctor poked around and everything and couldn't find anything. "Now look, right now he hasn't got 'em. If he gets them tomorrow or the day after, I can't . . . right now the child hasn't got it." Well, sure enough, to make a long story short we . . . we started calling up everybody and calling off the party. Archie woke up with one side of his face just a little red and I was sure he had the measles. Now he may have had the measles . . . now I do not know, but I called one of the women . . . and I told her I said I was at the doctor yesterday with Archie and he didn't have them. He's crying because I'm calling off the party, everything was already purchased, everything was set up. She said, "Look, Mrs. Merrill, I have three children of my own and . . ." by the way her child did actually come down with the measles after that . . . but if Archie actually had them I couldn't tell you to this day.

This kind of thing probably happens often in the Merrill household.

For Mrs. Merrill, nothing ever goes right—if trouble does not happen of its own accord her own anxieties will create it. It is also important to note how her son suffers in this process and is victimized by his mother's fearfulness.

Her response to such real and fancied dangers is a relentless intrusiveness into Archie's life. Her inability to leave him alone or give him any freedom is apparent at many levels. First of all, it comes out in Mrs. Merrill's inability to separate from her boy. She cannot send him away to camp, weakly rationalizing this on the basis that he would not have a rest hour there; she took him out of the hospital against medical advice even though she was well aware of the fact that improvement was contingent upon his staying there; when she had to have an operation she was convinced he cried all the time she was away although there was no evidence for this. As she sums up her feelings, "I was scared to leave him alone for fear he would catch the wrong type of a breath."

Yet difficulty in separating is only one manifestation of Mrs. Merrill's intrusiveness. There is another, more basic aspect. Mrs. Merrill says that when Archie was an infant he vomited a good deal and she thought he never had enough food. "I was so anxious for him to eat you know that I practically stuffed it down his throat . . . I always fed him. He didn't like that. He used to fight with me. He wanted to eat himself. But I would not let him." From the very beginning, then, Mrs. Merrill was a "stuffing" mother—a woman who actively and relentlessly forces herself upon her child.

Yet this does not end the matter. Because of her instability, Mrs. Merrill not only stuffs but subsequently resents her son's helplessness. She gets angry at his dawdling in the morning, his inability to stand up for himself in a fight, his incessant demands that he be shown how to do things. She feels worn down and embittered by the constant effort to supervise and protect and control every minute of his life. This combination of weariness and resentment has resulted in a certain element of doubt as to whether she had been a good mother. In talking of weaning, she said, "I never had any trouble. He was a very wonderful child. I mean, naturally. He did everything himself—except when his mother interfered. She wanted to do everything for him for fear that he would do this wrong and that wrong. And I did and I know I did wrong." She said something similar in relation to toilet training. She had no trouble because he was left free to go to the toilet when he wanted; had she tried to train him there would have been difficulties. Thus Mrs. Merrill does seem to be aware, at times, of the destructiveness of her intrusive control. Whether she can use this insight constructively, or whether it will only serve to make her behavior more inconsistent and unpredictable, is a moot question.

Finally, the interview shows that Mrs. Merrill's closeness goes beyond the point of intrusiveness and becomes, at times, a feeling of identity with the child. There is a frequent drawing of parallels between the two of them. Mrs. Merrill interrupts others but Archie has this habit also; she is messy but so is he; his fear of cats comes from her identical childhood fear; neither of them makes friends easily; when he cried because he could not do a problem for his tutor "I listened and it isn't actually hurting me, but it is again"; after his birth "we almost died." Interestingly enough, bad qualities are the ones which are shared, the mother identifying Archie's good qualities with those of her father. The following is even more revealing of her feeling of identity: "We really never lived a normal life. It is always been Archie, Archie. We lived Archie's life and Archie . . . lived ours." This characteristic of living through others, especially children, harks back to what was said about her poorly differentiated ego.

As may be seen, Mrs. Merrill is both more disorganized and more direct than Mrs. Fenster. She has no defense of perfectionism to unify her personality, and contradictory feelings and ideas find immediate expression. She also lacks Mrs. Fenster's facility for blaming her child for everything that goes wrong. Instead she fluctuates between hostility and guilt. Some of her anger is realistic, some results from her anxiety and helplessness when she fears she cannot control a situation, some is a kind of childish opposition, some results from the impossible demands she makes on Archie, such as becoming angry if he lies but also if he tells the truth. There is also a streak of what appears to be a more deliberate kind of punitiveness; e.g., she forced Archie to wear underpants he had accidentally soiled although she knew this was greatly distressing to him. Although such instances are rare they directly expose the destructiveness which always seems implicit in her intrusive domination. Yet, for every hostile action, there is a guilty reaction. "I know and I feel confident, and maybe I should not, that I am a handicap to Archie in more ways than one." "I think it is my fault that he is fearful," "I know Archie wants my affection; I know I don't show him the affection that the child really feels is his." "It is my fault [that he truanted] . . . I made too much of an issue over it." Also relevant here are the previously mentioned instances of identifying Archie's bad qualities with her own. Such self-accusations are genuine and are part of a generally depressive undertone which runs through much of the interview material.

If one adds the previously discussed anxious concern, intrusiveness, and the glimmers of affection and pride to these elements of anger and guilt, the picture is complete.

As for Archie, he is both more disturbed psychologically and more completely victimized by his mother than is Darlene. Although Mrs. Fenster offers a false model for her child to copy, it is at least an integrated one, whereas Mrs. Merrill's instability serves to bewilder her son and increase his sense of helplessness. His World Test and his Witch stories are saturated with themes of destruction and violence and indicate a high level of unmastered anxiety. Such a preoccupation with the dangers of life might well have come from his mother. However, because he is a child, his fantasies seem more compelling and terrifying to him than his mother's imaginary disasters are to her.

In a superficial way he is like Darlene in that he is continually demanding and pestering. The mother mentions his unpopularity and it is easy to see why he would be a very wearing little boy to have around. Like Darlene he also has learned to use his mother's techniques against her, his intrusiveness serving to irritate and exhaust Mrs. Merrill. Yet this behavior has little of the exhibitionistic quality that was so striking in Darlene. Granted that it is partly retaliatory, it is also more desperate and relentless, more an incessant, panicky bid for help in the face of tremendous anxiety.

A significant aspect of Archie's pathology is the impoverishment of his defenses. His schoolwork is poor, he has few friends, he usually plays with very young children. In an effort to protect himself from overpowering dangers he is retreating from interpersonal relationships into a preoccupation with taking apart and reassembling inanimate objects. One might assume that this not only represents an island of safety for him but also an area relatively free from his mother's suffocating influence.

Mrs. Kranek: A Neurotic Mother

For Mrs. Kranek, motherhood is a thankless chore. "Everything that is done I have to do. I have to make sure they [the children] eat. I have to make sure they wash. I have to make sure they go to the store. I have to make sure they take the dog out. I mean everything is left up to me." She is a simple woman whose image of the good life is one in which nothing happens to annoy her and whose idea of a good time is going to a movie. Her characteristic reaction to difficulties is an angry outburst, although she becomes quite anxious at times and is not without her reflective moments. If she has little maternal warmth to give Kathy it is because she herself has received little; if she fails to impart any feel for the niceties of human relationships it is because her life has been rather bleak and unadorned.

Although Mrs. Kranek probably was not severely deprived as a child, she certainly was brought up on a minimal subsistence basis, both physiologically and psychologically. The eighth of nine children, she early learned that life was hard—"Oh, very hard. We lived on relief. My father was on WPA and what money he did get he drank up. And my mother had a hard life with him, very hard. She had a child every year. He was very mean. He never hit her or anything but I mean he used to take his money and drink it all up and the kids would go hungry. . . . He used to punish us [children] by not letting us go out or—we used to go to the show maybe on Friday. The show used to be a nickel. If we weren't bad during the week we could go to the show. I mean that used to kill me cause I loved the show, but that's the way he used to make—make us mind." Such early experiences conditioned Mrs. Kranek to an uncomplicated view of life whose central values are material possessions, justice, discipline, and simple pleasures.

In Mrs. Kranek's scheme of things, being a mother means, at a very literal level, providing food for her children. The subtle interplay of communication which is intrinsic to feeding activities rarely enters the picture. All she knows is that as a child she was always hungry; now, as a mother, she provides food for her family; this in itself should be a precious enough gift to qualify her as a good and giving woman. "Many times we went hungry. And every time my —I give the kids something to eat I always say to them, 'When I was your age I wish I had that to eat.' And it's wrong. Me and my oldest sister talk about it lots of times. She says it's wrong to tell the children—it isn't the children's fault that you didn't have that to eat. But— I mean you just do it you know." Incidentally this quotation also represents one of the few reflective passages in the interview, since Mrs. Kranek is usually too caught up in the immediacy of her feelings to be self-critical. By the same token a good father is defined in terms of being a good provider. When asked, "Is your husband good to your children?" her reply was, "Yes, I mean, ah—I mean he makes sure they've got to have their food on the table and—if they need clothing right away, he says, 'Well go buy it.' He never ah—refused them anything."

In all this emphasis on material things there is nothing grasping or exhibitionistic. It is just that, having known deprivation, Mrs. Kranek's main concern is still with the necessities of life. To distinguish the gift from the spirit of the giver is a refinement which rarely occurs to her. Since she herself has never outgrown the wonder of having food, she cannot understand why her children do not experience the same feeling, nor can she imagine what more they could want of her. In fact, her children's expectations that she be more than a good provider arouse anger in her, perhaps because such expectations imply demands which she is incapable of meeting, perhaps because they impinge on her own unfulfilled longings for something more than she got.

However, a good parent must not only provide, she must distribute her attentions with justice. When asked if she favored any of her children, Mrs. Kranek became defensive and denied that she did. Also she resents the fact that her husband pays more attention to the boys and more or less neglects the girls. Having herself been in a large family with so little to go around, she has a keen awareness of the resentment which is touched off when one child gets more than the others.

If providing the necessities and distributing them justly are the core qualities of a good parent, then a good child is defined as one who does not give his parents too much trouble. He is easily satisfied in infancy (in the interview Mrs. Kranek carefully graded her children along this dimension), and later on he minds and assumes responsibilities. Her boy is an example of a good baby: "I haven't had a bit of trouble with anything since the day he was born. He was never sick, he never cried, he ate and he slept all day, all night." Or, note the revealing example of what a good older child does: "She'll be so good. She'll go down—you say, Kathy go to the store, she goes without saying a word. Kathy do something and she does it right away." When children behave in such a manner, the burdens of the mother are tolerable. Undue raucousness, stubbornness, or defiance arouse immediate anger and are met with whippings or yelling. Such disciplining serves to bring the child back in line. However, this is an endless and thankless task made even worse by the fact that she must do it all herself. Mrs. Kranek's frequent arguments with her husband center around the fact that he is too easygoing. "He says, 'I'm going to spank her.' He never spanks her though. I said maybe if you did spank her once in a while she wouldn't do it."

A very important facet of this orientation is that Mrs. Kranek is much more tolerant of children during infancy than later on. There is little evidence that she feels great tenderness for infants but, in her scheme of things, babies just are not as much trouble. "The older they get it seems the worse they get. They just don't want—I mean—they just don't want to do anything for you. And you have to keep telling them over and over." Thus the early caretaking activities she can more or less handle; it is the later problems of obedience and performance of daily chores that Mrs. Kranek finds such a grinding burden. One might again infer that some of her own childhood resentments at being given too much responsibility and too little love are reactivated and displaced on to her children.

The pleasures in Mrs. Kranek's life are not only simple ones but are usually extraneous to her role as mother. Going to a show remains the ultimate and almost exclusive source of enjoyment, and the unseen pictures of childhood have made her an insatiable movie-goer as an adult. It is true that she also enjoys going visiting and dressing up the children on such occasions. Although this might appear to be a family-derived pleasure, it seems that it is something she does for her own satisfaction regardless of the child's wishes in the matter. The only evidence of more genuinely positive feeling is the pride with which she described her daughter's prettiness and her sexual maturing.

This then is Mrs. Kranek's schema for motherhood. It is a simple one and only rarely does she go beyond it in an attempt to understand what has been omitted or incorrectly formulated. Characteristically she is oblivious to complexities and unaware, even at an intuitive level, of more subtle motivational factors. Also impressive is the directness with which her present values grow from her childhood frustrations and joys, as if all subsequent experiences have been ineffectual in modifying or even enriching her approach to life.

This limited outlook and lack of resources significantly affect the difficulties she has with Kathy. Her refrain, when talking of such problems, is, "I can't understand." "I can't understand it. I mean, I never had any trouble with the other two [children]." "That's what I can't understand; why is she so slow when I want her to be—you know—when I want to go some place." "I can't understand why she is like that. She don't take after either my husband or me as far as I can see. I mean I loved geography when I was a child and she hates it; she hates her reading and my husband said he loved reading when he was in school." This refrain is, in all probability, literally true. Mrs. Kranek is not the kind of complex or devious person whose lack of comprehension would reflect some emotional blocking or some disguised hostility; she is genuinely baffled by anything which lies outside of or runs counter to her own limited set of values. About the only explanation she comes up with periodically is the stereotyped one that her children misbehave because they are given too much: they take food and clothes and toys for granted, and instead of being satisfied, continue to make demands for more. Such an explanation serves only to reinforce the impression that Mrs. Kranek is a woman of limited resources.

If the limitations of Mrs. Kranek's schema of motherhood are apparent, there is also an important asset. Being a mother might be a somewhat grim and unadorned experience, but, by the same token, there is nothing mysterious or frightening about it. When asked if she were worried when she learned she was pregnant during a time when Kathy was very ill and she was estranged from her husband, she said, "I mean it never bothered me and—I mean it just came natural to me. I always took care of kids when I was little. My sister had a boy, he's—ah—I was ten years old and he was born. And he, I mean, he was little and I used to take care of him. I mean it just, came natural to me. When I had my own I just know what to do, see . . . I was always strong enough right after the baby was born. A week or two later I mean I was back doing all my own work. It never affected me, never got me sick or anything." Motherhood is to her like earning a living is to her husband, nothing more or less than one of the basic facts of living. Any feeling of excess, whether it be love or anxiety, rarely enters the picture. This is the bedrock stability which underlies Mrs. Kranek's loudly broadcasted resentments against her husband, her daughter, and her lot in life.

Mrs. Kranek's personality is not geared to maximizing the psychological development of her offspring, but there is also nothing intrinsically destructive about it. In fact, two of her children seem to be developing adequately. It is only with Kathy that an impasse has been reached. Even Mrs. Kranek's fantasies during pregnancy were ominous and atypical. "All the time I carried her I felt there would be something wrong with her when she was born. I just had that feeling, I don't know why. I just had that feeling that she was going to be born—deformed or mentally ill or what." Unfortunately, the dynamics of this crucial fantasy are not revealed by the data. There is evidence that Mrs. Kranek fears her temper and the destructiveness of her rages. At one point she told how she stopped whipping her oldest child for fear she would hurt her physically or "injure her mind." But what peculiar combination of hostility and guilt motivated these preoccupations during pregnancy, and why they appeared only with Kathy, remain a complete mystery.

Although Mrs. Kranek was reassured her child was all right after delivery, the first few months were exasperating ones. "She just cried all the time. She never ate and—I mean—up until she was a year and a half or more she—there wasn't any good point about her. I mean because she cried all the time and she was constantly wet and everything." Naturally it was the feeding problem which was most upsetting since it struck at one of Mrs. Kranek's primal values. "She cried—it seemed like she—was never satisfied. I mean I'd give her the bottle and she'd finish it and I even—I had the doctor increase the milk and everything. I thought she wasn't getting enough. And it still didn't help. She still cried. I mean the minute the bottle got empty she'd cry. So I'd give her some more and she'd still cry." Mrs. Kranek's feeling of helpless exasperation comes out clearly in such a description.

Yet, there was another source of distress; this was an implicit fear that poor nourishment would produce some devastating illness. "I worried that if she doesn't eat her resistance will be low. And that's always on my mind that she, that she is going to get something and she ain't going to be able to fight it off." Thus the fantasies during pregnancy were only dormant. Reality factors brought them out into the open when, at five months, Kathy contracted a severe case of whooping cough, probably complicated later by croup. Mrs. Kranek responded with protectiveness and overconcern. "They saved her and for a year and a half I sat up nights with her—I was afraid she would choke to death. I was afraid to lay down. I was afraid she'd fall you know and gag and choke over night. It takes an infant—it doesn't take much for them to gag on you know." This concern over health and poor nourishment has persisted in less dramatic form up to the present. Although Mrs. Kranek realizes how unrealistic such ideas are, she still has a chronic expectation that her daughter will be the first to catch a contagious disease.

In spite of this worry there was a period of relative calm when

Kathy was five and six years old. She still presented problems, but they were not very burdensome ones and Mrs. Kranek expected that school would "straighten her out." Just the opposite happened, and mother and daughter have become locked in a hostile interaction which is the predominant feature of their present relationship. Again it is not clear why this happened and why Kathy chose to use her new-found freedom in a retaliatory manner. However, she has shown a child's uncanny facility for hitting upon the most sensitive areas in her mother's personality—she does not mind, she does not shoulder responsibilities, she does not behave herself. At home Kathy's techniques are mainly ones of passive resistance; she dawdles, she dreams, she is standoffish, she fibs; at school she is more directly provocative, only finishing half her work, passing notes, and disrupting the class to the point of being expelled; with her contemporaries her aggression comes out directly and she is constantly fighting with them. Mrs. Kranek is infuriated by all this and is hard pressed to find anything good to say about her daughter. Her immediate reaction in the interview is one of total condemnation of Kathy, and only after getting this resentment out of her system can she go on to relate some ameliorating factors. Characteristically, her only explanation of her daughter's behavior is that she probably was given too much attention when she was sick.

Although the data do little to clarify the dynamics of the antagonism, they do show that Mrs. Kranek has not misread her daughter. Kathy is an angry little girl. Her Witch stories have a number of poison themes, and her World Test is saturated with a kind of senseless destructiveness (e.g., "This cow is looking at this dog because he wants to stamp on him"). Yet she is by no means an impulse-ridden child; her capacity for self-control is good, she has a lively and imaginative intellect, and the energies consumed by anger might easily be redirected into constructive channels if she were handled more sympathetically. Under the existing circumstances, however, a continued deadlock seems likely.

If little mention has been made, so far, of affection, it is because this is a rare commodity in the present mother-child relationship. At one point Mrs. Kranek is critical of her husband: "He never shows them—I don't know why—I mean I have never seen him take my daughters around and hug them and kiss them. He sees they have the necessary things, let's say, but he does not give them much love or affection." This is an unusual distinction for Mrs. Kranek to make between "things" and "love," and it is revealing that she applies it only to her husband rather than to herself. Also on the positive side of the ledger are the facts that she wanted a girl and looked forward to breast-feeding Kathy. However, her primary enjoyment seems to have come from holding and cuddling her baby girl. The most clearly affectionate statements about Kathy center around this area. "I think she loved to be held. I did hold her a lot because of being sick. I did hold her the first year and a half. To this day even—I mean there are times I like to pick—I will take her in my arms and hug her and tell her, 'Gee you're going to be a pretty girl when you grow up.' I, I try sometimes, sometimes so hard to, to love her and she just isn't the type that you—she doesn't like you to touch her or something. I like to hold her and love her and she, she doesn't like it." Such instances of genuine tenderness are rare. However, they suggest that Mrs. Kranek's year-and-a-half vigil while her daughter was sick was not motivated by guilt alone, but that the illness somehow gave her license to indulge in a closeness which otherwise could not be permitted. It is also interesting that it is the indulged infant who later, as a child, became so rebellious at the minimal subsistence mode of living which her mother offered. Thus Mrs. Kranek's stereotyped explanation may be partly true at least; Kathy did come to expect not too much but more than her mother was later capable of giving; the other children, having known so little tenderness, could more easily tolerate their mother's limitations.

A comparison between Mrs. Kranek and the two mothers of children with psychosomatic disorders reveals some important similarities and differences.

Mrs. Kranek's multifarious complaints about Kathy are very much like Mrs. Fenster's total condemnation of Darlene. True, Mrs. Kranek's list is not quite so encompassing, e.g., she reacted to illness with concern rather than irritability, but it is still an impressive one. However, the significant difference between the two mothers is that Mrs. Kranek makes no pretense about the way she feels; she is mad at her daughter and she does not care who knows it. The elements of deviousness and deception do not enter the picture, and there is no facade of perfection with underlying irritability.

Mrs. Kranek's overconcern about illness is reminiscent of Mrs. Merrill's but again there are important differences. Mrs. Kranek is not relentlessly driven to read destructive implications into very minor unpleasantness; on the contrary, she can recognize that her fears are unrealistic and can easily regain her balance when a major crisis is past. In addition, her oversimplified, unresourceful, unimaginative approach to life is at the opposite pole from Mrs. Merrill's emotionally lush and wildly undisciplined one.

More important, in light of the hypothesis of the project, is the fact that Mrs. Kranek can leave her child alone. This was true even in the distressing period of early infancy. "I never really forced her to eat anything. My sister-in-law used to follow her kid around all day long with food. I couldn't see that. I just—I never did that. I felt that when they were hungry they'd eat." This is true at present, although for a different reason. "I used to stand there and holler at her for an hour. I don't any more. I, I get so tired of hollering at her and it didn't do any good anyway. She takes an hour whether I holler or not, so I just leave her. . . . Sometimes I tell her she can't do this or she can't do that and—I figure, 'Oh there's no sense in doing it, she doesn't care anyway.' I mean if [punishment] would do some good, I would. With her it just doesn't help." The observed interaction also revealed this factor since Mrs. Kranek was distant and unresponsive to Kathy throughout the period. Thus Kathy is given some freedom out of sheer weariness and defeat on the part of her mother. This can by no means be regarded as a healthy situation and contrasts sharply with the respect for individuality shown by the next mother, Mrs. Pitney; it is more like an armed truce which periodically breaks out into open antagonism, each side well aware of the tactics of the other. But even such an uneasy armistice, with the mother smoldering and the child dawdling, means that lines of separation are clearly drawn. The Psychosomatic mothers, with their relentless intrusiveness, cannot allow even this state of affairs.

Mrs. Pitney: An Illness Mother

A casual reading of the interview material might tempt one to conclude that Mrs. Pitney is a good mother by default. Aside from her daughter's illness, she seems to have had a rather bland existence after her marriage. Under such circumstances, any reasonably adequate woman could be a good mother. It is only after more careful study that the magnitude and severity of the problems she had to cope with are clearly revealed. A chronology of realistic burdens runs as follows: Mrs. Pitney was married quite young and her father, whom she admired a good deal, died soon afterwards; as soon as she found out she was pregnant with her first child, her husband was drafted into the army; he was away when she delivered a girl, who died shortly after birth; a few months later she became pregnant with Cleota and her husband was shipped overseas; although he was back before the baby was born, he was visiting his relatives during the actual delivery; six months after this, Mrs. Pitney was hospitalized for minor surgery; two weeks before she delivered her third child, Cleota was hospitalized; Cleota was three years old at the time, and contracted both chicken pox and mumps during her ten months' stay in the hospital. Such a series of trials, while not quite so distressing as those Mrs. Merrill had to face, certainly exceeded anything in Mrs. Fenster's married life. The stresses during pregnancy and delivery are particularly striking.

The impression of blandness, then, does not arise from the facts themselves but rather from Mrs. Pitney's method of dealing with them. Both Mrs. Fenster and Mrs. Merrill are given to exaggerated reactions to their children: Darlene's high activity level was inflated into a "battle of wills" by her mother, while Mrs. Merrill saw each minor deviation from health as a matter of life or death. Mrs. Pitney goes to the opposite extreme. The more stressful the situation the more she minimizes it or glosses over it. She characteristically denies that a problem was disturbing and takes an impunitive, almost Stoic attitude of "life's like that." In regard to the death of her first child she said, "It was just one of those things . . . I didn't let it bother me too much because—but—I mean as long as I could have another one—that was the main thing." During her pregnancy with Cleota, "I wasn't worried about her; I was more or less puzzled why the first baby died because there was nothing the doctors could find that was wrong." The interview material itself reflects this trait; it is largely descriptive and factual, with a paucity of words expressing intense affect. At times she seems on the verge of talking about her resentment or her loneliness but she never does; instead she is more likely to cite some minor pleasantry, such as talking to a friendly nurse before delivery, to show that things really were not as bad as they seemed. Any questions about significant friction or any hint that she had more than her share of troubles met with complete denial. She could not express resentment even when it would be perfectly understandable to do so, nor could she blame anyone for the things which went wrong except, occasionally, herself.

This constant effort to smooth over difficulties touches on a characteristic which goes to the core of Mrs. Pitney's personality. In spite of her friendliness and vitality she is, at heart, a very reserved, self-contained person. "I don't know—I just don't get too close to people. I just think that most things are better kept to yourself than telling everybody about it. . . . I growl at the kids a lot but still things that I know—the big things, I try to keep from 'em, when just the other way probably should be the case . . . I probably don't talk things over with my husband as much as I should. . . . Things that happen to me or to my family they are my business and I just don't share all those things with everybody else." This puts her denial in its proper perspective. In effect she is saying, "Keep out." Her personal reactions, especially her negative ones of resentment or loneliness, are her own and not for public display. (She was irritable while telling stories to the psychologist and during the observed interaction; in both instances she might have felt that the investigators were prying into matters which were none of their business.)

What problems trouble her so deeply that she has to wall up some of her innermost feelings is impossible to tell from the data. There are only hints and these might be misleading: she identifies herself temperamentally with her reserved father rather than with her gregarious mother; she enjoys vigorous sports; Cleota's middle name is masculine; she slipped in referring to her children as "both my boys"; she had a good deal of trouble stating the sex of the children on the picture material; and, as will be seen later, she seems more at home with the "masculine" values of self-assertiveness than with the "feminine" ones of docility. One might speculate that this all points to a deep resentment of the feminine role and an equating of passivity with weakness or vulnerability; or, more conservatively, one could merely say that she has some important, unmastered problem of sexual identification. The data suggest little beyond these not too helpful generalities.

However, this quality has affected Cleota, both in terms of her identification with her mother and in certain indirect ways. "She [Cleota] keeps things to herself unless they are pretty tough. . . . You have to draw everything out of her. She—she—well, she complains too but the things she complains about are the things that don't amount to anything. She fusses about this little thing and that little thing but when there is anything that probably I should know about, she keeps it to herself." In addition to this similarity to her mother there is also a pervasive apathy about Cleota. Her mother calls it laziness in that she tends to let things slide unless definitely directed to do them. Her teacher describes her as a "Southern magnolia" which, when translated into everyday language, referred to a certain languorous quality, a need to be told what to do before she can mobilize her resources. Such lethargy might represent a technique of passive resistance designed to irritate her mother, since the mother figure in the Realistic stories was presented in fairly negative terms; yet it might well be a response to the lack of affective spontaneity in her mother. The fact that Mrs. Pitney must keep an important part of her personality walled off means she does not have free access to positive feelings; just as she cannot let herself go and be deeply angry, she also cannot be deeply loving. Because of this, Cleota, in spite of the many other kinds of positive stimulation she receives from her mother, has a strong depressive trend resulting from her basic deprivation of maternal affection.

This might seem a gloomy way to introduce a "good mother." However, there is an important distinction between a good mother and an ideal one. Certainly Mrs. Pitney is not a woman who has ready access to deep, inexhaustible springs of maternal warmth and affection, but then it may be that very few women do. She has definite inadequacies which go to the core of her personality and present major difficulties in her relationship with her daughter. If this were the whole story there would be no reason to single her out as an example of goodness.

However, this is not the whole story. In fact the problem just outlined might well be submerged most of the time or remain at an unverbalized level. Certainly as one shifts his focus to attitudes which are more representative of the everyday give-and-take in the family, a very different picture emerges. Thus it is only the level of deep personal feelings which trouble mother and daughter; in the less intense areas of interaction there is a good deal of freedom.

In the first place, even Mrs. Pitney's reserve has certain positive consequences. Although it may rob Cleota of some of the maternal tenderness she needs, it also carries with it a respect for individuality and a fostering of self-reliance. In describing her handling of a minor upset during Cleota's infancy, Mrs. Pitney said, "I used to tell the doctor how much she weighed and how she was getting along and if he had any suggestions I would abide. And that was that. Most of the time I used my own judgment." Statements such as these reflect a deeply ingrained sense of self-trust: she will seek competent advice when necessary but she does not hesitate to rely on her own common sense, with the belief that it will somehow see her through. In a like manner she usually respects her daughter's wishes and decisions. All this, of course, is in striking contrast with the intrusive control of Mrs. Fenster and the relentless overconcern of Mrs. Merrill; it is hard to imagine Mrs. Pitney ever in the state of exasperation and distress over Cleota's behavior which is so characteristic of both Psychosomatic mothers. Mrs. Pitney is not an intellectual mother, and maybe not a wise one, but her laissez-faire philosophy embraces both a trust of her own integrity and respect for her daughter's.

All this still makes Mrs. Pitney sound much too grim. She is a Southerner, not a New Englander, and many of her attitudes are casual and indulgent rather than strict and disciplined. While putting up with the difficulties which lie beyond her control she also manages to enjoy the pleasures which come her way.

Her casual, take-things-as-they-come attitude contrasts strikingly with the restless, even driven, quality of the Psychosomatic mothers. Recall how intensely both Mrs. Fenster and Mrs. Merrill were involved in becoming pregnant and contrast Mrs. Pitney's attitude when asked if she were anxious to have another baby after the first one died: "I mean we just let nature take its course. We didn't go and see any medical doctors one way or the other about it . . . because I mean I took the doctor's word that I was alright as far as having another one was concerned. And we had waited that long without having the other one so I thought well, there is no use to get anxious about it." In regard to sex preference: "We would take whatever they could give us [laugh]." She was perfectly content during her pregnancy to pass the time away gossiping with friends or cooking and taking care of the house. She was not motivated enough even to work in a nearby defense plant although the extra money would have come in handy.

After Cleota's birth this casualness was supplemented by an indulgence in training. Her casualness is seen in her reaction to a stomach upset Cleota had at six months of age. "After we brought her home from the hospital she cried for about an hour . . . and I don't know what that was all about because she was never sick one way or the other. And when she stopped, well, that was the end of it." Thus, for Mrs. Pitney a crying infant is nothing more or less than a crying infant; if signs of real distress appear, you take care of them; if not, why make a fuss. In contrast to Mrs. Merrill she sizes up Cleota's early illnesses as follows: "She had an upset stomach just for a day's time—and you know how a little tiny child like that is—the minute they are over their sick spell they are up and gone." Part of this casualness stems from the fact that Mrs. Pitney makes decisions on the basis of practical considerations rather than delving into motives. She describes her final revolt against the two o'clock feeding in such terms: ". . . it was in the winter time and we didn't have ah . . . central heating so I thought I don't see no point at all in this because she should have been rid of the bottle by three months . . . I mean . . . at this hour of the night so I just took it away from her. First couple of nights she got up I got up and gave her milk out of the cup and went along as long as she was alright. As long as she ate during the daytime . . . she was perfectly alright."

Mrs. Pitney's indulgence is shown in her easygoing attitude about toilet training and her tolerance of "accidents" when Cleota returned home after being hospitalized. It also comes out in minor details. At one point she was describing Cleota's behavior immediately preceding the illness. "That night she was in the middle of the bed and . . . I've got one of these 18th century . . . not four posters . . . but you know what I mean . . . she stood by that thing and bounced and bounced until I thought sure that mattress would go through on the floor." The important point is that Mrs. Pitney made no effort to stop Cleota and put her daughter's pleasure above the life expectancy of her mattress.

However, Mrs. Pitney is not always so offhand. She talks of hollering at the children, of whipping them, of threatening to skin them alive or beat the truth out of them. Unlike Mrs. Merrill, however, there is no guilty reaction; to her way of thinking short tempers and friction are inevitable when one has a family. There is another facet of this attitude toward hostility: Mrs. Pitney is upset by direct aggression such as fighting, but she admires a kind of headstrong self-assertiveness. She was quite proud of her daughter when she "screamed bloody murder" in the hospital and insisted the nurse bring her a pottie; she was vastly amused by Cleota's fury when the doctor pulled her pants down during a medical examination; in talking of Cleota's tendency to be bossy and outspoken, she has the same mixture of mock exasperation and implicit pride that a father would have when describing what a scrappy troublemaker his son is. The motive behind this admiration comes out when she is asked whether Cleota screamed bloody murder because she was finicky about being dirty. "No . . . it wasn't that . . . it was the idea that . . . I don't really know what it was . . . but I mean . . . the fact that that was something grown up and they were making her a baby again . . . I think that was more or less it." In another place she mentions the importance of being oriented toward the future rather than looking back at the past. There is no hint anywhere that her child's assertiveness means an inevitable "battle of wills"; for her it is a sign of sticking up for one's rights and an antidote to regression.

However, it should also be noted that the psychological data on Cleota indicate that this mother underestimates the depressive, despairing elements in her daughter. It is quite possible that she is threatened by such feelings in Cleota and they call forth all her defensive denial. Mrs. Pitney is probably best in her ability to accentuate the positives and to face up to the reality of bad breaks in life. But this is not enough for Cleota; what she needs in addition are just those feelings of warmth and protectiveness which her mother has been forced to wall up. Even her mother's spiritedness might serve to increase the child's discouragement by widening the gap of communication between them.

Self-trust, casualness, indulgence, practicality, ready outlets for anger and self-assertion—all are qualities which can be associated with good mothering. Yet two essential ones are still missing, those of tenderness and joy. As was mentioned before, deep feelings do not come easily to Mrs. Pitney and, for some reason, she must defend herself against showing strong resentment or love. Yet, in the context of the generally factual, defensive, emotionally inarticulate interview, the tender, happy feelings do filter through.

Throughout the sessions there are vignettes which, while presented in an unadorned, sometimes halting manner, point to a kind of immediate delight in her child, which mothers in the other groups lack completely. When asked to describe Cleota's disposition she said, "Just happy as a lark . . . I can't . . . everybody she met . . . everybody she saw . . . why she was . . . they could just go and she would just go . . . she never saw a stranger. . . . When bedtime came . . . you put her in her bed and that's all there was to it. You could go in and wake her up any hour of the day or night regardless of how long she's been asleep . . . she'd come right up smiling." Or, describing Cleota as an infant: "I used to put her out in the yard in the afternoon . . . that is, when weather permitted. The leaves were on the trees and she'd lay out there all afternoon long and lay there and laugh and look at the leaves on the trees, as long as they were moving, when the sun made shadows." Or this memory: "She's always loved animals. And flowers. When she was a little bit of a thing, I could give her an old buttercup or some kind of a little old flower like that and she would sit and just play with it and play with it and never would give it up." There was an obvious element of delight when she described her little boy's sudden concern that his angry outburst had hurt his father's feelings, or when she told of the grand things both children fantasy they will do for their parents when they grow up. It is her response to a question about discipline, however, which aptly brings out Mrs. Pitney's combination of overt anger and practicality with inarticulate tenderness.

"Sometimes I holler and sometimes I hunt me up a little belt of some description, but there's one thing I never did—I never hit either one of them anywhere except across their bottom. And I don't do much of that either. I used to . . . when my little girl first came home from the hospital I swatted her with my hand and I hurt my fingers on her brace more than I did her, so I finally quit that and I've gotten to the point where I don't hardly touch her at all now because . . . I don't know. At first it didn't bother me so much . . . but now . . . she's so big for one thing and then . . . instead of crying like she would when she was little . . . she'd just act like you'd taken her best friend away from her and goes around all mulled up at you for about a half a day and I didn't figure it'd do much good anyway. So now, usually when they get into something that they got no business . . . well . . . we just run them upstairs and let them play by themselves for a little while."

There was only one point at which Mrs. Pitney's feelings were more explicitly stated, and it was very revealing when this happened. The interviews were just about complete and the worker asked a final "catch-all" question, "Can you think of anything in Cleota's first year of life that comes to mind? We've talked pretty much about the usual things." The question itself would make a defensive reply legitimate. Instead, Mrs. Pitney said

Well . . . I think about the only thing I remember so very well was in the hospital . . . she was three months old. My mother brought her there for me to see. And she got to making such a racket and was enjoying herself so much that the doctor came in out of the hall and he said, "That's the biggest baby I ever delivered and, in fact, I don't even remember delivering her" [laugh]. But oh, she was just tickled to death. She just laughed and cooed and just had the biggest time you ever seen in your life. She didn't want to go. She . . . you know . . . whined a little bit when my mother took her and started dressing her . . . she didn't want to go. But I'm just almost sure that she recognized me . . . I mean . . . even as small as she was because I've never seen a little baby have as big a time as she did.

Such a spontaneous memory must certainly tap a larger reservoir of maternal delight and tenderness, even if such feelings are relatively inaccessible in Mrs. Pitney's day-to-day living.

Thus it can be seen why Mrs. Pitney is regarded as a good mother, not an ideal one. While she avoids the devastating entanglements of the Psychosomatic mothers, her need to deny her stronger feelings of resentment and affection have robbed her of the depth of feeling an ideal mother might have. Also, Cleota is not an ideal child; although genuinely friendly, easygoing, and charming, she has a depressive streak which results in moodiness and lassitude.

Fortunately, the existence of significant problems does not prevent a woman from being a good mother. Not only does Mrs. Pitney's problem seem less destructive to her child than Mrs. Fenster's or Mrs. Merrill's, but, more important, she has a host of assets to bring to the maternal relationship. She is down to earth and casual, allowing her daughter freedom and giving her a sense of her worth as an independent individual; anger is accepted as a fact of life and self-assertiveness is admired; her children can be a source of genuine pleasure for her; although her characteristic attitude is one of making the best of bad situations, she is not Spartan or cold; on the contrary, there is an inarticulate kind of tenderness which constantly softens her practical realism.

Since psychologists know so much about pathology and so little about health it might be worth while to note, in closing, that Mrs. Pitney was considered to be the best mother on the project.

11 --- Summary

This chapter will present both an enumerative and an interpretative summary of the results of the study. The numerous specific findings are assembled here to save the reader the inconvenience of having to refer to previous chapters and to present the factual framework for the interpretative integration of the data which follows.

ENUMERATIVE SUMMARY

Findings Concerning the Mothers

1. The mother-infant relationship as revealed in interviews with the mothers.

Experts rated this material in terms of the mother's attitudes toward pregnancy and toward child training and care, her general maternal attitudes, and the physiological status of the infant, while the social worker who did the interviewing made a descriptive evaluation of the mother's relation with the infant.

The Psychosomatic mothers[1] were distinguished both by their positive attitudes toward pregnancy and the absence of such positive feelings about actual training and care of the infant. Although they did not have a particularly extensive and varied list of negative maternal traits, they were characterized as being striving and controlling in relation to their infant. The infant himself did not have any more physiological distress than would be found in Neurotic or Illness infants, in regard either to general or to specific organic difficulties.

----

[1] See Chapter 3, pages 34-36 for a discussion of nomenclature.

However, the Psychosomatic mothers were burdened with an unusual number of problems arising from their general life situation.

The Neurotic mothers were judged as having negative attitudes both toward pregnancy and toward child training and care, although the feelings toward the latter were not as extreme as in the case of the Psychosomatic mothers. The group was marked by a variety of negative maternal attitudes rather than falling within the more circumscribed area of striving, controlling behavior. The Neurotic mothers were also burdened with distressing situations arising from areas other than infant care.

The Illness mothers were judged as having positive attitudes in all areas, although they did not feel quite so strongly about pregnancy as did the Psychosomatic mothers. The mothers were almost completely lacking in the striving, controlling attitudes so characteristic of the Psychosomatic group, and the first year of the infant's life was also relatively free of distress from sources extraneous to infant care. It is important to reiterate that the physiological status of the infant in this group did not differ from that found in the other groups.

2. The mother-infant relationship as reflected in the mother's thematic material given in response to specially selected pictures.

In *the Psychosomatic group* there was a general lack of feeling in regard to infant care, and the absence of positive attitudes was particularly striking. The role given the infant was a negative one, with little positive or even ambivalent feeling in this area; while the role of the mother was also negative, there was more ambivalence than clear-cut negative feelings about it. Both the nature of the mother's negative role and the accuracy of identification of interpersonal situations depicted in the stimulus material, showed a hypersensitivity to a close relationship with the child. The Psychosomatic mothers accurately recalled more pictures than did the mothers of the other groups. Finally, the stimulus material called forth fewer references to her own experiences in infant care than were found in the other groups, and those which were elicited tended to be negative.

The Neurotic group was characterized by the expression of strong feeling; their general attitudes about child care, the role they assigned to the mother and to the child were all permeated with positive or negative affect. Unlike the findings in the Psychosomatic group, the negative role assigned the mother concerned matters unrelated to infant care, and pictures of individuals were more accurately identified than those showing interpersonal situations. The accuracy of recall was inferior to that found in the other groups.

The Illness group was characterized generally by feelings ranging from neutral to positive; very little negative affect was present in any of the thematic material. The most ambivalence was seen in regard to the role assigned to the child. The accuracy of their recall was high, and the pictures elicited not only the greatest number of personal references, but also the largest proportion of positive ones.

3. The contemporary mother-child relationship derived from rating a brief period of direct observation.

The Psychosomatic and Neurotic groups were similar in the atmosphere of the interaction they generated. Both showed relatively little positive closeness and relatively greater anger and irritability as compared with the Illness group. Both showed relatively low mother-empathy and relatively high over-all discomfort. However, the Psychosomatic group was characterized by domination and competition, with the child seen as victimized by his mother, while the Neurotic group was characterized by low domination, competition, and victimization and high independence and encapsulation on the part of the child. The interaction in the Illness group was generally positive in respect to all the ratings.

Another approach to the contemporary mother-child relationship was that of having a mother predict what response her child made to a questionnaire about his everyday feelings and attitudes. The Psychosomatic group was the most accurate in its predictions.

4. Two subgroups of Psychosomatic mothers could be distinguished on the basis of the agreement between their rating of their child's infancy and the expert's rating of the interview material. In the case of the "High" Psychosomatic mothers there was a high mother-judge and judge-judge agreement, while in the case of the "Low" Psychosomatic mothers there was a low mother-judge and judge-judge agreement. The "High" mother's interview material was well organized, clear, and consistent, while the "Low" mother's material was confused, inconsistent, and disorganized.

The "High" mothers had the most positive anticipations during pregnancy, were more accurate in the recall of pictures used to obtain thematic material, and predicted their child's response to the questionnaire with greater accuracy than the "Low" mothers. In the observed interaction, the "High" mothers were self-contained and benign while their children were dominating, competitive, and angry; by contrast, the "Low" mothers were lacking in empathy, dominating, competitive, and angry while their children were helpless and victimized.

No other significant difference between the "High" and "Low" mothers was found although all the results were systematically analyzed in terms of the subgroups.

Findings Concerning the Children

1. Attitudes toward being mothered as revealed in thematic material given in response to a specially designed set of pictures, half of which depicted realistic mother-child situations, and half of which showed witches with children.

The Psychosomatic children evidenced the least responsiveness to the positive elements in the stimulus material and the greatest responsiveness to the negative elements. Being mothered was rarely associated with pleasure and gratification. Although there was no quantitative difference in negative thema over that found in the Neurotic group, a unique kind of interaction was found which consisted of a mixture of positive and negative elements: in some instances the mother was pictured as manipulative and giving to the child only if he were a model of good behavior; in other instances she was seen as inconsistent and both she and the child were caught up in a pattern of irresistible attraction and inevitable antagonism. The intensity of the Psychosomatic child's negative feelings about being mothered saturated their Witch fantasies with traumatic imagery and was more disruptive of their reality contact than was the case with other children.

The Neurotic children's thematic material falls between the extremes represented by the illness groups: they have neither the Illness group's abundance of positive feeling nor the Psychosomatic's paucity; at times their negative feelings outstrip those found in the Psychosomatic group but at other times such feelings are notably absent. In their negative themes, they, like the Illness children, tended to picture the mother as depriving or delaying gratification rather than as manipulative or inconsistent. These children were also relatively free of the traumatic fantasies about the destructiveness of the bad mother which were found in both illness groups. Finally, there was evidence that the lack of extreme feelings about mothering which characterized the Neurotic group was due, to a considerable extent, to their defensive non-involvement in the technique itself.

In *the Illness children* there was a sharp contrast between the positive feelings which characterized their realistic thema and their preoccupation with traumatic fantasies. This latter was never so extreme as it was in the Psychosomatic group, but it did contrast with the many themes of pleasure and gratification which were given to the pictures of realistic mother-child interactions.

2. Personality characteristics of the Psychosomatic children as revealed by the Rorschach, the World Test, and specially designed techniques.

Rorschach data indicate that the Psychosomatic children were less emotionally responsive than children in the other groups, and both the World Test and the Rorschach indicated that they were also more disturbed psychologically. Their response to being offered a present and their Rorschach and World Test symbolism provided evidence of increased mistrustfulness and suspiciousness in this group. Finally, a specially designed series of techniques showed that, in the Psychosomatic child's fantasies, etiology of illness was more intimately connected with interpersonal situations and with negative emotional states than it was in the fantasy of the other children. Both illness groups fantasied more aggression and transgression as producing sickness.

INTERPRETATIVE SUMMARY

The Psychosomatic mothers might be epitomized as follows: they are ambitious, controlling women who have high expectations for their child during pregnancy but find the actual caretaking of the infant unrewarding or disagreeable; because of their emotional investment, however, they are irresistibly drawn to this ungratifying activity to the point of becoming entangled in a close, mutually frustrating relationship. It will be worth while to trace some of the details of this pattern in terms of both the mother and the child.

The Psychosomatic mothers seem to be intense women in that they tend to be driving, rigid, and to expect conformity; moreover, these qualities are relatively unrelieved by tenderness or spontaneous enjoyment or casualness. Their heightened anticipation during pregnancy cannot be regarded solely as intensification of a healthy desire for fulfillment through motherhood; rather, it represents an overinvestment in specific goals ulterior to those of giving and receiving gratification from the infant. This can take many forms: a mother might want to duplicate exactly the pattern of childbearing of her own idolized mother, or she might have a strong competitive need to have a child at the same time as her sibling, or she might be determined to prove she can give her infant more love than she herself received. It is probably true that in every expectant mother there is both an anticipation of fulfillment which will enable her to obtain gratification through the infant's happiness, and a number of needs extrinsic to such fulfillment; it is just that, with the Psychosomatic mothers, the latter are disproportionately strong.

Once the infant arrives, there is a dramatic change in the mother's attitude. In spite of her high expectations, she finds very little gratification in caring for him. There is no evidence of ministering to the child out of the fullness of her love, of spontaneous pleasure and pride in him, of the harmonious interplay of maternal tenderness and infant pleasure. Caretaking and training are done either in a wooden manner or with distaste, and the infant is clearly regarded as an irritant or a source of concern, anxiety, and frustration. This is particularly true in regard to feeding activities, which is significant both because of the importance of feeding to the physiological well-being of the infant and because it constitutes the most intimate of caretaking procedures. Finally, there is an impersonality in her attitude which gives the impression that the mother has no deep emotional commitment to her relationship with the infant. Such basic and striking lack of gratification in infant care constitutes the strongest evidence for a lack of motherliness in the Psychosomatic group.

The hypothesized effects upon the infant are twofold. At the somatic level, he does not receive the type of continuous protection from distress which is so important to the achievement of physiological integration. This serves to perpetuate a pattern of diffuse, extreme, and erratic response to stress. The second consequence is that, in the infant's first dim awareness of his interpersonal environment, intimacy is closely associated with distress.

What accounts for the lack of motherliness which has such damaging implications? Certainly not the fact that the infant places more demands upon the mother because of physiological difficulties. There is no evidence that undue organic malfunctioning serves to mobilize the mother's negative feelings which, in turn, intensify the malfunctioning. There is evidence that the mother's general life pattern at this time is marked by an unusual number of stressful events; some of these, like separation from her husband due to military service, are beyond her control, while others, like marital discord, are partly her own making. Whatever the source, such events tend to distract the mother and interfere with the development of a close positive relationship with the infant. Yet, this cannot be the whole story, since the Neurotic mothers face situations equally as burdensome and still manage to obtain a certain amount of gratification from their infants.

There is no clear answer to the question, but it seems reasonable to hypothesize two closely related factors. It is possible that, with this particular infant, the mother has very little genuine maternal feeling even during pregnancy. This means that the positive anticipations are almost completely in terms of ulterior gratifications the mother wishes to derive from having a child. Closely related to this is the possibility that her unrealistically specific and rigid expectations increase the chances for frustration and disappointment. The mother has little tolerance for the many unpredictable features of infant organisms, the sex, the activity level, the responsiveness, etc., since any or all of these may be viewed as major obstructions to her own gratification. Thus she personalizes the infant's behavior in terms of its facilitating or blocking the satisfaction of her non-maternal needs; for example, an infant who temporarily refuses to eat is seen as undermining her adequacy as a mother or as deliberately entering into a power struggle.

Whatever the dynamics of the mother, it is clear that her child comes to have as arid a concept of what it is like to be mothered as she has of mothering him. There is a paucity of love or enjoyment or sharing or any of the positive feelings which enrich the experience of closeness; the emotional substance of intimacy is lacking. This does not mean that, concomitant with the emptiness, there is an exaggeratedly negative image of the mother; at least she is not regarded as any more angry or punitive or depriving than she would be in a group of neurotically disturbed youngsters. Thus, one would not expect dramatic overt expressions of antagonism to be characteristic of these children. It is only when one turns to their more personalized fantasy life and observes the rage and terror which saturate their preoccupations with witches that one realizes their great concern over the destructive potential of their mother. In order to avoid the arousal of such potentially traumatic feelings of destructiveness, the Psychosomatic child has to resort to a more extensive distortion of reality than is found in either of the other groups.

The other outstanding feature of the relationship in the Psychosomatic group is the mutual entanglement of mother and child. In spite of the fact that the mother finds infant care unrewarding and unpleasant, she cannot relinquish her closeness to the infant. In all probability the strength of the ulterior needs plus the rigidity in her personality make her persist tenaciously in her efforts to make the infant serve her purposes. It can also be speculated that guilt over her chronic hostility serves to reinforce the closeness.

This inability to let go of the infant is the beginning of a vicious circle. The more relentless the mother's determination, the more frustrating are the child's deviations and, consequently, the more unrewarding he becomes. On his part, once the infant is no longer helpless, he quickly becomes aware of his mother's vulnerabilities and learns to repeat just that behavior which she finds least tolerable. Although the child can retaliate against his mother, he also frustrates the fulfillment of his needs for maternal affection. Thus mother and child are irresistibly drawn to a mutually frustrating relationship, neither one able to derive any real gratification from the interaction, and each equally helpless to relinquish his destructive hold on the other. Incidentally, the Psychosomatic mothers are more knowledgable about their child's everyday feelings and reactions, probably because of this pathological closeness, but such intellectual understanding in no way helps them to become more empathetic.

Within this general context of negative closeness there are two distinct styles of maternal behavior. One group of Psychosomatic mothers is shrewd, complex, and cold. They are well organized, planful, and have particularly high expectations during pregnancy. They are quite often cagey in interpersonal relations, knowing the right thing to do and say while managing to be evasive and self-protective. They are not without some positive feeling for their offspring and, if they are given to playing the part of the good and intelligent mother, such a role can offer them some gratification. Basically, however, they are manipulative women who give to the child only on condition that his behavior be congruent with the image of her as a good mother. The other subgroup of Psychosomatic mothers is quite different. They are overreactive, unstable, and disorganized. They lack the integration which would result in a consistent handling of their child or an organized accounting for their behavior. Feelings find ready expression when they are with their children, and the obliviousness of these women to incongruities subjects their children to bewildering inconsistencies in behavior.

On their part, the Psychosomatic children have two images of mothering which complement the subgroups described above. In certain cases the mother is seen as constantly manipulating the child by giving to him only on condition that he be a model of good behavior; because she is driven to maintaining a facade of perfection, her child must be perfectly behaved. On his part, the child is caught between his feeling of outrage at being given conditional love and a strong identification with the mother which makes him condemn his own rebelliousness. In the other image, the mother is a person who has little sense of direction and continuity but is buffeted about by strong feelings of love and hate, concern and irritation, closeness and anger. Both mother and child are caught up in a pattern of irresistible attraction and inevitable antagonism.

Direct observation of mother and child furnish ample evidence of the negative entanglement which is the hallmark of the Psychosomatic group. The general atmosphere of the relationship is one of discomfort, with a minimum of empathy and a maximum of irritability and anger. More important, domination and competition keep both mother and child tightly enmeshed in the antagonistic relation. The well-organized mothers add to their underlying hostile, competitive attitude an adroitness at maintaining a benign facade which seems absent from the unstable subgroup. In an observed interaction, therefore, the organized mothers become the well-meaning but innocent victim of their petulant, depreciating, overweening child. By contrast, the prototype of the unstable subgroup is the domineering, controlling mother of the helpless, victimized child.

Finally, there are certain later characteristics of the Psychosomatic children which, theoretically, can be related to their ungratifying infantile period. To begin with, they lack the spontaneity, richness, and vitality of emotional expression, the freedom to react quickly and intensely to the environment, which is so characteristic of normal children; although they can evaluate reality adequately and are intellectually alert, they tend to be overcontrolled and bland. It has been speculated that this is the result of their failure adequately to integrate their physiological functioning during infancy so that, in later childhood, the ordinary stress which emotional responsivity places on the organism cannot be sustained and it reverts to an undifferentiated, primitive state. Thus the physiological components of emotional behavior are short-circuited into distressing physical symptoms and, instead of being able to carry out an emotional response in relation to the environment, the child is diverted to attending to his bodily needs. Interestingly enough, in his fantasies about etiology of illness the

Psychosomatic child makes this very connection and sees emotional states as direct causes of illness; in his fantasies, illness is also more directly connected with interpersonal situations than it is for other children, which is again congruent with the theory that, in psychosomatic disorders, the interpersonal variables have particular etiological importance.

The mistrustfulness which is found to be characteristic of the Psychosomatic child can also be traced to his inadequate mothering. From the beginning, intimacy and distress have been associated and, later on, the pattern of maternal closeness without maternal love serves to reinforce the connection. Thus the children, in spite of developing very good social techniques in certain instances, have an engrained suspiciousness of any deep affection which is offered them no matter how genuine the spirit. Finally, this basic mistrust of such a basic emotion as love might well be a significant factor in the increased severity of psychological disturbance to be found in Psychosomatic children as compared with Neurotic ones.

The Neurotic mothers can be epitomized as being relatively free in their approach to infant care and quick to express feeling, either positive or negative. There is no discontinuity between their anticipations during pregnancy and their attitudes toward the infant during its first year. In the face of the highly charged negative relationship which develops, both mother and child erect protective defenses to distance themselves from one another.

Such a picture presents many contrasts with the Psychosomatic group. Interestingly enough, the crucial difference is not in the quantity and variety of negative feelings the Neurotic mother has; in fact, in terms of this variable alone she far outstrips her Psychosomatic counterpart. However, the important thing is that this is just one facet of a larger pattern of being generally more feelingful. If they are often angry or rejecting or controlling, they also have their moments of genuine pleasure and affection and pride in relation to the infant. There is not that impersonality, that wariness, that noncommittal quality which characterizes the Psychosomatic mother in spite of her continual closeness.

Another important difference is the continuity of feeling from pregnancy to infancy in the Neurotic mothers. If they find pregnancy unwelcome and unpleasant, then the birth serves only to confirm their pattern of negative anticipation. There is little of the Psychosomatic group's high expectation followed by empty and frustrating experiences during infancy. In this sense the first year of life is not a pivotal one in the development of the mother-infant relationship.

These characteristics of the mother are mirrored in the child's attitude toward being cared for. As might be expected of children with behavior problems, there is a considerable amount of negative feeling, with the mother seen variously as angry, depriving, competitive, and burdened. However, the child is not subjected to the unrelieved pressure of unrewarding closeness since there are times of genuine pleasure and the image of a truly gratifying mother is a very real one to them. Such compensatory factors might account for their relative freedom from the intensely traumatic fantasies about the destructiveness of the mother which are so striking in the Psychosomatic group.

The third differentiating factor, and a crucial one, is that the Neurotic mother, unlike the Psychosomatic mother, can distance herself from her child. Perhaps this is because she is never as strongly invested in ulterior purposes which she expects the infant to serve in her life, or perhaps she is characterologically less intense and controlling; however, it is definitely not because her general life situation is easier for her or because the infant presents a picture of significantly better health. Whatever the reason, the Neurotic mother is able to achieve some sort of separation from the infant; for example, she more readily becomes involved in independent adult preoccupations which do not concern her offspring, and she can conceive of the child being sufficiently detached to be bewildered or unhappy about incomprehensible adult behavior. Thus the incessant personalizing, that readiness to interpret infant behavior in terms of enhancing or impeding the achievement of non-maternal goals, which is so characteristic of the Psychosomatic group, is relatively unimportant here.

As a consequence, both mother and child are able to build up defenses of non-involvement. They are angry and irritated with one another, but they can also wall one another out. This is why their observed interaction resembles an uneasy truce; the underlying tension of antagonism is there and may erupt into overt anger at times, but the mother puts a good deal of physical distance between herself and her child, and both insure the maintenance of psychological distance by studiously directing their attention to different pursuits. Of course, this type of defense solves nothing and serves only to sustain the impasse between the two. However, it does have the advantage of avoiding the kind of mutual entanglement which is so prominent in the Psychosomatic group.

The Illness mothers present the most positive picture in many respects. They are the freest and most relaxed of the group, have the largest reservoir of positive feeling to bring to the relationship with the child, are relatively exempt from the ambitiousness, control, and impersonality which characterize the Psychosomatic mothers, and the variety and intensity of negative feelings to be found in the Neurotic mothers. The over-all picture is one of realistic, uncomplicated pregnancy anticipations fulfilled in positive ways by the events of the first year of the infant's life. Their general life situation during this time is not so distressing as it is for the other mothers but this might be due as much to their adequacy as women as to good fortune. It is important to repeat that the infant itself presents no unusual problems in terms of physiological difficulties.

This does not mean the Illness group embodies all the qualities which comprise the image of an ideal mother; there are tensions and problems which make them feel quite ambivalent about their child, and there is also a tendency toward blandness rather than richness of feeling. In general, however, they approximate the ideal much more than do the mothers in the other two groups.

Their positive qualities are reflected in their children's attitude toward being close to them. In everyday living there is a healthy expectation of love, protection, and sharing, and a minimum of antagonism, anger, and manipulation. It is therefore surprising to find that in their fantasy life the Illness children have a terrifying image of the destructive power of the mother which, while not as extreme as that found in the Psychosomatic group, is definitely out of keeping with the whole tenor of the mother-child relationships. The speculation here is that chronic illness increases the likelihood that being cared for by the mother will become associated with the pain, anxiety, and frustration accompanying the illness. The child probably cannot understand why he suffers or why his mother cannot prevent such suffering; also he might well react to the increased strain his illness places upon his mother with exaggerated fantasies of destructiveness on her part. Thus, illness serves to fixate the split image of a "good" and "bad" mother found so often in children. It is also probable that illness predisposes a child to think in terms of aggression or transgression as etiological agent. The implication here is that a certain amount of disturbed fantasy is a concomitant of any chronic illness and that psychosomatic theories which are not cognizant of the nature and extent of such disturbances are open to serious error.

The observed interaction provides ample evidence that the child's frightening fantasies do not significantly contaminate his relationship with his mother. Here the atmosphere is one of positive closeness and comfort, with relatively little anger or irritability. The child can both maintain his individuality and can share with his mother his pleasure at being close to her.

It will be recalled that the basic hypothesis of the project is that mothers of children who develop psychosomatic disorders lack "motherliness," i.e., gratification of the infant's needs for body care and pleasurable stimulation in ways which also provide the mother herself with satisfaction. It is further hypothesized that the mother-infant interaction is a close, mutually frustrating one. The study contains ample evidence to support both hypotheses. It also reveals a good deal of unforeseen information about both the mother and child. Two distinctive patterns of faulty maternal behavior were discovered along with their counterparts in the children's attitudes about being mothered; also, important leads were uncovered as to the reasons these mothers cannot let go of a relationship which is so ungratifying. Finally, specific characterological traits and fantasies of the children were delineated which possibly have their roots in the faulty mother-infant interaction. Thus, a more explicit and detailed account of the relationship between the mother and her child can be given.

As is so often the case in research, we end the project with the feeling that this is a promising beginning.

PART TWO

Details of Methodology

12---Evaluation of Design

The following chapters will present a more technical analysis of methodology than was contained in Part I. Details of design, procedure, and scoring will be discussed along with the statistical treatment of results. Critical evaluations are also made whenever these throw some light on the technique being considered. However, both the rationale for the procedure and the interpretative discussion of results have already been given in Part I and will not be repeated here.

Before analyzing the individual techniques, however, two general matters deserve special attention. The first of these concerns the validity of the techniques as indices of "motherliness"; the second involves an evaluation of a multitechnique approach in testing the central hypothesis. As will be seen, these are closely related matters.

Validity

The recently elaborated concept of "construct validity"[1] plus the traditional rules for hypothesis verification form the theoretical substrata of the present investigation. It will be helpful therefore to discuss these two factors in some detail.

"Motherliness" is one of the many fruitful concepts in personality theory which lacks clearly defined, objective referents. Not only are there no satisfactory operational definitions of the term, but there are also no well-established behavioral derivatives; for example, there is nothing corresponding to "school achievement" which was so helpful

---

[1] Lee J. Cronbach and Paul E. Meehl. "Construct validity in psychological tests," *Psych. Bull.*, 52, No. 4 (1955), 281-302.

in the early work on measuring intelligence. This lack of adequate criteria, while generating special problems, need not prevent research from being objective, cohesive, and fruitful.

In the present instance the initial problem, that of defining "motherliness," was no different from what it is in any research which utilizes hypothetical constructs. The problem is essentially a rationalistic one: using all available information, such as the accumulated wisdom of experts and the relevant objective evidence, one must evolve a clear and consistent concept of the meaning of "motherliness." A comprehensive definition is not necessary and might even be impossible if the experts or the evidence disagree violently or if an ungainly number of ideas are encompassed by the construct. What is essential, however, is that the investigator state as definitively as possible the meaning which "motherliness" will have for him in his research. In the present study this was done in Chapter 2.

This definition is an abstract one, not an operational one. Furthermore, the experimental techniques were not designed primarily to verify or measure it. This would be a major undertaking in itself which, while eminently worth while, would be tangential to the primary interests of the project. Rather the construct was accepted on a rational basis as being clear and relevant to the kinds of behavior the investigators would be concerned with.

The factor of relevance mentioned in the preceding sentence is an important one since it served to set limits on the otherwise sprawling construct. The hypothesis made it possible to focus on a particular aspect of mothering—intimate, caretaking activities—and a particular kind of faulty mothering—mutually frustrating closeness. Just as it was not necessary to have a comprehensive definition of "motherliness," it was not necessary to include all varieties of mothering activities and all possible deviations in delineating the kind of faulty mothering to be investigated.

After "motherliness" was conceptualized in terms which satisfactorily met the requirements of clarity and relevance, it became a kind of focal idea which unified the diverse procedures. The only remaining step was that of fitting this construct into a broadly defined psychoanalytic theory of personality development in order to arrive at specific predictions for the three groups used in the study. The details of this integration have been given in Chapter 2 and nothing further will be added at this point in defense of using the psychoanalytic theory.

At this point, then, the investigators had a construct of "mother-liness" and an hypothesis that the lack of this quality is an essential feature of the mother-child relationship in the Psychosomatic group. The theory of personality development dictated the choice of the Neurotic control group, as well as integrating empirical findings about the personality characteristics of the Psychosomatic children, such as their suspiciousness and the severity of their psychological disturbance. All of this was still at the level of intangibles.

In the actual conduct of the experimental work the investigators reasoned as follows: If we accept this concept of motherliness and the attendant theory of personality development, then we would expect characteristic kinds of behavior from each of the groups of mothers and children in response to techniques concerned with the mother-child relationship. Since the construct has so many manifestations, no single technique seems sufficient to encompass it; rather, a whole series of procedures must be designed—some projective and some observational, some contemporary and some reconstructive, some capitalizing on individualized fantasy and some dealing with actual interaction—each reflecting a certain aspect of it. In this manner the behavior of the mother and child in different situations could be predicted on the basis of the previously established theoretical construct. The more frequently these predictions were verified, the more confidence could be placed in the idea that the diverse behaviors could be conceptualized in terms of a unifying construct. Thus no single technique was regarded as *the* operational definition of motherliness any more than any single result was considered as confirming the hypothesis. Rather, validity in the present study is a matter of the relevance of a number of previously predicted empirical findings to a previously established construct. A happy by-product of this approach is that, in the process of evaluating the experimental results, the construct itself can be more objectively defined and can also be enriched by unexpected results.

To recapitulate: At the conceptual level a construct of motherliness was evolved which was clearly stated, internally consistent, and pertinent to the hypothesis of the project. Integrating this construct into a broadly defined psychoanalytic theory of personality development permitted the differentiation of the Psychosomatic, Neurotic, and Illness groups along the dimension of motherliness. A number of techniques were devised which were relevant to the construct, and behavior on each technique was predicted. Positive findings could be regarded as evidence for concluding that the construct had a number of behavioral referents, or, stated conversely, that the diverse behaviors could be unified in terms of the construct. Such findings also served the more traditional function of verifying the hypothesized differences between the Psychosomatic group and the Neurotic and Illness ones.

Finally, the results might well have the added advantage of anchoring the construct more firmly in the realm of observables and of enriching its meaning.

This is not only an ideal description of the procedure but it is also an idyllic one. In reality there were thorny problems at every stage, whether it was that of theorizing, designing techniques, or evaluating results. Some of these problems deserve to be reported in detail.

The difficulties at the level of defining motherliness were no different from those any investigator encounters when dealing with a construct which is both comprehensive and vague. Biological and cultural considerations are as relevant as psychological ones; within the realm of psychology, conscious and unconscious attitudes play a significant part, as well as more general personality factors such as the mother's acceptance of the feminine role, her marital adjustment, her relation to her own parents. A study which could include all these factors would be impressive indeed. Until it appears, the investigator has no choice other than selecting the aspects of motherliness he believes to be relevant to the problem he is investigating. This means he is always open to the objection that he did not take X other factors into account. Such a criticism is never warranted. All any investigator can do is to define his construct as clearly as possible and then see how far he can go in accounting for behavior in terms of the definition he has chosen to adopt. The act of defining itself sets up legitimate parameters of experimentation and interpretation; as long as such limitations are understood and observed the investigator cannot be criticized for shortsightedness or bias. Fortunately it is not necessary to know everything about everything in science before one can learn something about something.

A more pragmatic critic might insist that, in spite of the rationale set forth at the beginning of this section, the construct of motherliness is still too vaguely defined and too tenuously anchored in observables to be used. Research such as the present project, while not unscientific, would be regarded as premature. There is a good deal to be said for such an objection. In designing the present studies there was much floundering, inefficiency, and waste which could have been eliminated had a valid set of objective criteria of motherliness existed. On the other hand, there is no way of telling whether something can be done other than trying to do it; blind alleys and fruitless effort are the inevitable price that is paid for the lack of established criteria. Viewed more positively, there is always the possibility that some studies will pay off and that an evaluation of the successful and unsuccessful ventures will bring the field much closer to establishing the objective measurements which are so badly needed.

Thus the investigators have no basic qualms about the theoretical aspects of the study; they seem as solid as our present understanding and the exigencies of conducting research permit. However, more troublesome feelings are aroused in evaluating the techniques which were used to tap this hypothetical strata.

One concern involves the shrinkage which takes place when one goes from the theoretical level to the actual experimental procedures. The construct of motherliness as presented in Chapter 2 is rich in implications and broad in scope. None of the techniques does justice to this breadth and scope, and even the totality of findings represent an attenuation of the original idea. More extensive observations of the mothers and children or more exhaustive case history material might have helped allay this vague sense of anticlimax; as it stands, the behavior sampled by the studies seems rather meager when compared with the theoretical conceptualization.

A more fundamental concern arises from the fact that new techniques first had to be devised before an area of interest could be investigated. Quite frequently the only guides were common sense, face validity, and knowledge of procedures used in similar studies, all of which can be extremely misleading. Because measuring devices had to be improvised, negative results were always confounded, as it was impossible to tell whether the technique itself was faulty or whether the hypothesized group difference was nonexistent. It does no violence to an operational approach to be concerned about the possibility that important differences in motherliness actually existed but that the techniques were not sensitive or ingenious enough to elicit them.

However, the most disturbing issues arose at the last stage, that of evaluating the totality of results in light of the construct and the hypothesis. Ideally the hypothesis should have been clearly verified, the construct of motherliness enriched and objectified; in reality, integration of the data involved many doubts and compromises. Ideally there should be a finality about the statement "Confirmed" or "Rejected"; in reality some results were strikingly positive, some hopelessly negative, while many fell into a tepid region of mildly confirmatory. This applies both to the statistical significance of the data and to its psychological richness. Under such circumstances the task of arriving at a final evaluation becomes quite a difficult one.

To begin with there is the matter of tolerance of negative results. How many statements of "no significant differences among groups" can the data analyst return before one becomes suspicious that the basic hypothesis is not supported? There are certainly no rules for answering this question. A good deal depends on the standard of scientific rigor set by the individual investigator, plus his subjective confidence in, or the previously established validity of, his measuring instruments. In the present research there were few completely negative findings; only Toy Choice gave results which might just as well have been drawn from a table of random numbers, so the soundness of the central hypothesis was never seriously questioned. However it must also be admitted that the novelty of the techniques was a significant factor here. Although results were always predicted, the investigators realized that, because so little was known about the measuring device, unforeseen findings might also come to light. A procedure usually yielded relevant and significant data even when it did not turn out as expected. For example, in GIFT the predicted differences in choice of pictures did not prove significant, but the fantasies given in response to an inquiry about the choices did reveal group differences consonant with the hypothesis. Of course there is no guarantee that such results will not prove ephemeral; good scientific procedure requires, at this point, that the technique be repeated on a new group in order to see whether the unpredicted findings can be independently verified.

The necessity of re-evaluating results from individual techniques touches on the most vexing problem of all, that of arriving at the most meaningful integration of disparate data from different techniques. In effecting this integration, many unexpected things had to be done: a mother's agreement with a judge's rating and her correct prediction of her child's response to the questionnaire, originally thought to be evidence of empathy, were finally regarded as products of overintellectualization; when over half of the Rorschach signs of emotional emptiness failed to differentiate the groups of children, the remaining signs were still regarded as sufficient to support the hypothesis being tested; the Mixed Themes, while statistically significant, were few in number but were weighted heavily as to psychological significance. Where does integration leave off and arbitrariness begin? Were not the investigators overinvested in their hypothesis to the point of making the Psychosomatic group look bad regardless of what it did?

Such questions are not easy to answer. When it comes to interpretation, the rules of science are vague, and individual judgment must take over. The process of integration means that results from many techniques must be compared and evaluated, decisions must be made as to which are basic and which must be brought into line. The main bulwark against arbitrariness in the present research was the solid blocks of congruent findings. For example, the lack of positive feeling which characterized the thematic material of both Psychosomatic mother and child, plus the lack of positive closeness of the interaction, constitutes a rather impressive clustering. To cast doubt on such results because of the somewhat inconclusive data from the questionnaire would not seem sensible. Or, the emphasis on the Mixed Themes can be justified not only on the basis of their uniqueness but also on the basis of the fact that they nicely complement certain findings about the "High" and "Low" Psychosomatic mothers. In addition to such reassuring consistencies within the empirical data, the clinical understanding of mother and child which this type of research design affords served to increase the investigator's confidence in their decisions. For example, the overwhelming clinical impression of Mrs. Fenster was that she is intellectualized, narcissistic, and has little warmth for her child; thus the fact that the judges agree with her rating and that she can predict Darlene's choices on the questionnaire had to be evaluated in terms other than empathy.

The goal of all these attempts at integration was the clarification of the mother-child relationship in the Psychosomatic group, and the hope is that the final interpretations have served this function. In the last analysis, however, the question of whether the investigators have been perceptive and flexible, or whether they have been merely arbitrary, has no answer. All one can do is make the facts public and trace the steps of integration clearly. If the process seems strained and the conclusions unwarranted, then others are free to evaluate the findings for themselves.

It is the investigators' feeling that the temptation to arbitrariness has been resisted as much as is humanly possible; but they are not so sure they have avoided the sin of oversimplification. One of their gravest concerns is that, in an effort to integrate and be consistent, violence has been done to the richness of the findings and the richness of personality in general. It is true that a number of faulty patterns of relationships were revealed in the Psychosomatic group, but it is also true that the mothers certainly do not represent an extreme in pathology nor are the children hopelessly disturbed. This means that there is the possibility that positive factors were revealed which were overlooked or neglected. For example, are some of the findings of "no significant differences between groups" in reality quite significant in that they show a positive participation in the common experience of mothering which would counterbalance the more deviant attitudes? Has the intellectualization of the "High" mothers and the inconsistency of the "Low" mothers been dismissed too readily as being faulty, without consideration of the importance to the child of the consistency of the former and the helpful protectiveness of the latter? In focusing on kinds of pathology, were important areas of health wrongly evaluated? Again, there is no answer to such questions except the inevitable one of further research.

A final point about design which is extremely important. At one level it was very pleasing to the investigators to find a methodology which would do justice to the richness of clinical concepts. Yet this also involved problems which, admittedly, the present study did not successfully solve. Paradoxically, the more complex the results, the less clear their relation to the hypothesis. Stripped to its empirical essence, the study mainly showed there were certain significant differences in the mother-child relationship in the three groups; yet, the hypothesis states that one of these groups is characterized by "lack of motherliness"; it is not at all obvious how one tests the hypothesis by such data.

Thus, in breaking away from the simplicity of a unidimensional approach—such as developing a scale of motherliness—the results seem to be unanchored and one is hard put to know on what basis one can say that group X has more or less of a characteristic than group Y. Of course, the situation is not all that bleak. The construct of motherliness was independently defined in terms of mutual gratification, and there is ample evidence that the Psychosomatic mother and child derived little pleasure from one another. One can also justifiably argue that findings which are consistent for mother and child and which appear on a number of different techniques are more stable than ones based on a single scale.

However, the other results are more troublesome. On what basis can we say that the cold control of the Psychosomatic mother represents a greater lack of motherliness than the overt anger and armed truce of the Neurotic mother? To appeal to "clinical wisdom" would scarcely be appropriate, and to point to the disturbance of the children would be circular. Certainly there is little in the hypothesis or in the theoretical framework which could help in this dilemma.

Thus, the most balanced evaluation of the findings would be that some confirm the hypothesis while others show that typical patterns of mothering are found in the various groups. In the authors' opinion it would be a mistake to ignore the latter for the sake of purity of design; at this stage of development of clinical psychology, too much needs to be learned about specific patterns of mothering to disregard the leads which appear in the data. Rather, it is hoped that such leads will be the stimulus for further research in mother-child interaction, and that the limitations in the present design can be successfully avoided by other investigators doing multitechnique research.

Multitechnique Approach

The multitechnique approach to investigating a single major hypothesis is certainly not unique in personality research, yet it is sufficiently novel to warrant a brief evaluation.

The most clear-cut advantages of such an approach are relevant to matters of secondary importance in research. For example, the efficiency of data collecting is unquestionably increased. It took almost two years to locate the present population because of the infrequency of some of the psychosomatic diseases and the rigorous standards for equating groups. From a strictly utilitarian viewpoint, it was imperative that the maximum amount of data be obtained from each mother-child pair. Although this meant that the investigators could not profit by experience and improve on their studies as they went along, it did eliminate the time-consuming job of locating new populations.

In the present state of personality research there is also an oblique advantage in having a series of studies associated with a specific group of investigators. It is quite clear that the personality of the investigator and the type of relationship he establishes significantly influence the results obtained. To make matters worse, there is no way of determining the nature and extent of this influence or correcting for it. In program research, such biases, while not controlled, at least are fairly constant throughout. The entire project might suffer because of the limitations or unconscious emotional investments of the participating personnel, but at least individual results can be integrated without wondering how much disparate findings are a function of personality differences of the investigators.

These are both rather peripheral matters however. The basic question is—Does a multitechnique approach justify itself in terms of an exponential increase in understanding of the problem being investigated? In the present instance, the answer is "yes and no"—it both clarifies and confuses.

Looked at from the point of view of techniques, one would hope that this procedure would yield a rich network of interrelated findings, e.g., that results from the Realistic pictures would correlate with certain Rorschach and World Test findings. At a theoretical level it would be gratifying to state that individual techniques were unified not only by their relevance to a central construct of motherliness but also by their intercorrelation. Unfortunately this is not the case. Some interrelations did appear, notably the "High" and "Low" mothers' behavior in the interaction and, to some extent, their response to the questionnaire. On the other hand, there were equally impressive instances of lack of correlation among the data; e.g., the evidence of suspiciousness which showed up in the Rorschach and World Tests did not similarly discriminate the groups on the Witch pictures. Although such pictures were not specifically designed to tap this area it seemed reasonable to expect that the proportion of themes of suspiciousness would correspond to that found on the other projective techniques. Such was not the case. Or again, it seemed reasonable to expect a much closer relationship than was actually found between the "High" and "Low" subgroups of the Psychosomatic mothers and the two kinds of Mixed Themes fantasied by their children. Thus, for every revealing interrelation there was a puzzling failure of correlation suggesting that nothing should be expected of a technique beyond its serving the specified purpose for which it was designed.

The project did succeed in highlighting some of the reasons for this lack of interrelatedness. Observing a child in a number of different situations clearly revealed the importance of individual differences in "test-taking" attitudes; some children were reticent or exuberant regardless of the stimulus, some blossomed out if they were alone or could isolate their activities but froze up if they had to speak to the investigator, while others needed the stimulation of communication and would become restless and impoverished without it. To give a number of techniques a similar label such as "projective" is no guarantee that they will neutralize such deeply embedded patterns of responding. Thus a multitechnique approach has to reckon not only with the divergent dimensions of the stimulus material—projective, structured, verbal, performance—but with the highly individualized ways of reacting to such dimensions. In view of the complexity of these variables, intercorrelation of techniques should perhaps be regarded as a rare and fortunate occurrence rather than an expected one.

In certain cases it was possible to understand why expected consistencies failed to appear. For example, it was easy to see why Archie Merrill gave defensive, descriptive stories instead of chaotic Mixed Themes; he was so desperately in need of security that he could not trust himself to go beyond the obvious implications of the Realistic pictures. Yet, in a number of other instances the responses to different situations were completely unexpected and mystifying. Who could predict that such an intense, controlling person as Mrs. Fenster would retreat to one corner of the room during the interaction, and more or less leave her daughter alone? Or there was the case of a sweet, conforming, docile little girl who constructed the pleasantest little World and, five minutes later, when she was alone with her mother, was merciless in her haughty depreciation and her contemptuous rejection of all the mother's positive approaches. Such observations suggest that the concept of the consistency of personality might be a misleading one in evaluating research results in that it offers too great a temptation to overgeneralization; certainly there is evidence for a striking inconsistency of personality, at least at the level of observable behavior, which seriously complicated the problem of placing the results in their proper perspective.

There are two implications in this discussion of lessons learned from the multitechnique approach. First it implies that when a broadly defined personality variable is being investigated, the use of more than one behavior sample and one technique is almost essential. This should not be construed to mean that single technique studies are useless or unscientific; operationally they can be immaculate, and interpretation of results can stay well within the bounds of modesty and appropriateness. It is just that the shrinkage between construct and technique is often considerable and the area of legitimate generalization quite limited. To make statements about the amount of hostility in groups of children on the basis of a single doll-play session, or to infer differences in empathy on the basis of predicting responses to a questionnaire, is a very risky matter. The variables of personality theory are often complex in their conceptual properties and their overt manifestations; it would seem reasonable, therefore, to gear research to such intricacies. If this is a difficult task it also might well prove the most fruitful means of advancing the understanding of personality.

The second implication is that research results, in the area of personality, are determined not only by the nature of a specific technique but also by temporary and permanent sets in the subject to respond to certain stimuli in characteristic ways. This considerably complicates the problem of research design and interpretation of data. Until recently such extratechnique factors have been acknowledged but, with a few notable exceptions, largely ignored; future research will probably be forced to find methods either to control them or include them in the evaluation of results. For instance, it might be that groups will have to be equated on a much more sophisticated basis than they are at present, and it might be that the assumption that all personality variables will be randomly distributed except those relevant to the investigator's interests is a rather naïve one. If it is not possible to control such factors by equating the groups, then it might be that the results themselves will have to be evaluated as individual protocols are in a clinical setting. For example, if a certain response is not given, it might mean that the attitudes underlying that response are not particularly characteristic of the individual, but it also might mean that he was too frightened or too shrewd to give the response. Merely to score presence or absence of a response might be too gross a measure when important personality variables are being investigated.

Of course there is little that is new in all this; it is merely another variant of the clichés, "personality is complex" and "different techniques tap different levels." Both statements are absolutely correct, yet there is a danger that they will be used to explain away contradictory and confusing experimental findings. Their true function is to serve as an antidote to complacency and a constant stimulus to a frontal attack on the methodological problems raised by intricacies of personality research.

One final word before leaving the area of techniques. It would be gratifying to report that some of the procedures used in the project were fruitful enough to warrant wide application in other research. No such report can be made. Most of the techniques proved adequate to the limited purposes for which they were designed or yielded information which was valuable when placed in the context of other research data. Some might have wider applicability if modified along lines suggested in the relevant methodological sections, but none should be uncritically transplanted to other research or clinical settings.

The clearest advantage of the multitechnique approach is not tied in so much with the interrelatedness of specific findings as it is with the increase in clinical understanding of the mothers and children. Because they were usually seen a number of times and in a variety of situations, and because their behavior was discussed by different investigators, these mothers and children frequently became quite vivid personalities. Far from being an exciting but useless by-product, this understanding figured prominently in every stage of interpreting the data. It meant that the bare bones of statistical findings could be elaborated with a greater richness of detail than would otherwise be possible; it provided a much needed frame of reference in the difficult process of integrating the findings, and finally, it meant that speculation, those leaps into the unknown which are so important to all research, could proceed from a much firmer grasp of what was and was not characteristic of the mothers and children in the study. Such advantages are not to be lightly regarded in personality research.

13 --- Methodology of Studies
of the Picture of the Past

Material concerning the child's first year of life was obtained from the mother during a series of interviews by the social worker. The interviews were neither highly structured nor completely free; the worker systematically covered the areas of pregnancy, delivery, and the main events of child rearing during the first year of life: feeding, toileting, general physiological status, sleeping, playing, responsiveness, and the like. The mothers were left free to comment on other matters and to introduce discussions of their own problems and those of their children within rather wide limits. With the mothers' knowledge and permission, the interviews were recorded on tape as they were made. Verbatim typescripts were made from the recordings. Forty-six mothers provided sufficient interview material for the systematic analysis of the first year of life provided here.

QUANTITATIVE ANALYSIS OF INTERVIEWS

Procedure

Judges were asked to read the interviews, edited to eliminate identifying information and all content referring to topics other than the first year of life. The judges were then asked to rate the interview content by sorting a series of items referring to the common events of the first year of life. The mothers, when the interviews were over, were asked to make ratings on the same items, basing their sorts on their recall of the first year of life rather than upon their recorded interview content. A number of statistical analyses of the data thus obtained were made, ranging from intergroup comparisons of item positions, studies of judge-judge and mother-judge correlation in sorts, to a factorial analysis. Detailed descriptions of the steps in the quantification of the interview material follow.

(1) *Items.* From a much larger pool of items, suggested by many different persons and discussed in detail in group meetings at the outset of the project, 84 items were finally selected as the basis for sorting. These items describe realistic events and easily observable surface attitudes concerning the first year of a child's life. They seek to quantify the information obtained in the interview and do not invite deep interpretation of conscious or unconscious processes. Each item is referable ultimately to the major hypothesis of the investigation.

Two lists of items were prepared, one for the use of the judges and one for the mothers. The content of the two lists is nearly identical; the differences between them are largely in vocabulary. The two lists are presented below. It will be noted that the numbers of corresponding items are the same for both lists. Thus, for example, Item 11 on the judges' list has been translated into Item 11 on the mothers' list.

JUDGES' ITEMS FOR SORTING

1. Mother manifested excessive concern about bowel function.
2. Father manifested excessive concern about bowel function.
3. The baby physically resisted attempts at bowel training.
4. Baby received unwholesome physical contact.
5. Baby was comfortable in relation to feeding.
6. Bowel training was begun before the child was physiologically ready.
7. Mother seemed unusually fearful and agitated in relation to baby.
8. Mother ate unusual amounts or was unusually selective in her diet during pregnancy.
9. Mother presented external appearance of good adjustment.
10. Comfortable physical facilities for bowel training were available.
11. Considerable physical coercion was employed by the mother to effect bowel training.
12. Considerable physical coercion was employed by the father to effect bowel training.
13. Too high a love premium was placed on bowel performance.
14. Mother seemed to resent caring for baby when he was ill.
15. Mother seemed to enjoy showing off the child rather than developing an interrelationship with him.
16. Baby seemed unusually upset by any change in care.
17. Baby was exposed to severe physical suffering at the hands of its father.
18. Mother seemed unduly concerned over baby's constipation.

19. Mother seemed unusually dependent upon her own mother for help with the baby.
20. Mother seemed unusually ambitious for the baby's training.
21. Mother seemed unusually disgusted by baby's stools and diaper changes.
22. Baby was cared for largely by persons other than the mother.
23. Mother seemed hypersensitive to the baby's crying.
24. Mother was inconsistent in her treatment of the baby.
25. Mother often neglected this baby.
26. Mother regarded the birth process as excessively traumatic.
27. Mother had specific designs for the future of the child.
28. Father manifested idiosyncrasies about diet and other habits during pregnancy.
29. Father had specific preference for sex of child.
30. Mother had appropriate concern over the realities of the birth process.
31. Mother had specific preference for sex of child.
32. Mother was very happy to know of pregnancy.
33. Mother had a wholesome desire to breast-feed the baby.
34. Mother frequently had to use enemas and suppositories with this baby.
35. Baby did not seem to respond to affection from parents.
36. Baby was a cuddly baby.
37. Baby received inadequate physical contact.
38. Mother manifested excessive nausea and vomiting during pregnancy.
39. Mother showed excessive weight gain during pregnancy.
40. Mother seemed overanxious to learn about pregnancy.
41. Mother prepared appropriately for coming of baby.
42. This pregnancy was not wanted by the mother.
43. Mother availed herself of good professional service early in pregnancy.
44. Mother guarded her physical health properly during pregnancy.
45. During pregnancy mother's eating habits and other daily habits definitely changed.
46. Baby did excessive crying.
47. Mother seemed wholesome in her desire to have the child.
48. There was an extended period of lack of pregnancy before baby's conception.
49. Parents had planned for this pregnancy.
50. Baby was hyperactive in infancy.
51. Baby was slow in crawling and walking.
52. Baby showed preference for being handled by mother rather than father.
53. Baby was not given adequate opportunity to develop neuromuscular activity.
54. Baby seemed to develop hunger at irregular times.
55. Spoon and/or cup feeding were introduced unusually early.
56. Baby seemed contented between feedings.
57. Baby had an unusually large appetite.
58. Mother was unusually anxious about feeding.
59. Father was unusually anxious about feeding.

60. Baby seemed to be satisfied with three meals a day earlier than most babies.
61. Specific food or foods did not seem to agree with baby.
62. Baby was held and fondled regularly during feeding.
63. Mother enjoyed playing with the baby.
64. Father enjoyed playing with the baby.
65. Mother enjoyed watching for signs of baby's development.
66. Mother enjoyed "talking" with baby.
67. The number of diarrheal attacks in the first year of life was excessive.
68. Constipation was unduly severe.
69. Baby seemed to be excessively colicky.
70. Baby manifested excessive regurgitation and/or vomiting.
71. Father seemed to employ enemas and suppositories too frequently.
72. Father did not want this pregnancy.
73. Baby showed unusual respiratory difficulty in the first year.
74. Baby had excessive number of colds, coughs, or spells of croup.
75. Baby had excessive number of skin rashes.
76. Baby's skin was unusually dry or unusually sweaty.
77. Baby was unusually excited over visual stimulation.
78. Baby was unusually excited over auditory stimulation.
79. Baby never achieved a regular sleep schedule.
80. Baby seemed unusually alert.
81. Baby did excessive amount of thumbsucking.
82. Baby played with self and handled self excessively.
83. Baby engaged in unusual amount of rolling, rocking, or head-banging.
84. Mother rocked and sang to this baby a great deal.

Mothers' Items for Sorting

1. I was extremely worried about my baby's bowels.
2. My husband was extremely worried about my baby's bowels.
3. The baby physically resisted attempts at bowel training.
4. The baby was handled much too much in the first year.
5. The baby was comfortable in relation to feeding.
6. I thought it was all right to go ahead with toilet training before the baby could sit up.
7. I was extremely worried and nervous about this baby.
8. During pregnancy I ate much more (or less) than usual, or was picky about food.
9. I am proud of the fact that everything went so well in the baby's rearing.
10. Comfortable physical facilities for bowel training were available.
11. I had to use a great deal of forcing to toilet train this baby.
12. My husband had to use a great deal of forcing to toilet train this baby.
13. The best way to toilet train this child was to make him understand I loved him best when he performed like he should.
14. Like many mothers I found it was a nuisance to care for this baby when it was sick.

15. Nothing gave me so much pleasure as when other people admired this baby.
16. This baby seemed unusually upset by any change in care.
17. This baby was exposed to severe physical suffering at the hands of its father.
18. I was always very worried when the baby was constipated.
19. With this baby, I often needed my mother's help and advice.
20. I believed that this infant should be perfectly trained as early as possible.
21. I remember being very disgusted by this baby's stools and diaper changes.
22. This baby was cared for largely by persons other than myself.
23. I was extremely sensitive to this baby's crying.
24. I had to use a lot of different ways of training this baby.
25. Because I was so busy I often had to neglect this child.
26. This baby's birth was extremely frightening or painful for me.
27. I had a definite idea of what I wanted this baby to be like when it grew up.
28. When I was pregnant, my husband's eating habits and other daily habits definitely changed.
29. My husband definitely wanted this baby to be a girl (or a boy).
30. I knew there were realistic difficulties in giving birth and was concerned about them.
31. I definitely wanted this baby to be a boy (or a girl).
32. I felt a great deal of happiness when I learned I was going to have this baby.
33. I looked forward to breast feeding this baby if I could.
34. I frequently had to use enemas and suppositories with this baby.
35. No matter how much love we gave this baby, it did not respond.
36. This was a cuddly baby.
37. I thought it was better not to handle this baby except when absolutely necessary.
38. I had a great deal of nausea and vomiting during this pregnancy.
39. I gained a great deal of weight during pregnancy.
40. I tried to learn every single fact about pregnancy.
41. Before this baby came I got everything ready that was needed.
42. I would rather not have had this baby.
43. I took advantage of good professional service early in this pregnancy.
44. I was careful to take good care of myself during pregnancy.
45. During pregnancy my eating habits and other daily habits definitely changed.
46. This baby cried a great deal of the time.
47. I was very happy to know of this pregnancy.
48. There was a long period of lack of pregnancy before this baby's conception.
49. My husband and I planned for this pregnancy.
50. This baby was always too active and restless.
51. This baby was slow in crawling and walking.

52. This baby showed a preference for being handled by me rather than by my husband.
53. I thought this baby should not move around too much too soon.
54. This baby seemed to develop hunger at irregular times.
55. Spoon and/or cup feeding were introduced unusually early.
56. This baby seemed contented between feedings.
57. This baby had an unusually large appetite.
58. I was very nervous about feeding.
59. My husband was unusually nervous about feeding.
60. This baby seemed to be satisfied with three meals a day earlier than most babies.
61. Specific food or foods did not seem to agree with this baby.
62. This baby was held and fondled during feeding.
63. I enjoyed playing with this baby.
64. My husband enjoyed playing with this baby.
65. I enjoyed watching this baby change from day to day.
66. I had a great deal of fun "talking" with this baby.
67. This baby had many attacks of diarrhea (loose, runny bowel movement).
68. This baby was very constipated.
69. This baby had a great many bad stomach-aches.
70. This baby did a great deal of spitting up and vomiting.
71. My husband frequently had to use enemas and suppositories with this baby.
72. My husband would rather not have had this baby.
73. This baby did a great deal of panting, gasping, and choking when he was tiny.
74. This baby had many colds, coughs, or spells of croup.
75. This baby had a great many skin rashes.
76. The baby's skin was unusually dry or unusually sweaty.
77. The baby got unusually excited over lights, colors, or things moving.
78. The baby got unusually excited over sounds.
79. This baby never seemed to get on a regular sleep schedule.
80. This baby seemed to notice everything.
81. This baby did a lot of thumbsucking.
82. This baby played with himself and handled himself a lot.
83. This baby did a lot of rolling, rocking, head-banging, or things like that.
84. I rocked and sang to this baby a great deal.

(2) *Sorting.* The sorting procedure is an application of Stephenson's Q-technique,[1] in which sorters are asked to arrange the items in terms of which are most and which least characteristic, according to a predetermined symmetrical distribution. A 9-step scale was used,

----

[1] Stephenson, W. *The Study of Behavior, Q-Technique and its Methodology* (Chicago: University of Chicago Press, 1953).

where "9" was most characteristic and "1" least characteristic. The frequency distribution was 1, 4, 10, 16, 22, 16, 10, 4, and 1. Each item was typed on a separate small card for convenience in sorting. Since the procedure necessarily varied somewhat from the judges to the mothers, the two procedures will be presented separately.

Judges were thirty-one trained persons, either psychologists, social workers, or psychiatrists.[2] They were provided with interviews which had been prepared in the following way: Two of the project investigators independently read each interview completely, and selected from it those parts of the material which referred only to the first year of the child's life. The two readers also independently eliminated any content which might identify the diagnostic group to which the mother belonged. Differences in editing between the readers, of which there were almost none, were resolved by discussion. The interview material describing only the first year, with identifying information omitted, was then assembled and presented to the judges. This procedure necessarily made for some awkwardness in the flow of mother's and worker's language; but the judges did not seem to find this unduly distracting.

Each judge read three interviews ordinarily representing at least two of the three diagnostic groups. Each interview was read by two judges. The assignments were arranged so that no judge was consistently paired with another judge. Along with the interview material, the judges were provided with an envelope containing the 84 items, and nine guide cards indicating the nine categories for sorting. The following typed instructions were also handed to the judges:

INSTRUCTIONS TO JUDGES

Your task is to describe the first year of life of the child whose interview material is given you, in terms of the 84 descriptive items which are provided.

1. First read the material over, in order to get a general picture of the child and his family in the first year of life.
2. Then take out of the envelope the 9 guide cards and arrange them in front of you in numerical order. In addition to the guide cards, the

[2] We wish to thank the following individuals who served as judges: Drs. Mary Arnold, Don Dysinger, Marshall R. Jones, Gerald Miller, Boyd Sisson, Elise Elkins, Marion C. Tolpin, Marcia Hughes; and Paula Hern, Pat Wright, June Yoxall, Mary Towne, Emily Smith, Mary Ann Ryerson, Pat Grossman, Mildred Mailick, Edna Ford, Frances Perce, Kate Anderson, Jan Smith, Dorothy Large, Lois Binns, Natalie Seltzer, Eleanor Merrifield, Alviva Bressler, Ella Ross, Elizabeth Reichert, Paul Reizen, Lillian Kaplan, Nettie Klein, and Janet Korhman.

envelope contains 84 descriptive statements. We want you to describe the child with these statements by arranging them into piles, on the basis of how well each statement applies to him—how characteristic of him each statement is.

3. Sort the 84 statements into three or four rough piles, according to how well they describe the child.
4. Put the *most descriptive, most characteristic statement in Pile 9*, the four next most descriptive statements in Pile 8, etc. Your nine piles should have the following frequencies: 1, 4, 10, 16, 22, 16, 10, 4, 1. The *least* descriptive, *least* characteristic statement goes in Pile 1.
5. There will be some descriptive items for which you can find no information in the interview material. Put these items in one of the "middle" groups.
6. When you have finished sorting all the statements, recheck the count for each pile. Then pick up the guide card for Pile 1 and the statement for that pile, and replace them in the envelope. Do the same for pile 2, and for each of the other piles. Make sure that you keep the piles in numerical order.
7. Seal the envelope. Make sure your name is on the envelope before returning it.

Mothers sorted the 84 items after the interview series had been concluded, and were asked simply to characterize the first year of their child's life in terms of this set of items. The same predetermined distribution was used. Although the instructions used were similar to those given the judges, the difficulty of the sorting technique for these women made necessary some elaborations of the procedure. The mothers were first asked to read through the cards and sort them into three piles: "like my child," "not like my child," and "in between." When this first rough sorting was completed, the mothers were taken to a large table where a graphic frequency distribution had been prepared on a large piece of white cardboard. There was a space for each of the 84 items and the meaning of the two ends of the scale was clearly indicated. The mothers were then asked to place each item in the space that seemed appropriate for it. The mothers were left alone to do this task, although the investigator checked from time to time to be sure the instructions were being followed. The majority of mothers had difficulty with the job, and needed both specific instruction and reassurance as they worked on it.

Both the judges' and the mothers' sorts were transcribed onto data sheets immediately after the rating was completed.

(3) *Judge Agreement.* Since two judges sorted each interview, it is possible to calculate the judge-judge agreement on these cases. The correlations range widely from mother to mother, between the limits

of .134 and .759. The mean judge-judge correlation for all mothers is .52; for the Psychosomatic group it is .50, for the Neurotic group .59, and for the Illness group it is .52. This degree of agreement is probably as high as could be expected from the estimated reliability of this sorting technique, but it leaves much to be desired so far as the dependability of further statistical analysis is concerned.

Closer study of the range of judge-judge intercorrelations, however, raises some provocative questions. For example, the spread of correlations differs markedly from one diagnostic group to another. In the Neurotic group, all the correlations are above .40; in the other two groups, there are about equal numbers of cases above and below this point. Furthermore, certain mothers seem to earn low judge agreement regardless of the identity of the judge, while other mothers seem to inspire high interjudge agreement.

Such findings raise questions which only separate methodological studies can answer. Many variables must contribute to differences in judge agreement: interview length, level of discourse, linguistic skill, openness of personality, the nature of the items, and the aptitude and devotion of the judges. The present investigation yields only two suggestive lines of evidence concerning these points. One, the relationship between judge-judge and mother-judge agreement, is presented later in this chapter. The other stems from a minor methodological analysis of the only variables easily manipulated within the framework of this research—the degree of training and experience of the judges and their interpretation of the items. This study was conducted as follows:

Two highly skilled social workers,[3] not members of the original group of judges, agreed to sort five cases which had earned exceedingly low interjudge correlations, ranging from .13 to .34. These workers not only had long experience in interviewing adults, but also had served as sorters in another comprehensive clinical research, and were thoroughly familiar with and experienced in the sorting procedure. They met together with one of the project research team for a lengthy discussion of the procedures used in the present research, based upon actual interview material. Eventually they arrived at agreement as to exactly what level of interpretation they would use, how they would evaluate common inconsistencies, and what meaning they would accept for each of the 84 items. It seems fair to conclude that, after

----

[3] We wish to thank Mrs. Charlotte Kobrin and Mrs. Helen Klehr for their contribution to this phase of the study.

this session, these two workers were not only highly experienced but highly pretrained judges. The expectation was that, if judge aptitude and item clarity were the determiners of judge-judge correlations, these two judges would achieve significantly higher agreement on the five cases than did the original sorters.

Table 3 presents the results of this study. It is clear that the results do not confirm the expectation. Although the second interjudge correlations are all somewhat higher than the originals, in only two instances (Cases 1 and 5) is the shift dramatic.

Table 3

COMPARISON OF ORIGINAL JUDGES WITH PRETRAINED JUDGES IN AGREEMENT ON FIVE CASES

	Original	Pretrained
Case No.	Judge–Judge r	Judge–Judge r
1	.250	.574
2	.134	.347
3	.338	.407
4	.306	.477
5	.174	.551

Inspection of the actual sorts reveals that major disagreements among these pretrained judges still exist over extreme items. Much of the increased agreement seems due to increased consistency in the middle range of the scale. It is also important to note that the agreement on approximately half the remaining cases sorted by untrained judges exceeded the highest agreement obtained by the trained judges. Finally, in regard to the Psychosomatic cases, in no instance was the increase in judge-judge agreement sufficient to change a mother from the "Low" to the "High" category. Such results suggest that the source of at least some judge disagreement lies in the picture the mother gives of the first year, rather than in judge training or item ambiguity.

(4) *Mother Agreement.* Both the difficulties which the mothers experienced in applying the sorting technique and the time schedule of activities for the research raised questions regarding the reliability and validity of the mothers' sorts. It will be recalled that the mothers made their sorts after the interviews with the social worker were over—an arrangement that invited interference between the interview situation and the mother's more quantitative evaluation of the

first year. The interview, in its interpersonal aspects as well as in the content reviewed, might easily affect the mother's later appraisal of the crucial early months of her child's life.

A second minor methodological study was therefore undertaken to shed light on these two major difficulties. A subgroup of seventeen mothers, representing all three diagnostic groups, was chosen from the original population to participate in a separate investigation. These mothers sorted first at the time of their second project appointment, before the interviews began. They sorted again, under the same instructions, at the close of the interview series. The time interval between before-and-after sorts varied from mother to mother; the range was from twenty-two days to ten months eight days. A control group of ten mothers was chosen from the general clinic population as a basis for comparison with this sample. These mothers all had children within the age range used in the larger study, although their children did not necessarily suffer from the same sorts of disorders. The time interval between before-and-after sorts in the control group varied for the most part in accordance with that found in the experimental subgroup.

This minor study serves two purposes. The before-after correlations in both groups should provide one estimate of reliability for the sorting technique. A comparison of the correlations for the two groups should constitute an expression of the effect of an interpolated series of interviews upon the order of items in the pool.

The mean before-after correlation for the subgroup of mothers from the larger project is .659; the corresponding correlation for the control group is .681. The difference between the two coefficients is not significant. Apparently participation in a series of interviews concerning her child's development has no discernible effect upon the way the mother evaluates the common events of the first year of the child's life. It is equally apparent, however, that the sorting technique does not call forth behavior consistent enough to yield particularly high reliabilities as expressed by a sort–re-sort technique. The range of correlation coefficients is from .352 to .852 in the project group, and from .204 to .826 in the control group.

Since the time interval between the two sorts varied widely from mother to mother, the question of the effect of time upon consistency of sorting arose. When *rho* is computed between sort–re-sort correlation and time interval between sorts, no significant relationship emerges. The value of *rho* is .215 for the project group and .042 for the control group.

The relatively low reliabilities are, of course, cause for concern. At the level of statistical interpretation alone, they set a ceiling on the values which could be obtained in judge-judge comparisons. These correlations, presented earlier, are probably as high as could be expected from the reliability of the technique. But the lack of before-after agreement in sorting is at variance with some of the published literature on this technique.[4] Certainly the mothers' difficulties in comprehending and accepting their task, as described above, are a prime source of unreliability. Many of the more reliable sorters in other studies have been persons of higher intellectual and educational status than these women. But this cannot be the whole story. Consistency in a sorting task must depend heavily upon the nature of the instructions and upon the kind of phenomena described by the pool of items. Common sense alone suggests that sorting to a concept of one's ego-ideal (as employed in a number of the high-reliability studies) must be a very different task from that of sorting to the early developmental events in the life of one's ten-year-old child. The present findings lead to the tentative suggestion that, in advance of a tryout, one really cannot accurately predict under what circumstances this technique will or will not work reliably. More important, they call for extreme caution in interpreting the results of the mothers' sortings.

Results

(1) *Factor Analysis.* The Q-technique is, of course, primarily a correlational method which properly ends in the location of subjects within factorial space. Originally it was hoped that some light would be shed on the characteristics of the first year of life for the three groups of children if the judge's sorts were carried through a complete factor analysis. Consequently, the intercorrelation matrix was found for 16 Psychosomatic, 14 Neurotic, and 14 Illness mothers, using the Pearson r. This 44 x 44 matrix was factored using the centroid method. Five factors were extracted, which accounted for 98 per cent of the variance present. These five factors were then rotated using an oblique rotation method. Simple structure was not obtained.

----

[4] Carl R. Rogers and Rosalind Dymond (eds.), *Psychotherapy and Personality Change* (Chicago: University of Chicago Press, 1954).

Some clustering of cases was found for three of the five factors: Factor A, made up of a group of mothers from all three diagnostic groups; Factor B, comprised chiefly of Illness mothers; and Factor E, comprised largely of Psychosomatic mothers. When the individual items most responsible for this clustering are examined, however, little helpful information emerges. To take Factor E (which shows some clustering of Psychosomatic mothers) as an example, a number of items concerning pregnancy seem to be high on this factor: happiness at learning of pregnancy, preparation for the baby, good professional care during pregnancy, planning for the pregnancy. In the same factor, the low items include statements which might be considered negative or unwholesome: forced toilet training, annoyance at illness, disgust over diaper changes, frightening or painful birth, for example. In Factor B (which shows some clustering of Illness mothers), some of the same pregnancy items are high, along with a number of other "positives": comfortable feeding, comfortable facilities for toileting, wish to breast-feed; but the low items form no discernible pattern. While such findings are not at variance with those obtained from other techniques in the study, they neither add new information nor are they sufficiently significant to be used in support of the other results.

In view of the failure to obtain simple structure, and the lack of clear-cut grouping of mothers on the various factors, the results of the factorial analysis are not included in the interpretative body of this report. It is probable that the absence of grouping of mothers is due to the same low reliability of the sorting technique which pervades all the other findings in this section.

(2) *Analysis of Item Groups.* A more meaningful analysis of the results proved possible when the individual items were organized into groups according to similarity of content. Table 4 presents this organization of items. It will be recalled that some items are expressed in negative terms and some in positive; Table 4 distinguishes also between these two classes.

(a) *Results of Judges' Sorts.* The judges' sorts were now examined according to this organization of items. Only extreme item placements were considered: the analysis focused on the items rated "1" or "2" ("not characteristic") and those rated "8" or "9" ("very characteristic"). The occurrence in each area of some items which are positive or desirable and some which are negative or undesirable necessitates a double statistical analysis. Consequently, two chi-squares were com-

Table 4

ORGANIZATION OF ITEMS INTO CONTENT AREAS

AREA	ITEM NUMBER	
	POSITIVE	NEGATIVE
Pregnancy	43, 44, 47	8, 28, 38, 39, 40, 45
Anticipation	32, 41, 49	27, 29, 31, 42, 48, 72
Birth	30	26
Feeding	5, 33, 56, 60, 62	55, 57, 58, 59
Toilet Training	10	3, 6, 11, 12, 13, 20, 21
Gastrointestinal (Digestive)		54, 61, 68, 69, 70
Gastrointestinal (Eliminative)		1, 2, 18, 34, 67, 71
Activity Level		23, 46, 50
Responsiveness	77, 78, 80	35
Respiratory		73, 74
Skin		75, 76
Sleep		79
Neuromuscular		51, 53
Autoerotic		81, 82, 83
General Stimulation	36, 62, 63, 64, 66, 84	4, 17, 37
Attitude of Mother	9, 65	7, 14, 15, 19, 22, 24, 25

puted for intergroup differences in each area, one for the positive items and one for the negative ones.

Table 5 presents the number of times judges placed an item belonging to a particular content category in either extreme location: "not characteristic" or "very characteristic." Items in Table 5 are again subdivided into positive and negative groups. It will be noted that the areas are now organized into four larger groups as well: Total Pregnancy, Total Training and Care, Total Physiological Status, and Mother's Attitude. It is these four inclusive categories which form the basis of the interpretations made earlier in this report.

Results of the chi-square analysis, based upon the data in Table 5, may be summarized for the major areas as follows:

Total Pregnancy. There is a significant intergroup difference for the positive items; P is $> .01$. The most deviant group is the Neurotic, which is least characterized by positive items; there is a tendency for the Illness group to be somewhat distinguished by the positiveness of their attitudes. It is the Psychosomatic group which is most positive in its attitude toward pregnancy. There are no significant intergroup differences in the negative items. Since some of these items are con-

Table 5

JUDGES' LOCATION OF ITEMS IN EXTREME CATEGORIES

AREA	PSYCHOSOMATIC				NEUROTIC				ILLNESS			
	POSITIVE		NEGATIVE		POSITIVE		NEGATIVE		POSITIVE		NEGATIVE	
	1[a]	9[b]	1	9	1	9	1	9	1	9	1	9
Pregnancy	4	13	4	13	7	4	7	12	4	11	8	15
Anticipation	17	11	17	31	23	3	11	34	17	4	14	27
Birth		1	2				1	5	1	2	5	5
TOTAL PREGNANCY	21	25	23	44	30	7	19	51	22	17	27	47
Feeding	20	6	2	7	10	7	1	1	8	11	3	3
Toileting			5	5			5	5		1	12	9
General Stimulation	16	10	10	6	11	7	9	5	11	11	10	2
TOTAL TRAINING AND CARE	36	16	17	18	21	14	15	11	19	23	25	14
Gastrointestinal (Digestive)			6	19			8	9			2	9
Gastrointestinal (Eliminative)			16	5			7	7			11	9
Respiratory			3	4			2	1			1	7
Skin			6	1			6	0			1	4
Sleep			3	2			2	1			1	1
Activity			7	12			3	7			8	5
Responsiveness	3	1	5	1	1	3	0	3	2	5	3	0
Neuromuscular			3	2			3	2			3	3
TOTAL PHYSIOLOGICAL STATUS	3	1	49	46	1	3	31	30	2	5	30	38
MOTHER'S ATTITUDE	1	4	25	4	2	4	10	9	3	7	24	8
Autoerotic			5	0			5	1			8	5

[a] Judge placed item in "1" or "2" ("not characteristic").
[b] Judge placed item in "8" or "9" ("very characteristic").

CHI-SQUARE RESULTS

Area	X² (df = 2)	P
TOTAL PREGNANCY		
Positive	11.20	.01
Negative	1.52	n.s.
TOTAL TRAINING AND CARE		
Positive	5.52	.07
Negative	1.80	n.s.
Specific Training		
Positive	6.59	.03
Negative	1.64	n.s.
General Stimulation		
Positive	.89	n.s.
Negative	1.57	n.s.
TOTAL PHYSIOLOGICAL STATUS		
Negative	1.44	n.s.
MOTHER'S ATTITUDE		
Negative	6.67	.03

cerned with paternal reactions, and the hypothesis focuses largely upon mothers, a second analysis was made omitting all items which described fathers. This revision made no difference in the results reported above.

Total Training and Care. The positive items differentiate among the three groups at the .07 level of significance. The Psychosomatic group is striking in its lack of positive attitudes, the Illness group has an abundance of positive attitudes, and the Neurotics fall between. There is no significant intergroup difference in negative items. When the items referring to fathers are eliminated from this analysis, the intergroup difference in positive items becomes significant at the .03 confidence level, with the same direction of difference as noted above. The negative items now distinguish among the groups at the .20 level of confidence, with the Psychosomatic group having more negatives, the Illness group fewer, and the Neurotic group in between.

The Total Training and Care category was also broken down into Specific Training (feeding and toileting) and General Stimulation. In Specific Training (feeding and toileting) there is an intergroup difference on positive items which is significant at the .03 level of confidence. Again the Psychosomatic group is striking in its lack of positiveness, the Illness group in its abundance of positiveness, and the Neurotic group is in between. The negative items yield no significant results. General Stimulation considered separately is not significant on either positive or negative items.

Total Physiological Status. There is no significant intergroup difference on either positive or negative items. Reference to Table 5, however, will indicate that the Psychosomatic group is characterized by a lack of negatives. This area may be subdivided into Organ System Intactness (gastrointestinal, respiratory, skin, and sleep characteristics) and Activity and Responsiveness. On Organ System Intactness, the negative items differentiate among the groups at the .07 level of confidence; here the Illness group has a large preponderance of negatives; the Neurotic and Psychosomatic groups have a lack of important negatives. On the Activity and Responsiveness items, the negative items differentiate at the .18 confidence level, and the Neurotic group has a predominance of negative items.

A further analysis was made in which items pertaining to maternal reactions to physiological status ("Mother manifested excessive concern over bowel function") were omitted, leaving only items descriptive of the infant himself ("Constipation was unduly severe"). There were too few positive items to analyze, and the analysis of the negative ones yielded at P of .30. Although the group differences are negligible, the Illness infants were judged as having the greatest physiological difficulty. The maternal reactions were then analyzed. Again the positive items were too few to merit statistical treatment, while the negative ones yielded a chi-square significant at the .15 level of confidence. It was the Neurotic group which had the greatest number of negative attitudes and the Psychosomatic group the fewest.

Attitude of Mother. Here again the negative items distinguish reliably among the three groups, at the .03 confidence level. The Psychosomatic group shows a significant lack of negative attitudes, the Neurotic group many such negatives, and the Illness group falls between. Because the items in this category seemed to represent a rather narrow sampling of maternal attitudes (neglect, inconsistency, nervousness), a more comprehensive grouping of such items was made and a second analysis performed. Ambitiousness was defined in terms of Items 6, 11, 13, 20, 27, 31, and 55. This group of items differentiates among the three groups at the .03 confidence level, with the Illness group significantly lacking such attitudes and the Psychosomatic and Neurotic groups both showing them. Neglect (Items 22, 25, 37) distinguishes among the groups at the .03 confidence level, but the theoretical frequencies are so low as to make the interpretation questionable. The Neurotic group is highest on these items. Nervousness (Items 7, 18, 23, 26, 40, and 58) yields no significant differences.

(b) *Results of Mothers' Sorts.* An identical analysis in terms of the same grouping of items was carried out on the basis of the mothers' sorts. Two chi-squares were computed for each of the four areas (Pregnancy, Total Training and Care, Total Physiological Status, and Mother's Attitude), one for the positive items and one for the negative ones. Only one of the eight comparisons achieves significance: in the area of Pregnancy, the Psychosomatic mothers rate themselves as less negative than do the mothers in the other two groups. Chi-square for this comparison is significant at the .01 level of confidence. Table 6 presents these data, along with the analysis made when all items referring to fathers were omitted.

(3) *Judge-Mother Agreement.* The question of degree of agreement between mothers and judges in sorting the items was next raised. It was hypothesized that, either because of defensiveness in the project

Table 6

MOTHERS' LOCATION OF ITEMS IN PREGNANCY AREA

POSITIVE ITEMS: *nonsignificant*

NEGATIVE ITEMS	LOCATION			
	1 [a]	9 [b]		
Psychosomatic	34	5		
Neurotic	12	12		
Illness	20	13		
			X^2 9.115	P .01

NEGATIVE ITEMS REFERRING TO MOTHER ONLY				
Psychosomatic	18	5		
Neurotic	8	10		
Illness	14	9		
			X^2 5.06	P .08

[a] Mother placed item in "1" or "2" ("not characteristic").
[b] Mother placed item in "8" or "9" ("very characteristic").

situation or because of lack of understanding of what was going on during the early months of their children's lives, the Psychosomatic mothers would agree less closely with the judges than would the mothers in the other two groups. In a sense, this implies that the judges' sorts are a criterion of validity against which the mothers' sorts might be tested.

The results are not in line with the prediction. The mean mother-judge correlation for the Psychosomatic group is .36; the mean mother-judge correlation for the Neurotic group is .39; and the mean mother-judge correlation for the Illness group is .37. There is clearly no significant difference among these mean correlations.

When the Psychosomatic group is examined separately, however, two distinct groups of mothers emerge, defined by the degree of mother-judge agreement on the sorts. Because the identification of these two groups of mothers assumes considerable importance in the final interpretation of results, the values of the mother-judge and judge-judge correlations for the two Psychosomatic groups are presented in Table 7. The terms "High" and "Low" refer to the degree of mother-judge agreement: the "High" group shows high mother-judge agreement, and the "Low" group shows low mother-judge agreement. It will be noted from the table that the mean mother-judge correlation in sorts for the "High" group is .52, while the mean mother-judge correlation for the "Low" group is .25. The range of mother-judge correlations for the "High" group is from .484 to .572; the range for the "Low" group is from .063 to .361. The table indicates also that the "High" group is characterized by high judge-judge agreement (mean correlation between judges is .63); and that the "Low" group earns low judge-judge agreement (mean correlation between judges is .40). The two control groups, it will be recalled, fall between the "High" and "Low" Psychosomatic groups on mean mother-judge correlations and on mean judge-judge correlations. On the basis of these findings, the presumption seems justified that the "High" and "Low" mothers represent two distinct groups, separated not only from one another but also from the Neurotic and Illness groups.

Table 7

MOTHER-JUDGE AND JUDGE-JUDGE CORRELATIONS FOR "HIGH" AND "LOW" GROUPS OF PSYCHOSOMATIC MOTHERS

	HIGH			LOW	
CASE	r	r	CASE	r	r
	MOTHER-JUDGE	JUDGE-JUDGE		MOTHER-JUDGE	JUDGE-JUDGE
1	.568	.616	1	.132	.394
2	.496	.606	2	.357	.500
3	.572	.644	3	.232	.338
4	.484	.611	4	.287	.356
5	.500	.593	5	.359	.653
6	.500	.718	6	.092	.174
			7	.361	.472
			8	.252	.375
			9	.359	.366
			10	.063	.306
Mean r	.52	.63		.25	.40

(a) *Analysis of items for "High" and "Low" Groups.* The "High" and "Low" groups of Psychosomatic mothers were compared on the basis of the four major groups of items employed earlier, utilizing the judges' sorts. In only one of the four areas, that of *Pregnancy*, did significant differences between the "High" and "Low" groups emerge. Table 8 presents these data. All other analyses yielded nonsignificant results.

Table 8

JUDGES' LOCATION OF ITEMS FOR "HIGH" AND "LOW" MOTHERS IN PREGNANCY AREA

POSITIVE ITEMS	LOCATION			
	1^a	9^b		
High	2	17		
Low	19	8		
			X^{2c} 13.88	P .01
NEGATIVE ITEMS				
High	12	6		
Low	11	25		
			X^2 4.9	P .03
NEGATIVE ITEMS REFERRING TO MOTHER ONLY				
High	7	5		
Low	7	23		
			X^2 3.29	P .07

a Judge placed item in "1" or "2" ("not characteristic").
b Judge placed item in "8" or "9" ("very characteristic").
c Corrected for continuity.

Apparently it is the "High" mothers who are judged most positive in their statements about pregnancy.

Examination of individual items placed in the two extreme locations by the judges suggests some further differences between the "High" and "Low" groups. While no statistical analysis of these data is warranted, the items are identified here for purposes of completeness of record. The following items showed marked differences between the "High" and "Low" groups in judges' location:

7. Mother seemed unusually fearful and agitated in relation to baby. (judged "very characteristic" of "Highs")
20. Mother seemed unusually ambitious for the baby's training. (judged "very characteristic" of "Highs")
31. Mother had specific preference for sex of child. (judged "very characteristic" of "Lows," "not characteristic" of "Highs")
34. Mother frequently had to use enemas and suppositories with this baby. (judged "not characteristic" of "Highs")
49. Parents had planned for this pregnancy. (judged "very characteristic" of "Highs," "not characteristic" of "Lows")
50. Baby was hyperactive in infancy. (judged "not characteristic" of "Highs")
62. Baby was held and fondled regularly during feeding. (judged "very characteristic" of "Highs")

63. Mother enjoyed playing with the baby. (judged "very characteristic" of "Highs")
64. Father enjoyed playing with the baby. (judged "very characteristic" of "Highs")
69. Baby seemed to be excessively colicky. (judged "very characteristic" of "Highs")
80. Baby seemed unusually alert. (judged "very characteristic" of "Highs")
81. Baby did excessive amount of thumbsucking. (judged "very characteristic" of "Highs")

When the analysis of items by groups is performed in terms of mothers' sorts, no differences emerge between the "High" and "Low" groups. The lack of significant difference seems due largely to the occurrence of too few cases in the extreme locations employed in the analysis.

SOCIAL WORKERS' EVALUATION OF INTERVIEWS

When all the interviews were completed, the social worker reviewed them all and tabulated the occurrence of certain phenomena not covered by the items. This analysis of the interview data made it possible to capitalize on the trained and experienced judgment of the social worker in ways that were impossible when the sorting technique was employed. Since the same worker had interviewed all the mothers, she had a broad background of information against which to evaluate the cases. Although many interesting facts emerged from this review of the interviews, only those which were reported earlier as relevant to the major findings are summarized here.

(1) *Stress on the mother during the child's first year.* The worker identified three sorts of stress which she deemed particularly significant in influencing the mothers' attitude toward the child during the first year of life: father away from the home for long periods of time; mother away from the home working, whether or not the mother's employment seemed necessary on an economic basis; and severe marital discord. Eight mothers in the Psychosomatic group were considered subject to these stresses; two of these mothers worked, two fathers were away because of military service, and three mothers were judged to have an extremely poor marital relationship. Eight mothers in the Neurotic group were also judged to be in a stressful situation during the child's first year; of these, three were considered to have a poor marital relationship, and five were without their child's father for long periods of time, four because of military service and one be-

cause the child was born out of wedlock and no permanent relationship between the parents was established. Only two mothers in the Illness group fell within the category of stressful first year; one mother, who had a poor relationship with her husband, worked full time; the other was separated from her husband because of military service.

It is, of course, possible that these stresses are no more common in these three groups than in a group of unselected mothers. In order to shed some light on this problem, the above figures were compared with those obtained from a representative sample in another study.[5] Since the codings of stress may differ somewhat as between the groups studied here and the unselected sample, only rough comparisons are justified, and only tentative conclusions may be drawn. In this control group 46 out of 110 cases had difficulties during the first year of the infant's life which, on the basis of percentages, makes them resemble the Psychosomatic and Neurotic groups more than the Illness group. However, a X^2 of 2.9 showed that over-all group differences were not significant. Although such findings are suggestive, a more definitive answer to this question awaits further research.

(2) *Mothers' attitudes toward children.* The social worker also wrote brief summaries of each mother's major attitudes toward her child. These summaries are presented in Table 9. It is from this material that the statement of the maternal attitudes as "ambitious, controlling, demanding of conformity" is derived. The social worker's final count shows that fourteen of the Psychosomatic group can be described as ambitious; six mothers in the Neurotic group were judged ambitious for their children; no mothers in the Illness group earned this characterization. Eleven Psychosomatic mothers were called "demanding of conformity" by the social worker; five Illness mothers fell into this group; and six of the Neurotic group were considered to expect conformity of their children.

(3) *Intellectual level of mothers.* The social worker and the investigator who dealt largely with the mothers in the test situations discussed together the probable intellectual level of the mothers. The social worker had information on school grade completed for most of the mothers, and in addition had general impressions of the mothers'

----

[5] We wish to express our appreciation to Dr. Jean Walker Macfarlane for making available to us the comparable data from the 126 Berkeley children in the representative sample employed in the Guidance Study at the University of California Institute of Child Welfare, and to Dr. Marjorie Honzik for her painstaking and helpful analysis of the data to make possible the necessary comparisons.

intelligence. The second investigator based her judgments on the mothers' performance in the storytelling and sorting techniques. Table 10 presents the pooled judgments of the two investigators on those mothers for whom sufficient information was available to warrant an evaluation.

Table 9

MOTHERS' ATTITUDES TOWARD PATIENTS

Psychosomatic Group

1. Extremely overprotective, rigid in demands upon the child, threatened infant to secure compliance. Seemed incapable of giving any warmth to the child at any time.
2. Driving and ambitious for the child, pleased that the child is "mother's girl" and totally without any insight as to why the child is so attached to her. Extremely possessive of the child.
3. Little satisfaction from the child. More satisfaction from her son, and admitted that she enjoys him more than daughter. Expects conformance and has high standards of behavior for her children.
4. Defenses extremely strong. Denied that the child was unwanted, that he interfered with her work plans, totally without insight. She was unaware of the fact that actually she has not cared for any of her children. She does not understand the child's illness and is frightened by it. She resents the medical expense that has been necessary.
5. She did not want child and shunted the care off on an older daughter. Mother expects conforming behavior and has little warmth to offer the child.
6. Denied any problems despite the extremely difficult health situation from infancy on. Is ambitious for her child and eager for her to achieve.
7. She is warm toward child. She is overwhelmed by the child's severe illness and cannot understand it. She denied having many difficulties with child prior to the illness and because of the language handicap it was difficult to get much detailed information from her.
8. Bland, fearful, and guilty about illness. Denied that child presented any problems prior to illness. She has rigid standards and expects conformance from her children.
9. She was ashamed of the illness but denied it. She is ambitious for her children, and has deep-seated feelings of inferiority which child's illness and daughter's difficulties do not lessen.
10. Intellectualized about difficulties. She is guilty about child's illness, but defended herself by verbalizing an intellectual understanding of the emotional factors usually associated with the illness. She has high standards for herself and her children.
11. Very inhibited, little warmth to give to child. She expects complete conformance.

12. Indifferent and cold toward the child. Identifies her with the natural father, her first husband. In asking for help in the situation, mother indicates that the child is totally to blame for the difficulties that have arisen.

13. No satisfaction from the child. Is actually such a disturbed person that she has never been able to give to child nor handle him properly. She seems to get occasional flashes of insight which are very upsetting to her.

14. Resentful of child's birth so early in the marriage and the need for her to assume total care of the child while her husband was in service. No satisfaction at any time from the child.

15. She was sharp and critical of the child. She was unaccepting of him, his twin siblings, or of her husband. She is resentful and guilty about the illness.

16. Intelligent woman who overintellectualizes. She identifies with her younger daughter, but thinks that she is closer to her sick child. She is extremely driving and ambitious for her children. She expects conformance. She is guilty about the illness.

Neurotic Group

1. She is indifferent toward the child and finds her totally lacking in any satisfactions. Mother is irritated at the child's behavior and has no insight nor any desire to better the situation.

2. She has been physically cruel toward the child and at all times, even in the child's infancy, she demanded complete conformance. She cannot relate to the child in any way whatsoever.

3. She is indifferent toward the child. She denied that the child has presented any problems, which indicates her lack of involvement.

4. She is overanxious and overprotective of the child. She keeps the boy infantile. She denied that she continues to be anxious and guilty regarding the boy. Mother still clings to the idea that child's problems are the result of a childhood accident rather than face the fact that she and the father cannot modify their handling of him.

5. Anxious, overprotective. She denies problems yet seems quite helpless in trying to cope with the child and his demands. She still says that she wants a girl to replace the child who died.

6. Rejecting of child because of the circumstances of his birth. He was conceived before marriage, and since father has always taunted mother with this, she in turn, has reacted against the boy.

7. This mother is so involved with her husband and the continuous marital conflict that she cannot relate to her children. She has no understanding of the child nor of his problems.

8. Warm toward the child but baffled by his behavior. She is proud of the fact that he is bright, but feels defeated because of his reading handicap. His hyperactivity since infancy overwhelms her.

9. Although she stated that she likes girls best, she seemed much more relaxed while talking about her boys. She is insensitive to the child's needs.

10. She does not understand the child. She is of low average intelligence and has lacked guidance in the rearing of her child. She is irritated by his behavior and has always punished him severely for misdemeanors.

11. She is indifferent toward the child's emotional needs. She would tease the child as a tiny infant and at other times be harsh with her. She gave the early history as being uneventful, but she is able to say that the child's behavior today is extremely displeasing to her.

12. She has no understanding of the child's needs. She derives little satisfaction from him and identifies him with the father. She described the father as being peculiar and feminine. She blames the father for the child's problems.

13. Anxious, insecure, and confused, but with some underlying warmth toward the child. She is guilty that her immaturity prohibited her from giving to the child when he needed her. She really was afraid to handle him in his infancy and placed him with an aunt. She now reacts to the child's acting-out with regret and anger.

14. She intellectualizes and denies that there are problems. She gives lip service to wanting to understand and know her child.

Illness Group

1. Indifferent toward the child. She has not been unduly concerned over problems or illnesses as she has not become too involved with the child.

2. Overprotective and guilty. Was frightened of the responsibility involved in caring for the child and has intellectualized as a defense. She has turned the care of the child over to others for most of the child's life.

3. Guilt makes her deny that the child has ever caused her any difficulties. She is overburdened by the severity of the illness and her many other responsibilities. She intellectualizes.

4. She admitted that the care of the child was difficult because she was so concerned about her physical condition. She has found the child's whining and demanding ways hard to take. She has had litttle satisfaction from the child.

5. Openly admitted that she has had little pleasure from the child. The child's physical condition and overattachment to mother have been burdensome to her.

6. She is guilty over the illness and feels that this is punishment for her sins. She is an immature and dependent woman who cannot give emotionally to her child. She expects rigid conformance to high standards. She is impatient toward the child.

7. She did not want this child and was extremely eager to secure an abortion. Then she was excessively guilty and angry when child was such a sick child. She expects complete conformance.

8. Warm and accepting of child. She is anxious over handicap and somewhat ashamed of child's crippled condition.

9. Cold and indifferent toward the child. He has been a problem to her since the age of two. Physical perfection is important to her, and she cannot tolerate this child's severe handicaps.

10. Great anxiety over the child. She feels extremely guilty over the illness and thinks that she has tainted the family for generations to come.
11. She denied that there were any problems, but then was inconsistent in that she could tell me that the child did present behavior difficulties as an infant. She gave extremely short answers which told little.
12. Overprotective of the child. Guilty over illness. She denied any resentment of child. She is a very religious person and feels that difficulties with the child or difficulties otherwise are to be borne with stoicism.
13. She identifies with the child in many negative aspects. She is guilty about his illness. She is most ashamed of his small stature.
14. She is guilty over the death of patient's sibling, a girl, and her desire to replace the child. She is both resentful and guilty over the physical problem that this child presented. She has always been extremely overprotective.
15. She denied problems and had as a defense a hale and bluff exterior. She could remember little detail concerning the child and yet showed some guilt over the illness.

DIRECT QUESTIONS TO THE MOTHER

The picture of the past was filled in somewhat through the mothers' answers to two direct questions posed by the investigator at the close of the storytelling technique. The two questions were, "Was there any way in which this child was different from other children when he was tiny?" and "What came easiest in rearing him? What was hardest?" Diversity of response prevented the occurrence of statistically significant findings, since breakdowns into categories yielded too few cases for analysis. Summaries of the mothers' replies, however, are given in Tables 11 and 12. It will be noted that Psychosomatic mothers deny any "difference" in their child more often than mothers in the other groups, and that both the Psychosomatic and the Illness groups have a preponderance of negative over positive mentions in answering the question as to whether their children were different from other children. Replies to the questions of what came easy and what came hard were not only diverse but did not yield discernible group differences.

Table 10

ESTIMATED INTELLECTUAL LEVEL OF MOTHERS

	EDUCATION	ESTIMATE
PSYCHOSOMATIC		
High		
1	Some college	Above average
2	High school graduate	Above average
3	High school graduate	Above average
4	Some college	Above average
5	No information	Above average
6	No information	Above average
Low		
1	High school graduate	Above average
2	3 years high school	Above average
3	High school graduate	Above average
4	3 years high school	Above average
5	No information	Above average
6	Some college	Above average
7	High school graduate	Above average
NEUROTIC		
1	Quit 1st year high school	Average
2	No information	Average
3	High school graduate	Above average
4	No information	Average
5	High school graduate	Above average
6	Quit high school at age 16	Average
7	No information	Average
8	High school graduate	Average
9	No information	Below average
10	High school graduate	Above average
11	No information	Above average
12	No information	Average
ILLNESS		
1	Some high school	Average
2	No information	Average
3	High school graduate	Above average
4	High school graduate	Above average
5	No information	Above average
6	No information	Average
7	High school graduate	Above average
8	No information	Above average
9	High school graduate	Above average
10	1 year college	Above average
11	6 months high school	Above average

Table 11

MOTHERS' ANSWERS TO DIRECT QUESTIONS

	PSYCHOSOMATIC	ILLNESS	NEUROTIC
HEALTH			
Good	1	0	0
Sick	5	11	2
ACTIVITY LEVEL			
High	0	2	4
Low	1	0	0
FAST DEVELOPMENT			
Walking	1	4	5
Talking	3	1	1
"SMART"	3	4	3
SLOW DEVELOPMENT			
Walking	0	2	2
Talking	0	0	3
ANXIETY SYMPTOMS			
Fear, crying	4	1	4
Temper, spoiled	1	1	2
Sleep disturbances	1	1	1
FEEDING	4	6	2
TOILETING	0	0	1
REMOTE	1	0	1
APPEARANCE			
Pleasant	3	2	3
Unpleasant	2	5	1
NO ANSWER			
Preoccupied with present	2	0	1
Denial	5	4	1
OTHER PROBLEMS			
Thumbsucking, breath-holding	3	3	2
Conforming, likable	1	4	2
Total Mentions	41	51	41

Table 12

**SUMMARY OF MOTHERS' ANSWERS TO QUESTION:
WAS THIS CHILD DIFFERENT FROM OTHERS?**

	PSYCHOSOMATIC	ILLNESS	NEUROTIC
"PROBLEMS" OF PSYCHOLOGICAL NATURE (anxiety, feeding, toileting, thumbsucking, etc.)	13	13	16
DEVELOPMENT PRECOCITY			
(High activity, fast, smart)	7	11	13
Positive responses	12	17	18
Negative responses	22	30	21
ATTITUDE OF MOTHER			
Satisfaction	5	9	11
Complaint	13	9	9
Ambivalence	4	5	5
No response	4	3	0
Positive	5	9	11
Negative	21	17	14

14---Methodology of Indirect Studies of Maternal Attitudes Toward Infant Care

As a less direct approach to the events of the child's early months, mothers told stories to a series of specially constructed pictures.

PROCEDURE

Stimulus materials

Twenty photographs of situations related to pregnancy, delivery, and early child care were obtained from a variety of sources. The photographs were then reprinted by means of a blueprint reproductive technique so that they were uniform in size. Since this procedure usually involved an increase in the original size of the photograph, the resulting stimulus material is somewhat more hazy than the ordinary photograph. Each picture was then mounted on a 9" × 12" sheet of heavy white cardboard.

Descriptions of the twenty pictures follow:

1. Mother and daughter "loving noses" in a scene of pleasant intimacy.
2. Young pregnant woman sitting alone before a wall, knitting.
3. Father bathing daughter.
4. Boy leaning with head against abdomen of pregnant mother.
5. Woman trying to pick up protesting infant from crib.
6. Boy in high chair drinking milk; mother sitting beside him with head resting on tray of high chair.
7. Baby alone, looking straight ahead with solemn expression.
8. Little girl standing, clutching blanket.
9. Mother in labor on hospital bed, fingering wedding ring.
10. Mother breast-feeding baby while older boy looks on, eating cracker.

11. Little girl smiling as she holds up a child's collapsible toilet seat.
12. Mother bathing crying infant while older boy watches, biting the end of the bathinette.
13. Crying newborn infant, dressed in fancy, beribboned shirt and sweater.
14. Little girl engrossed in hitting pounding-bench with hammer.
15. Mother's hands lowering smiling infant into crib.
16. New mother dressing baby on hospital bed for the first trip home.
17. Father holding newborn son for the first time.
18. Mother stooping beside solemn, diapered little girl who holds an open safety pin.
19. Pregnant woman on examining table in doctor's office; doctor reading chart in background.
20. Mother and father in bed; mother nursing baby, father awake and yawning.

Instructions

Since the pictures were presented on the first visit of the mother to the laboratory, the examiner began by reminding the mother that she was interested in information concerning pregnancy and early child rearing. She then presented the pictures, with the following instructions:

"This is a test of imagination. I am going to show you some pictures about pregnancy, babies and little children, and I want you to make up a story about each picture. You can make up any kind of a story you want. Just let your imagination go, and tell what led up to the picture, what the people in it are thinking and feeling and doing, and how it will turn out."

The mothers' stories were recorded verbatim. At the end of each story, as many of the following questions were posed as were necessary to cover the four points indicated:

(1) "What sort of baby (child) is this?"
(2) "How does the baby (child) feel?"
(3) "What sort of mother (father) does this baby (child) have?"
(4) "How does the mother (father) feel about the baby (child)?"

After the twentieth picture, the examiner tested the recall of pictures by using the following instructions: "You saw a lot of different pictures. I wonder how many you remember now. Just describe all the pictures from this set that you can remember." The recalled descriptions were also recorded verbatim. The examiner encouraged the mother by the use of "Any more?" until it was judged the recall was exhausted.

Analysis of Stories

SCORING SCALES

Six different scoring scales were employed for quantifying the mothers' productions:

(1) *Accuracy of identification of the situation depicted.* This characteristic was appraised by comparing the mothers' interpretation of the pictures with the events known to be occurring when the original photographs were made. The scale locates the stories in one of three categories, as follows:

High. Accurate in detail; includes some elaboration to demonstrate that the point of the picture has been grasped.

Medium. Accurate in a general way; some elements of inaccuracy present, but main point correct.

Low. Inaccurate; totally or almost completely wrong interpretation.

(2) *Accuracy of immediate recall of pictures.* The score here is simply the number of pictures recalled out of the total group of twenty. While special record was made of any major distortions of pictures in the recall period, such distortions proved to be so infrequent that total recall score was the figure ultimately used in the analysis of results.

(3) *Personal references.* The major criterion for the judgment that a personal reference has occurred in a story is that the mother make an association to her own experience or that of a friend or relative. The personal reference need not be an inherent part of the story. It may be a brief comment ("That baby is breast-fed—mine weren't"), or a long description of how the story-teller handled the situation depicted on the stimulus card. Casual uses of the first person ("I think that . . .") and references to the subject's feelings about telling the stories ("I've never been good at this sort of thing") have been excluded from this scale.

Stories were located in one of three categories according to this procedure:

Negative context. Mother compares picture with self to own disadvantage, expresses own negative feelings, aligns self with pictured mother seen in negative light.

Positive context. Mother compares picture with self to own advantage, expresses own positive feelings, aligns self with pictured mother seen in positive light.

Neutral or undetermined. Mother makes personal statement of fact without feeling tone, or expresses ambivalence or confusion to such a degree that rating is impossible.

(4) *Attitude toward activities involved in child care.* Stories were located in one of five categories, as indicated in the following breakdown. An illustrative story has been included for each step to give the flavor of the scale.

0—No statement about child care or statement inappropriate to the picture.

No. 11 [sighs] What the Sam Hill has she got? Oh, that's her . . . the baby has her toilet seat, about to put it on the toidy, in preparation for showing how independent she is. She can go by herself and get down like a good girl. She's very proud of herself. Looks healthy, happy, well adjusted.

1—Positive attitude: enjoyment, contentment, pride, affection in caretaking activities.

No. 1 Well, it looks like the little child is just out of bed. And I guess she is . . . not quite two years old maybe. [Pause] Just looks like she might be up from sleeping at night—not a nap, because she has her sleeper on. Mother probably thinks a lot of the little girl. She's getting her up for breakfast. [Q] It doesn't look like she's sick, looks like she's well. [Pause] About two. She might be wearing diapers instead of panties, so she's not toilet trained. A pretty little girl, pretty hair. [Q] Looks like a very kind mother. She's very well groomed. [Pause] Looks like she thinks a lot of the little girl. [Pause] I don't know where to go from there. They'll probably have breakfast together. [Pause] She doesn't look like a hurried mother . . . might take things rather easy, and not be too impatient. She spends some time with the child, as far as play is concerned.

2—Neutral attitude: description only, no feeling expressed about child caretaking.

No. 15 Oh, she's putting him to bed, I think. He's very well contented. He's been diapered and fed and the bed so neatly made. The way he's looking at the mother, she's a good mother, 'cause he's laughing. That's all I can tell you.

2A—Ambivalent attitude toward child caretaking.

No. 16 What's she trying to do? [Pause] Put his shirt on? If she is, she's doing it the wrong way. [Turns picture] [Pause] This is not too much of a detailed picture. If she's trying to put the shirt on, she's not very intelligent. The baby is not very happy about it either. She's continuing with dogged determination. She obviously feels she's doing a very nice job. Baby is laying on a pad instead of a bed—it shows thinking in that respect. A middle-class or lower than middle-class family, doing the best they know how.

3—Negative attitude toward child caretaking; disappointment, anxiety, complaint, irritation.

No. 16 I don't know, she doesn't look very happy and the baby's not very happy. Everything bundled. It's not right, not right from any angle. The pad, the pile of diapers. . . . She's trying to put a binder on him. He's not lying in a good position. She doesn't look like she desired to care for the baby, doesn't . . [pause] .

(5) *Role assigned to the child.* This scale focuses on the position of the child in the stories and the role assigned to him by the teller. Again stories were located in one of five categories, as follows:

0—No statement about the child's role.

No. 2 This person seems to be very much concerned over her work. Maybe she has a feeling of wanting to be alone where it's quiet. [Pause] Mmmm. I don't think she's worried about it, she's just interested in what she's doing. [Straightens cards]

1—Positive: child a source of pride, independent, developing, learning, pleasing mother, helping mother.

No. 14 She's having a real good time, sort of clumsy but she manages pretty well. She's making all the noise she can make. She's outgoing and happy. She's a bubbly child. Her mother loves her dearly and is very responsive, though rather strict, and the baby minds and everything is rosy.

2—Neutral: description of child only, no feelings expressed about child's role.

No. 16 A very young baby . . . a young mother. Maybe it's her first child. She's dressing him, probably to go out. She's very concerned and anxious to get things just right. [Pause] Her attention is focussed on what she's doing. How she's pinning this . . . I presume a band. She is careful not to stick him, has her fingers under. [Pause] I think she is the type of mother who is very cautious. She'll give her child the best possible care.

2A—Ambivalent attitude toward child's role.

No. 8 Looks like this child has a companion that she drags around. Hugs it and loves it, even though it's dirty. She doesn't seem to be feeling too well about something. Probably getting ready to go to bed. Maybe she had an argument with another child. Not very happy, and getting comfort from the toy. Maybe she thinks this toy loves her.

3—Negative: child a disappointer, irritator, rebel, sick, anxious, or insecure.

No. 1 [Pause] This is hard for me. [Sighs] Is it this hard for everybody? [Laughs nervously] Well, she looks very happy but the baby looks sad. No, she looks studying. Looks like she's getting up in the morning, kind of dazed before she's wide awake. The mother looks very efficient— dressed so nice, so early in the morning. She looks like a little girl . . . maybe she's not a mother, maybe that's why she looks . . . that's hard.

(6) *Role assigned to the mother.* Here the position of the mother

in the story is central, and the rating is based on the role which the teller assigns to the mother-figure. Stories are located in one of seven categories, as follows:

0—No statement about mother's role.

No. 19   This is a sick lady. The doctor is in her room and she wants to know what's going on with her. She looks very interested and wants to know from the doctor what is wrong. [Q] I hope it will happen that everything will be o.k.

1—Positive: protects child, supports, gratifies, is patient, loving.

No. 18   This one looks like a little girl who's getting ready for bed. She's tired, and the mother is making a game of getting ready for bed. She has a safety pin in her hand—either she found it or she's just waiting. She isn't wearing diapers, too big for that. Probably they're playing peekaboo, enjoying each other.

2—Description of activities only; no feelings expressed about mother's role.

No. 4   Strikes me as a mother preparing her child for a new baby. Maybe telling the boy that the new baby is growing in her tummy, and letting him listen to the movements. Preparing him for the new baby. He seems to be taking it all in. Doesn't seem to be afraid or worried . . . interested more than anything.

2A—Ambivalent attitudes toward mother's role.

No. 6   [Pause, sighs] She could have been very tired. What seems strange to me is that the child would be drinking milk so unconcernedly, with the mother . . . it's not natural. Unless she's just very tired, and the child should go on eating. If it were very tragic, it would have been conveyed to the child and he wouldn't be drinking unconcernedly. Or she's getting him in a mood to take a nap.

2B—Mother's situation described alone, without reference to the child, as rejected, unhappy, worried about other things.

No. 2   [Pause] This girl seems to me to be married and in the family way. Very much alone. [Pause] Her knitting, or whatever she's doing, is . . . uh . . . just automatic with her. Her mind seems to be on things other than what she's doing. All I can say is she seems to be very disturbed inwardly, not happy at all. [Q] Actually it comes to my mind that her husband is away for some reason or another. Doesn't have her husband with her, which in turn calls for loneliness. And . . . uh . . . in general she seems to suffer from being alone, with no one at all to depend on. [Q] Actually . . . uh . . . it's very hard at this point because the girl is so . . . uh . . . how can I put it? Uh . . . I can't put it into words. She feels so rejected, I should think, and actually it will take some doing to bring her out of it . . . which would have a lot to do with the man involved. Just sort of leaves it in mid air. Not any final way out of it.

2C—Mother's situation described alone, without reference to the child, as happy, relaxed, gratified, about other things.

No. 15 Also looks like a very, very happy baby. It's smiling, looks like it has just been bathed, fed, and now ready for a nap. I remember such an expression on my children—very gratifying, the time when you love them most. The mother looks like she's dressed up. Not overworked. Looks like a woman who has time for her family and for herself. Better than average means. From her clothes and the things around her, it looks like she takes care of herself, her nails. The child doesn't look like it suffers. The woman has interests of her own.

3—Negative: rejecting of the child, irritated, criticizable, fatigued, impatient, punitive.

No. 1 [Pause] From the way . . . this child isn't responding. Maybe it isn't hers. [Q] [Pause] Looks like he has been set back in a corner, all the time. [Q] He can't accept her, he doesn't know how. [Q] I wouldn't say this is the mother. One with six or seven kids and not much time to spend with them . . . so many things she makes come first. [Q] It's there: "I gotta put up with you."

Rating procedure

One judge rated all the stories on each of the six scales. Ratings were made scale by scale and picture by picture; thus all stories to picture No. 1 on scale 1 were rated first, then all stories to picture No. 2 on scale 1, and so on through the twenty stories and the six scales. Identities of the mothers were concealed from the judge at the time of rating. Both the procedure of splitting the total protocol and the omission of names from the stories guaranteed that the ratings would not be contaminated by knowledge of the predictions made for particular groups.

Reliability of Ratings

The first two scales (Accuracy of Identification and Accuracy of Recall) seemed so straightforward and factual as to require no formal check on judgments. The Personal Reference scale involved some element of judgment, and was therefore evaluated by means of re-ratings. A random sample of ten cases (200 stories) was drawn from the total group of cases and ratings on Personal Reference made by the original rater after a lapse of a year's time. Agreement as to presence or absence of personal references in the stories, between the two ratings, was 94 per cent. In 81 per cent of the occurrences of personal references, the assigned value (positive, negative, or neutral) was

identical in both ratings; in no case was there a positive-negative reversal of ratings.

The last three scales (Attitude toward Child Care Activities, Role
Assigned to the Child, and Role Assigned to the Mother) were not
only more judgmental, but were crucial to the hypotheses to be tested.
Consequently, these three scales were subjected to two formal reliability checks.

For each of these scales, twenty-five stories were selected from each
of the three diagnostic groups, seventy-five stories in all per scale.
The stories represented both a sampling of the diagnostic groups and
a range of responses, so that a second rater would presumably have
the opportunity to apply all the categories of the scales. These stories,
together with the scales and illustrative materials described above,
were given to a second rater.[1] The second rater was not aware of the

Table 13

AGREEMENT BETWEEN TWO RATERS IN JUDGING STORIES ON SCALES 4, 5, and 6

	N STORIES	% EXACT AGREEMENT	% AGREEMENT WITHIN ONE SCALE POINT
SCALE 4 (Attitude toward Child Care)			
Psychosomatic group	25	60	84
Neurotic group	25	56	84
Illness group	25	52	84
Total	75	56	84
SCALE 5 (Role of Child)			
Psychosomatic group	25	40	84
Neurotic group	25	44	96
Illness group	25	56	88
Total	75	47	89
SCALE 6 (Role of Mother)			
Psychosomatic group	25	32	80
Neurotic group	25	34	84
Illness group	25	40	88
Total	75	36	84

identity of the tellers of any of the stories she rated. Results of this
study are presented in Table 13, which gives the percentage of exact

[1] We are most grateful to Dr. Marion Wieman for her assistance in this time-
consuming and exacting task.

agreements in ratings by groups and scales, and the percentage of agreements within one point on the scales (considering the numerical values only: 0, 1, 2, and 3, for each scale).

It is clear from this table that the degree of exact judge agreement leaves much to be desired; but it is equally clear that there is some core of interjudge agreement, since the two judges rarely diverge from one another in an extreme manner.

In a second approach to the question of rater reliability, the original judge re-rated a random sample of ten cases on each of the three scales. The interval between ratings was in no case shorter than one year, and identities of the mothers were concealed. Table 14 presents the results of this study.

Table 14

AGREEMENT BETWEEN TWO RATINGS BY THE SAME JUDGE ON SCALES 4, 5, and 6 FOR MOTHERS' STORIES

	N STORIES	% EXACT AGREEMENT	% AGREEMENT WITHIN ONE SCALE POINT
SCALE 4 (Attitude toward Child Care)	110	69	95
SCALE 5 (Role of Child)	200	79	98
SCALE 6 (Role of Mother)	190	88	99

The degree of exact agreement is clearly higher for one judge than for two independent judges, even when the interval between ratings is unusually long.

The sources of the unreliability of these ratings are probably most complex. Certainly the nature of the mothers' productions is implicated; the mothers gave more descriptive than narrative material, and their responses were characteristically brief and unrevealing. Such an outcome is partly the consequence of the nature of the stimulus pictures; in an effort to depict the concrete situations required by the hypothesis, the investigators unwittingly prevented the mothers from exercising much imagination. The scales, also strictly dependent upon the underlying hypotheses, called for much more variability and subtlety of response than the mothers were able to give to the pictures. Consequently, the raters found themselves continually depending upon minimal cues in the stories in an effort to tease out the sort of information which the hypotheses demanded. Such a situation can only lead to wide areas of disagreement among the judges. It is obvious that much of the negative character of the results to be presented later stems from the relative unreliability of the ratings. It is for this reason that the interpretative materials in Chapter 5 are presented in extremely cautious and tentative terms.

RESULTS

Results of the analysis of mothers' stories are best presented scale by scale. Table 15 presents results for Scale 1, Accuracy of Identification of Pictures.

Table 15

ACCURACY OF IDENTIFICATION OF PICTURES

	N STORIES	% STORIES
PSYCHOSOMATIC GROUP (23)		
Rating 1 (High)	191	41.5
Rating 2 (Medium)	170	36.9
Rating 3 (Low)	99	21.5
NEUROTIC GROUP (23)		
Rating 1 (High)	174	37.9
Rating 2 (Medium)	171	37.2
Rating 3 (Low)	114	24.8
ILLNESS GROUP (25)		
Rating 1 (High)	183	36.6
Rating 2 (Medium)	202	40.4
Rating 3 (Low)	115	23.0

Chi-square for all three degrees of accuracy for all three groups is 4.74, with four degrees of freedom; P is .30. A number of additional analyses were made, all equally nonsignificant. When accurate ratings (1 and 2) are contrasted with inaccurate (3), chi-square is 1.3 with two degrees of freedom; P is .50. When the analysis is made in terms of number of mothers who were most accurate (rating 1), chi-square among groups is 1.29, with two degrees of freedom; P is .50. When number of mothers who were least accurate (rating 3) is subject to intergroup comparison, the differences are so obviously nonsignificant as to warrant no computation. An H-test of accuracy of identification (rating 1) yields a value of 1.00, with two degrees of freedom; P is .50. Thus no significant intergroup differences emerge on the first scale.

The identification of individual pictures in terms of extreme ratings on Scale 1, however, yields significant results. The sum of "1" ratings and "3" ratings of accuracy was tabulated for each picture, and chi-squares computed for those pictures with the widest differences in score. Table 16 presents the results of this analysis.

Table 16

ACCURACY OF IDENTIFICATION OF INDIVIDUAL PICTURES

	Psychosomatic	Neurotic	Illness	X^2	P
DISTORTION					
(number of "3" ratings)					
Picture No. 1	3	12	5	9.05	.01
2	10	5	11	3.51	.20
6	3	9	2	7.54	.02
8	9	15	12	2.99	.25
14	6	3	1	8.10	.02
ACCURACY					
(number of "1" ratings)					
Picture No. 6	16	6	15	9.84	.01
7	2	5	7	3.90	.15
9	9	13	8	2.33	.30
12	8	14	2	12.18	.01
16	9	6	12	3.36	.20
17	10	5	5	4.42	.10
18	4	10	8	3.82	.15

Ten of the twenty pictures differentiate among the groups with a P of .20 or better.

Scale 2, Accuracy of Identification of Recall, differentiates significantly among the three groups. The mean number of pictures recalled by the Psychosomatic group is 11.5; for the Illness group the mean is 12.1; and for the Neurotic group it is 10.6. The value of H is 5.41, with two degrees of freedom; P is .05. Thus the Neurotic group falls significantly lower than the other two on direct recall.

Additional analyses of the recall data were performed by studying individual pictures, and by grouping the pictures according to situation portrayed (see Table 17). While individual pictures differed in the proportion of the various diagnostic groups recalling them, no difference was deemed large enough to be worthy of further statistical analysis. Study of the groups of pictures was made in terms of order of recall. These results, given in Tables 18 and 19, are likewise non-significant.

Table 17

BREAKDOWN OF PICTURES INTO CONTENT AREAS

Area	Picture Numbers
Child alone	7, 8, 11, 13, 14
Child with mother	1, 4, 5, 6, 15, 16, 18
Child with father	3, 17
Family	20
Sibling	10, 12
Pregnancy	2, 4, 9, 19
Feeding	6, 10, 20
Bathing	3, 12
Toileting	11, 18
General child care	1, 3, 5, 6, 10, 11, 12, 15, 16, 18, 20

Table 18

ORDER OF RECALL: NUMBER OF TIMES PICTURE WAS RECALLED 1ST, 2ND, 3RD, or 4TH

Picture Group	Psychosomatic	Neurotic	Illness
Child with mother	27	30	25
Child care	55	51	58
Pregnancy	16	17	20
Feeding	22	18	17
Bathing	6	8	10
Toileting	15	17	13

Table 19

ORDER OF RECALL: NUMBER OF TIMES PICTURE WAS RECALLED IN FIRST THIRD AND LAST THIRD OF SERIES

Picture Group	First Third			Last Third		
	P	N	I	P	N	I
Child care	53	47	54	43	39	48
Child with mother [a]	26	28	26	30	26	37
Pregnancy	18	18	17	21	20	15
Feeding	22	12	20	13	13	17
Toileting	14	17	12	9	7	6

[a] This difference yields a X^2 of 3.21 and a P of .20, but its size and isolation make it unworthy of note.

(P=Psychosomatic; N=Neurotic; I=Illness)

Results for Scale 3, Personal References, are presented in Table 20. Chi-square for the analysis of total personal references is 4.45, with a P between .05 and .10. When chi-square is computed for the Positive, Negative, and Neutral personal references, the value is 8.85, significant between the .05 and .10 levels of confidence. Thus the Psychosomatic group gives significantly fewer total personal references than the other

Table 20

PERSONAL REFERENCES

	PSYCHOSOMATIC	NEUROTIC	ILLNESS
Positive references	7	15	25
Negative references	33	30	31
Neutral references	13	21	22
Total references	53	66	78

two groups. That group also has significantly fewer positive personal references than the other groups and relatively more negative personal references.

Attitude toward Child Care Activities (Scale 4) is necessarily based upon a selection from the total number of pictures, since only those pictures showing mother and child together could yield information about caretaking. Consequently, the results, presented in Tables 21 and 22 reflect the mothers' stories to pictures 1, 3, 5, 6, 10, 11, 12, 15, 16, 18, and 20.

Table 21

ATTITUDE TOWARD CHILD CARE ACTIVITIES

	NUMBER OF STORIES					
	PSYCHOSOMATIC (23)		NEUROTIC (23)		ILLNESS (25)	
CATEGORY	TOTAL	%	TOTAL	%	TOTAL	%
0—No statement	23	9.1	15	6.0	24	8.7
1—Positive	65	25.7	83	33.2	86	31.2
2A—Ambivalent	26	10.3	19	7.6	20	7.4
2—Neutral	63	24.9	47	19.0	77	28.0
3—Negative	76	30.0	86	34.4	68	24.7

Table 22

ANALYSIS OF INTERGROUP DIFFERENCES ON SCALE OF ATTITUDE TOWARD CHILD CARE ACTIVITIES

Category	"H"	df	P
0—No statement	1.14	2	.60
1—Positive	1.27	2	.50
2—Neutral	5.69	2	.05
2A—Ambivalent	1.57	2	.50
3—Negative	1.52	2	.50

These tables indicate that only on Scale 2, Neutral Feeling, is there a significant intergroup difference; here the Neurotic group has significantly fewer neutral stories than the other two. This finding is further supported by an additional analysis, in which the three groups have been compared on "feelingful" stories (ratings 1 and 3) and "non-feelingful" stories (all other ratings). Chi-square for the number of "feelingful" stories is 6.14, with a P of .05; the direction of the difference indicates that the Neurotic group tells significantly more "feelingful" stories than do the other two groups.

Results for Scale 5 (Role Assigned to the Child) are given in Tables 23 and 24. Here the outstanding finding is that the mothers in the Psychosomatic and Neurotic groups assign the child a negative role significantly more often than do the mothers in the Illness group. The Neurotic group is again distinguished by relatively few neutral stories. The Illness group admits the most ambivalence about the child's role into its stories, while the Psychosomatic group is significantly low in

Table 23

ROLE OF THE CHILD

NUMBER OF STORIES

Category	Psychosomatic (23)		Neurotic (23)		Illness (25)	
	Total	%	Total	%	Total	%
0—No statement	24	5.2	21	4.6	33	6.3
1—Positive	89	19.3	100	21.8	126	24.2
2A—Ambivalent	67	14.6	77	16.8	89	17.1
2—Neutral	130	28.3	106	23.1	139	26.7
3—Negative	150	32.2	155	33.7	133	25.6

this category. There are indications that the Psychosomatic group tells fewest positive stories about the child's role, and that the Neurotic group tells the fewest stories which contain no statement about the child.

Table 24

ANALYSIS OF INTERGROUP DIFFERENCES ON SCALE OF ROLE OF THE CHILD

Category	"H"	df	P
0—No statement	3.63	2	.17
1—Positive	4.00	2	.15
2A—Ambivalent	4.15	2	.10
2—Neutral	5.27	2	.07
3—Negative	9.12	2	.01

In an effort to understand more fully the nature of the negative role assigned to the child, Category 3 was broken down into further sub-categories. These are presented, along with the relevant frequencies, in Table 25. The small frequencies make impossible any further statistical analysis.

Table 25

CONTENT OF CATEGORY 3 (NEGATIVE) ON SCALE OF ROLE OF THE CHILD

NUMBER OF STORIES

Subcategory[a]	Psychosomatic	Neurotic	Illness
1	57	56	38
2	56	54	52
3	5	7	5
4	16	20	16
5	5	13	7
6	17	12	14
7	3	0	1

[a] Definitions of Subcategories:
1. Child seen as anxious, insecure, unhappy, fearful.
2. Child seen as a positive frustrater; rebels, defies, source of worry to mother, angry, fussy.
3. Child withdraws.
4. Child seen as sick or hurt; colicky.
5. Child doesn't understand mother or situation; intellectual difficulty.
6. Child in physical discomfort other than injury or illness, hungry, wet.
7. Child unresponsive to mother.

The final scale, Role Assigned to the Mother, yields significant intergroup differences, as indicated in Tables 26 and 27.

Table 26

ROLE OF THE MOTHER

NUMBER OF STORIES

	PSYCHOSOMATIC (23)		NEUROTIC (23)		ILLNESS (25)	
CATEGORY	TOTAL	%	TOTAL	%	TOTAL	%
0—No statement	4	0.7	5	1.1	4	3.6
1—Positive	131	30.0	139	31.9	157	31.8
2—Neutral	144	32.9	119	27.3	165	33.4
2A—Ambivalent	46	10.5	43	9.8	52	10.5
2B—Mother preoccupied over unpleasant matters	19	4.3	25	5.7	18	3.6
2C—Mother preoccupied over pleasant matters	5	1.1	7	1.6	4	0.8
3—Negative	88	20.1	98	22.5	94	19.0

Table 27

ANALYSIS OF INTERGROUP DIFFERENCES ON SCALE OF ROLE OF THE MOTHER

CATEGORY	"H"	df	P
0—No statement	too few cases for analysis		
1—Positive	2.95	2	.25
2—Neutral	6.31	2	.05
2A—Ambivalent	2.99	2	.25
2B—Mother preoccupied over unpleasant matters	4.69	2	.10
2C—Mother preoccupied over pleasant matters	too few cases for analysis		
3—Negative	4.69	2	.10

The Illness group pictures the mother in significantly less negative terms than do the other two groups. The Psychosomatic group has relatively few positive stories of the mother's role and the Neurotic group relatively many. The Neurotic group maintains its pattern of fuller expression of feeling; this group has significantly fewer neutral ratings on this scale than do the other two groups. A further significant finding is that, to a significant degree, the Neurotic group pictures the mother as worried or concerned over matters unrelated to the child. On this scale the Psychosomatic group is highest in expressions of ambivalence toward the mother's role.

"High" and "Low" Mothers. Each of the six scales described above was analyzed separately for the "High" and "Low" Psychosomatic mothers. Only one significant difference between these two subgroups of mothers emerged: on Scale 2, Accuracy of Recall, the mean number of pictures recalled by the "High" mothers was 12.5 and by the "Low" mothers was 10.4. A "t" test for this difference yields a value of 2.23 and a P of .05, indicating that the mothers in the "High" group are significantly more accurate in their recall of the pictures than are those in the "Low" group.

15---*Methodology of Studies*
of the Contemporary Picture

INTERACTION

Direct observation of mother and child together in a relatively free situation was employed to examine the nature of the contemporary interaction between the two. Three psychologists observed the pairs and made independent ratings on a number of variables constructed to test the main hypothesis of the study. Comparisons among the three groups were then made, as well as comparisons between the "High" and "Low" groups of Psychosomatic mothers.

Procedure

On the second visit of the mothers and children to the laboratory, the mother participated in an interview with the social worker while the child took the World Test. When the World Test was completed, the experimenter took the child into an adjoining room and told him to wait there for a moment. He then interrupted the mother's interview with the social worker and, in the hall outside, gave the mother these instructions:

I am going to need your help in this part of the research. As you know, one of the things we want to find out about is the kind of toys children enjoy playing with—especially children who have been sick for a long time. Now I would like to see how your boy (girl) plays with this toy when I'm not in the room, since sometimes it does make a difference when I'm there. So, if you will take this toy in to him, I will observe his play through a one-way mirror. That means I'll be able to see what he does, but he will not be able to see me. You can do whatever you like. Just don't let him know I am observing him.

The experimenter then handed the mother a box containing stone blocks of various sizes and shapes and an instruction booklet with pictures of possible constructions. He led the mother to the door of the room and then left.

The room was arranged with a table against the wall which housed the mirror, with two chairs at the table facing the mirror. A table lamp contained a concealed microphone. In a far corner of the room was another chair, upon which were stacked a number of current popular magazines. Mother and child were left free to do as they liked for ten minutes; at the end of that time, the experimenter again interrupted the session and the mother returned to the interview, while the child participated in the illness-fantasy experiment.

Ratings

Three psychologists remained in the observation room of the suite during the ten-minute period, watched the interaction, and listened to the conversation over a public-address system. The raters took as complete running accounts of the interaction as possible. Immediately after the session was over, each rater independently made ratings of the interaction in terms of the following scale:

I. POSITIVE CLOSENESS (warmth, empathy, positive feeling regardless of understanding)
1. *Mother:* Child-centered (child's fun and satisfaction come first, regardless of technique; mother suspends other concerns and has set to give pleasure to child)
2. *Mother:* Empathy
3. *Child:* Mother-centered (puts mother's fun and satisfaction first)

II. DISTANCE (separateness, physical distance, little communication or interaction; little looking at)
1. *Mother:* Rigid (stony-faced)
2. *Child:* Rigid (inhibition, muscular stiffness)

III. DOMINATION (strangle hold, negative power)
Who has power in negative sense; active or passive domination; who does the most negative things:

Child dominating   Neither or both   Mother dominating
1   2   3   4   5

IV. NEGATIVE CLOSENESS (no over-all rating)
1. *Mother:* Irritable, impatient with child
2. *Mother:* Overtly angry with child (scolding, lose temper, harsh criticism)
3. *Child:* Irritable, impatient with mother
4. *Child:* Overtly angry with mother

5. *Child:* Negative dependency (demanding, pestering, whining)

V. COMFORT

VI. MATURING (constructive, developing vs. tearing down, inhibiting)

VII. AMOUNT OF INTERACTION—Also check whether Positive or Negative interaction.

VIII. COMPETITION (one member trying to outdo the other)
Who does the most competing

Child		Neither or both		Mother
1	2	3	4	5

IX. CONSISTENCY

A. ANXIETY
1. *Mother:* Anxious, overt (jittery, nervous)
2. *Child:* Anxious, overt (inhibited or hyperactive)
3. *Mother:* Anxious, covert (churning inside)
4. *Child:* Anxious, covert

B. HELPLESSNESS (good intentions but no techniques; lost)
1. *Mother:* Inept
2. *Child:* Inept

C. NARCISSISM
1. *Mother:* Self-centered (wants to show off child to observer as model; wants child to look good to others so it will credit her; puts audience before child)
2. *Child:* Depreciating, superior, haughty, in relation to mother

D. VICTIMIZATION
1. *Mother:* Victimized (at mercy of child, masochistic)
2. *Child:* Victimized by mother

E. DEPENDENCY
1. *Child:* Passive dependency (looking to mother constantly for structure, stimulation, initiative)
2. *Child:* Independent (self-sufficient; few needs for mother)
3. *Child:* Encapsulated (ignoring, non-sharing, water off a duck's back, secretiveness)
4. *Mother:* Encapsulated

Ratings were made strictly in terms of behavior observed in the situation and were based on the total period rather than brief episodes. Raters were instructed to evaluate the interaction, rather than to attempt to rate each member of the interacting pair separately. All ratings were on a 5-point scale, with "1" representing an absence of the variable being rated. The identity of the pairs in terms of diagnostic group was always known to one judge and never known to another, while the third varied in her knowledge of identity. An informal analysis of interjudge agreement revealed no systematic distortion which could be assigned to degree of knowledge of the case, although the judges did demonstrate the personal biases and emphases which are common to all rating procedures.

Results

(1) *Reliability of ratings.* As in most ratings of personality variables, the data obtained here are skewed and the range is narrow. For this reason, the assumptions underlying the commonly employed correlational techniques are not met. Consequently, reliability among the judges was analyzed in terms of the mean interclass correlation.[1]

Table 28 presents the mean interclass correlations among the three judges' ratings on all variables. The probability figure indicates whether a significant degree of agreement exists between the judges. Only those scales yielding an intraclass R whose P is .01 or better are considered in the results described earlier.

(2) *Intergroup differences.* Table 29 presents the mean judge ratings for each of the variables on the scale for each of the three diagnostic groups, as well as the "High" and "Low" Psychosomatic groups considered separately. It presents also the analysis of the significance of differences among the three diagnostic groups (Psychosomatic, Neurotic, and Illness) and among the four groups which emerge when the "High" and "Low" groups are considered separately ("High" Psychosomatic, "Low" Psychosomatic, Neurotic, and Illness). The H-test was used as a measure of the significance of differences. The categories of Anxiety and Helplessness are omitted from this table because their low reliability did not justify the computation of group differences.

Three departures from the usual H-technique were necessitated by three of the scales which did not lend themselves easily to the H-test. It will be noted that Variable VII receives two analyses, one labelled Amount of Interaction, the other Direction of Interaction. The former analysis employs the H-test; in the latter, where the number of positive and negative interactions is studied, a straight contingency table was employed. Items III-1, "Who has the power," and VIII-1, "Who does the competing" also required different analyses, since these are in a sense bipolar scales, and calculating a mean would obscure possible differences. A measure of the amount of domination or competition was obtained by overlapping the scales and converting them to three-point scales, where ratings 1 and 5 were combined, 2 and 4 combined, and 3 retained as the mid-point. The H-test was then appropriate, and

---

[1] Ernest A. Haggard, *Interclass Correlation and the Analysis of Variance* (New York: Dryden Press, 1957).

Table 28

MEAN INTERCLASS CORRELATIONS AMONG JUDGES' RATINGS

CATEGORY	R	P
I. Positive Closeness	.521	< .01
1. Mother: Child-centered	.364	< .01
2. Mother: Empathy	.441	< .01
3. Child: Mother-centered	.122	= .05
II. Distance	.729	< .01
1. Mother: Rigid	.412	< .01
2. Child: Rigid	.197	= .01
III. Domination	.460	< .01
1. Who has power	.607	< .01
IV. Negative Closeness		
1. Mother: Irritable toward child	.605	< .01
2. Mother: Angry with child	.419	< .01
3. Child: Irritable toward mother	.446	< .01
4. Child: Angry with mother	.343	< .01
5. Child: Negative dependency	.525	< .01
V. Discomfort	.347	< .01
VI. Maturing	.408	< .01
VII. Amount of Interaction	.321	< .01
VIII. Competition	.526	< .01
1. Who competes	.550	< .01
IX. Consistency	.201	= .01
A. Anxiety		
1. Mother: Anxiety overt	.067	> .05
2. Child: Anxiety overt	.294	< .01
3. Mother: Anxiety covert	.106	> .05
4. Child: Anxiety covert	− .014	> .05
B. Helplessness		
1. Mother: Inept	.040	> .05
2. Child: Inept	.209	> .05
C. Narcissism		
1. Mother: Self-centered	.300	< .01
2. Child: Depreciates mother	.508	< .01
D. Victimization		
1. Mother: Victimized	.416 −	< .01
2. Child: Victimized	.594	< .01
E. Dependency		
1. Child: Passive dependency	.585	< .01
2. Child: Independent	.339	< .01
3. Child: Encapsulated	.547	< .01
4. Mother: Encapsulated	.253	< .01

Table 29

MEAN JUDGE RATINGS AND ANALYSES OF INTERGROUP DIFFERENCES ON INTERACTION VARIABLES

Category	Psychosomatic Total					H-Tests	
	"High"	"Low"	Psych.	Neur.	Ill.	3 Groups P	4 Groups P
I. Positive Closeness	2.13	1.92	2.02	2.08	2.73	= .04	= .07
1. Mo.: Ch.-centered	2.73	1.87	2.05	2.18	2.58	= .17	= .13
2. Mo.: Empathy	2.40	1.76	1.95	1.93	2.55	= .02	= .03
3. Ch.: Mo.-centered	1.27	1.22	1.27	1.18	1.28	= .80	= .80
II. Distance	3.06	2.08	2.36	2.80	2.53	= .30	= .25
1. Mo.: Rigid	2.80	2.93	2.88	2.78	2.55	= .50	= .50
2. Ch.: Rigid	1.80	1.87	1.92	1.68	1.85	= .60	= .60
III. Domination	2.73	3.68	3.38	2.67	2.05	.01	.01
1. Who has power	2.54	3.83	3.45	3.24	3.13	= .50	.03
IV. Negative Closeness	(No rating)						
1. Mo.: Irritable to ch.	1.93	2.95	2.41	2.46	1.78	= .05	= .02
2. Mo.: Angry with ch.	1.13	1.78	1.44	1.56	1.13	= .05	= .06
3. Ch.: Irritable to mo.	2.93	2.35	2.44	2.18	1.83	= .10	= .10
4. Ch.: Angry with mo.	2.53	1.58	1.74	1.45	1.20	= .02	= .02
5. Ch.: Neg. dependency	2.20	3.25	2.49	2.02	1.92	= .30	= .02
V. Discomfort	3.34	3.38	3.35	3.24	2.65	= .01	= .01
VI. Maturing	3.13	3.17	3.18	2.95	2.90	= .40	= .40
VII. Amt. of Interaction	2.80	3.17	2.90	2.43	2.27	= .10	= .08
Direction of Interaction			+12	+21	+41	$X^2 = 26.43$	P = .001
			−44	−35	−19		

PSYCHOSOMATIC TOTAL

H-TESTS

CATEGORY	"HIGH"	"LOW"	PSYCH.	NEUR.	ILL.	3 GROUPS P	4 GROUPS P
VIII. Competition	2.00	2.10	2.14	1.42	1.48	= .03	= .03
1. Who competes	2.60	3.55	3.37	2.93	3.12	= .20	.01
IX. Consistency	3.60	3.48	3.51	3.83	3.97	= .20	
C. Narcissism							
1. Mo.: Self-centered	2.07	2.51	2.43	2.01	1.80	= .06	= .25
2. Ch.: Depreciates mo.	2.87	1.90	2.16	1.76	1.70	= .28	= .25
D. Victimization							
1. Mo.: Victimized	2.46	1.82	1.89	1.77	1.58	= .60	= .20
2. Ch.: Victimized	1.80	3.58	2.98	2.09	1.73	.01	.01
E. Dependency							
1. Ch.: Passive dependency	1.60	2.82	2.22	1.83	1.90	= .45	= .04
2. Ch.: Independent	2.73	1.75	2.20	2.95	2.93	= .02	.01
3. Ch.: Encapsulated	1.47	1.47	1.53	2.23	2.08	= .04	= .04
4. Mo.: Encapsulated	2.27	2.20	2.18	2.43	2.28	= .25	= .25

is reported in the table. Chi-square was used to determine whether
mother or child did the most dominating or competing.

Those scales which are earlier described as indicating the *techniques*
of interaction are: Direction of Interaction, Domination, Competition,
Child Victimized, Child Independent, Child Encapsulated, and Mother
Narcissistic. Those scales which are earlier described as indicating
the *general atmosphere* of the interaction are Positive Closeness,
Mother Empathy, Discomfort, and four aspects of Negative Closeness:
Mother Irritable, Mother Angry, Child Irritable, Child Angry.

QUESTIONNAIRE

The following are the multiple-choice items on the questionnaire:

1. Do boys like you better than girls?
   Do girls like you better than boys?
   Do both boys and girls like you just about the same?
2. How strong are you?
   Are you very weak?
   Are you not very strong?
   Are you strong?
3. When you are not very hungry and don't want to finish your dinner
   Does your mother let you leave your dinner or
   Does she want you to eat every bite?
4. What age would you like to be?
   Younger than you are?
   The same age as you are?
   Older than you are?
5. Does your father always feel strong and healthy, or
   Does he feel tired and sick lots of the time?
6. Which do you like best
   To go off by yourself and play?
   To play with one or two children?
   To play with lots of other children?
7. How good looking (pretty) are you?
   Are you not very good looking (pretty)?
   Are you sort of good looking (pretty)?
   Are you very good looking (pretty)?
8. Which would you like most?
   To have more money to spend?
   To grow up real fast?
   To play games better?
9. When you have done something wrong and know you will be
   scolded,
   Are you more afraid to have your mother scold you, or
   Are you more afraid to have your father scold you?

10. When you play hard and get dirty,
    Does your mother get cross at you, or
    Doesn't she care?
11. How many good friends do you have?
    None at all?
    One or two?
    A lot of friends?
12. When you play at home,
    Do you try to keep all your toys neat, or
    Do you like to make a mess, or
    Don't you really care what happens?
13. Which would you like most?
    To have boys and girls like you better?
    To be smarter than you are now?
    To be better looking (prettier)?
14. When you are very hungry between meals,
    Does your mother give you something to eat, or
    Does she tell you to wait until mealtime?
15. If you were going to the circus, would you rather go
    With your father
    With your mother
    With your best friend
    All alone?
16. Does your mother most always know what you are thinking about, or
    Doesn't she most always know what you are thinking about?
17. How often do children play mean tricks on you?
    Never
    Sometimes
    A lot?
18. How happy are you?
    Are you happy most of the time?
    Are you sometimes not happy?
    Are you sad most of the time?
19. When do people have most fun?
    When they are little babies?
    When they are the same age as you are?
    When they are grown up?
20. When your father is home
    Does he spend lots of time with you?
    Does he spend a little time with you?
    Is he usually busy doing other things?
21. Do you have most fun playing with real little children?
    Do you have most fun playing with children your own age?
    Do you have most fun playing with children lots older than you are?
22. When you get mad, what do you feel like doing?
    Do you feel like fighting?
    Do you feel like calling names?
    Do you feel like just forgetting about it?

23. How many friends would you like to have?
    One or two?
    A few friends?
    Hundreds of friends?
24. Suppose you wanted to stay up late one night
    Would it be easier to get your mother to let you stay up, or
    Would it be easier to get your father to let you?
25. Would you like to have a (another) little brother?
    Would you like to have a (another) little sister?
    Would you rather not have any (more) brothers and sisters?

The instructions to the children were simple. The investigator said, "I would like to know how you feel about some things," and proceeded with the first item. Usually the child caught on immediately, but if he blocked, the investigator said, "Just tell me what you think." The problem of hedging and circumstantiality were met by asking the child to choose what happens "most of the time."

The mothers were instructed as follows: "These are some questions that your child has already answered for Dr. Wenar. I would like you to go through them, please, and answer them the way you think your child did."

The principal measure was the number of "Agreement" items, defined by the number of instances in which the mother successfully predicted her child's response to an item. The mean number of Agreements was 13.05 for the Psychosomatic mothers, 11.05 for the Neurotic, and 12.45 for the Illness group. An H-test yielded a value of 4.40, which is significant at the .10 level of confidence. The U-test on the "High" vs. "Low" mothers in the Psychosomatic group was significant at the .20 level of confidence, with the "High" mothers being more accurate.

Although every effort was made to avoid socially acceptable choices, there is always the possibility that there would be some items where one choice was overwhelmingly favored. To check this, the total number of children making a given choice was calculated. After inspecting the data, it was decided that, if two of the three choices had less than ten cases in each item it might be considered too stereotyped to be useful. There were three such items in the children's data (Nos. 6, 12, and 23), indicating that the majority of children state they prefer playing with lots of other children, try to keep their toys neat, and would like to have hundreds of friends. There were no items meeting this criterion in the mothers' data. Now, one might argue that these stereotyped items might be particularly potent as a means of uncovering a group of deviant children. This is theoretically true, but examination of the actual data indicates that all three groups shared such deviant members about equally. It was concluded, therefore, that such items should either be omitted or revised in future research.

Pursuing this matter one step further, all choices which were given by fewer than ten mothers or children were examined. There were twelve such choices in the children's group and thirteen in the mother's. Interestingly enough there was an overlap on all but six of these twenty-five items, indicating that the choices which had little "pull" for the children, also had little "pull" for their mothers. Again the implication is that such choices might be eliminated or modified in future use and that the Agreement was probably raised artificially by them. Further examination of the data also reveals that all three groups shared equally in such deviant choices. Thus no single group of mothers was differentially insensitive to alternatives which lie pretty well outside the realm of possible preference on the part of their children.

A number of attempts were made to see if the data held more specific clues as to differentiating areas of knowledge and ignorance on the part of the mothers in the three groups. These attempts were not very fruitful but they will be described briefly.

The items on the questionnaire were divided into four groups according to whether they applied to parental behavior (such as Items 3, 5, 9, and 10), self-evaluation (such as Items 2, 7, and 18), peer relationships (such as Items 6, 11, and 17) and ideal self (such as Items 4, 8, and 13). The total number of agreements for each group of mothers in each of the categories was tabulated, but inspection of the results clearly indicated no group difference.

Next, the number of agreements on each individual question was examined for evidences of significant group differences. All but six items could be eliminated by inspection and, of these, only four were either significant, or showed significant trends.

Item No.	Psychosomatic	Neurotic	Illness	Chi-Square	P
	(n = 19)	(n = 21)	(n = 20)		
3	8	16	13	5.03	.07
10	15	10	6	8.63	.02
12	12	5	15	11.84	.01
14	9	5	15	10.79	.01

Since Items 10 and 12 refer to cleanliness and orderliness, and 3 and 14 to feeding, one might infer that the non-Psychosomatic mothers are less knowledgeable about the former and the Psychosomatic mothers are less aware of their child's feelings about the latter. Such an inference in terms of these data alone would be unwarranted, yet its congruence with findings from other techniques makes it worthy of mention, e.g., the finding concerning the Psychosomatic mothers fits in with the fact that these women disagreed with the judges in rating the comfort of the infant in relation to feeding. In general, then, this technique did not prove too valuable in providing specific insights into the mother-child relationship.

16---Methodology of Studies of Children's Attitudes Toward Mothering

As often happens in hypothesis-centered research, none of the standard thematic techniques was suited to the particular needs of the project. Although many of them include some pictures of mother and child together, they do not explore this relationship as specifically and thoroughly as was desired. Therefore a new technique had to be devised.

Pictures Used to Stimulate Fantasies of Mother-Child Relationships
REALISTIC PICTURES

1. A mother buttoning one of the suspenders on a little girl's jumper. The girl's expression is ambiguous, and the mother's face cannot be seen.
2. An outdoor setting, with a mother holding a boy in her arms. The boy has a pained expression, while the mother looks either concerned or angry. There is a broken swing in the background.
3. A two-year-old looking over the edge of a crib at its mother who is entering the room. The baby's expression is ambiguous, and only the back of the mother can be seen. The room is dark.
4. A mother and daughter sitting on a couch. The mother is smiling and fingering the string on an elaborately wrapped package. The child is looking at the package with an ambiguous expression.
5. A kitchen scene, with a smiling mother taking a turkey out of the oven. A boy is standing close to her, looking at the turkey with great interest.

All the pictures are photographs. Aside from Picture 3, the age range of the children depicted is between five and eight years. Pictures of infants were not used for fear that the stories might be contaminated by attitudes toward siblings. This hunch seemed justified by the fact that the three-year-old was occasionally identified as a sib and the story was saturated with rivalry themes.

WITCH PICTURES

1f. A young girl at a sink with a piece of soap in her hand. Behind her is a witch with her head down on a table, but watching the girl.

2f. A "princess" in a woods, looking up at a witch sitting on a branch of a tree and holding a lantern.

3f. A hooded figure showing a boy and girl at a table full of delicacies. The children's expression and stance could represent either surprise or hesitation.

4f. A young boy approaching a cottage in the woods. A very vague figure is standing in the doorway.

5f. An outdoor setting, with a witch standing in front of a boy. She has her face very close to his and her hand on his shoulder.

All the Witch pictures were drawings in which both the style and the amount of detail were roughly equivalent.

The choice of Witch pictures was dictated by certain empirical considerations. Observation of the ward children suggested that they were relatively uninhibited in their use of this symbol and relatively guarded in more direct expressions of negative feelings about their mothers. At no point were the Witch pictures thought of as getting at "deeper" or "more unconscious" attitudes.

However, the use of Witch pictures has an important methodological consequence—it destroys the homogeneity of the stimulus material. This is because the Realistic and the Witch pictures differ in their psychological distance from the mother; i.e., they differ in the obviousness of their referent. It is not unusual for the homey Realistic scenes to remind a child of events in his family circle; yet, out of all the children there was only one (a very sophisticated and priggish lad) who remarked about a Witch picture, "When a mother is angry she becomes a witch." One might assume that the attitudes expressed in the Realistic stories are more like those the child brings to his everyday relations with his mother. The way he feels and the object of his feelings are probably nearer to awareness. In the witch fantasies feelings center around a symbol with no direct referent in reality. Such feelings are not readily integrated into the pattern of daily living; they are more akin to nightmares or to the irrational fears and fascinations of childhood. As will be seen later, this difference between the Realistic and Witch pictures significantly affects the interpretation of results.

Instructions

The following instructions were given the children: "This is going to be a storytelling game. I am going to show you some pictures and

I want you to make up a story about them. Just tell me who the people are, how they feel, and what is going on in the picture. Then tell me what happens to them and how the story ends."

At the end of each story the child was asked: "From the way he looks in the picture, how does the child feel? Why does he feel that way?" or "What happened to make him feel that way?" The same two questions were asked about the mother. The only exception was when the child omitted the mother from the original story. In such cases the inquiry about the mother was made after all five stories had been told to the Realistic pictures.

The children were generally cooperative and some of the more exhibitionistic ones were enthusiastic about the task. All of them had had their intellectual evaluation and had been in a free play situation, so that much of the initial situational anxiety had been dissipated. Only one subject completely refused to tell stories. In some cases there was a great deal of resistance, but this was overcome by telling the child just to describe the picture, and asking specific questions as to what happened next or how the story ended.

Scoring

All scoring was done at the level of manifest content. No attempt was made to infer underlying or implicit feeling. For example, a story which sounded too good to be true was still scored as positive. To have done otherwise would have raised serious problems of reliability. Equally important was the fact that the stories themselves were rarely complex enough to justify a more interpretive kind of evaluation. Only those elements of the story pertaining to the mother-child interaction were scored.

Following is a comprehensive list of scoring criteria for each category.

CONTENT

1. Positive Content. This includes caretaking, positive concern over injury, sympathy, giving tangible things such as food or presents, teaching, helping, mutual sharing and enjoyment of activities, affection and love, pride, defending.

2. Specific Negative Content.

Am—Mother overtly angry. Mother seen as angry, mad, hollering, punishing, openly irritated.

am—Mild anger on part of mother. Mother pictured as irritated, punishing in such minor ways as sending the child to bed, ashamed of the child or unhappy about something he did.

Dc—Depriving mother. A mother who directly and finally refuses to give something to the child, such as food, love, attention.

De—Delaying mother. A mother who says "Wait" to a child's request, or who promises to give "later."

Der—Realistic delay or deprivation on part of mother. A realistic explanation is given for refusal or delay; e.g., the child cannot have any turkey because it is not done yet.

P—Competitive mother. A mother who wants what the child receives, or is jealous of what the child gets.

Lm—Self-centered mother. A mother who is depicted as putting her own needs above the child's by selfishly doing what she wants to do.

Bm—Burdened mother. The mother is described as tired or forced to sacrifice extensively for the child.

Im—Impatient mother. A woman who wants the child gotten out of the way as quickly as possible, so she can go about her own business and will not have to be bothered.

Cm—Controlling mother. The mother is pictured as manipulating, putting conditions, moralizing, demanding goody-goody behavior, trapping, insincere in her actions.

Ac—Child overtly angry. The child described as mad at the mother, openly defiant, blatantly demanding, fighting with the mother.

ac—Mild anger on part of child. Statements that the child does not want to do something, or evidence of passive resistance such as the child "won't go to bed."

Sc—Surreptitious child. A child described as behaving in an underhand, deceptive, or sneaking manner.

3. Neutral Content. The scoring here included descriptions of the picture per se, with no elaboration of the relationship; enumeration of details with no interpretation of the interaction; mother and child described separately and having separate activities; general descriptions from which neither a Positive or Negative score could be derived; thematic material only about the child.

4. Mixed Themes. This is the inclusion of both Positive and Negative content in a story. There are two main types: (a) The mother gives (affection, food, presents, pleasure) but puts conditions and restrictions, or uses giving as a bribe to get the child to do something, or expects conformity and good behavior in return. (b) Alteration of

clear-cut Positive and Negative content. At times this can be an un-explained switch from an overtly positive to an overtly negative atti-tude on the part of the mother; at times it is a jumbled mixture of themes of giving with themes of squabbling, provocativeness, and open conflict.

5. Another method of scoring the stories, which was not described in Chapter 7, was also used. This was called Consistency of Content. In certain cases a child's original story was incomplete and an ending had to be obtained in a special inquiry. At times this ending was con-sistent with the theme of the original story, but at times it reversed the original theme. It was reasoned that such inconsistencies might have special significance as a measure of defensiveness or conflict. However, no significant differences in Consistency were found among the three groups.

PERCEPTION OF FEELING

The criteria here were quite similar to those for the various kinds of Content. The only added factor was direction of feeling—whether it was centered within the interaction or directed to persons or events outside the interaction. The scoring here was sufficiently explained in the first section. As it turned out, this more differentiated method of scoring was of little value in the final interpretation, since the results were combined with those from Content when the data were evaluated.

The range of feelings expressed by the child was rather narrow and the reasons given to explain such feelings were often brief. Typically the mother or child was described as feeling happy, good, fine, mad, unhappy, etc., and the reasons would be a restatement of some ele-ment of the story. One might object that the children were resorting to clichés instead of expressing real feelings. However, it must be remembered that children at this age do not have a very rich vocab-ulary to express feelings and that, for the purpose of the research, the essential thing was the choice of a positive or negative adjective.

DEVIANT INTERPRETATIONS

These consisted of Perceptual Distortions and Unspecified Mothers, both of which were fully described in Chapter 7.

TRAUMATIC ELEMENTS IN WITCH STORIES

1. Traumatic oral elements. These included all references to poison, such as poisoned food or poisoned potions, biting and "eating up,"

and such idiosyncratic elements as exploding food or excessive illness from eating.

2. Excessive violence. This included intense struggle with gruesome details and exaggerated killing. In some cases there was an emphasis on the bloodiness of the struggle, in others there was the introduction of fire and themes of being burned to death, and in still others a large number of people were killed.

3. Negatively toned descriptions of the witch. The adjectives included here are spooky, terrible, evil, wicked, cruel, mean, and ugly.

4. Child killed. Stories ending with the child being killed were taken as indicative of failure to master the traumatic elements in a story.

Reliabilities

Self-consistency in scoring was used as the principal measure of reliability. The children's protocols were randomized and each story was scored for all the major categories. Two months later all the stories were again scored by the same investigator. The percentage of agreement on each category was used as a measure of reliability.

In the cases of Neutral Content and Consistency of Content the per cent agreement was not sufficiently high to indicate satisfactory reliability. The procedure was therefore modified in the following manner. Dr. Marion Wieman, a staff psychologist at the Neuropsychiatric Institute, was asked to score a group of stories comprised of all those stories originally scored Neutral plus 18 Positive and Negative randomly selected "duds." The stories were presented again one month later for rescoring, and the per cent agreement for Neutral themes was calculated. This turned out to be 98 per cent. A secondary but quite happy finding was the fact that there was 100 per cent agreement between Dr. Wieman's scoring of the Positive and Negative "duds" and the original investigator's scoring.

A somewhat different procedure was adopted in respect to the Consistency scores. In this case Dr. Wieman was given the 49 stories which were not consistently judged by the original investigator. Thus she had to score only those stories in which evidence of a change in theme was quite difficult to discriminate. The same stories were presented again after a month's interval for rescoring, and the percentage agreement as to Consistency was 85 per cent. This was considered sufficiently high to insure adequate reliability.

As a final step, all stories which neither Dr. Wieman nor the investigator could score consistently were eliminated from the data as being too ambiguous to be reliably evaluated. There were five of such stories in the Psychosomatic group, two in the Neurotic group, and two in the Illness group.

There are two noteworthy implications to these procedures. The first is that the scoring criteria for the different kinds of Content are sufficiently explicit and objective to enable an independent judge to evaluate the stories consistently. Therefore they are not the exclusive property of the investigators. The other important finding is the high interjudge agreement on those kinds of Content which were reliably scored by the original investigator. Although just a sample of such stories was used, the evidence again points to the clarity and communicability of the scoring criteria.

Table 30

RELIABILITIES OF DIFFERENT SCORING CATEGORIES

	% AGREEMENT
CONTENT	
Positive	95
Negative	83
Neutral	98 [a]
Mixed Themes	84
Changed	85 [a]
PERCEPTION OF FEELING	
Mother	
Positive to child	83
Positive to others	93
Negative to child	92
Negative to others	82
Child	
Positive to mother	87
Positive to others	96
Negative to mother	81
Negative to others	83
Neutral	87
SPECIFIC NEGATIVE CONTENT [b]	
Controlling mother	83
Surreptitious child	82
WITCH PICTURES	
Traumatic content	96

[a] Dr. Wieman's ratings.

[b] Reliabilities of other kinds of Specific Negative Content ranged from 82% to 100% agreement. Individual reliabilities are not quoted since very little interpretative use was made of these categories.

One might wonder why an independent judge was able to obtain a self-consistency far greater than that of the investigator. There are a number of possible factors. Most obvious is that she might well be a "better" judge in that her grasp of the criteria was clearer and her application of them more consistent. However, the magnitude of the task might also make an appreciable difference. Dr. Wieman had a limited number of stories which could be scored at one sitting, while the investigator had to score all the data. Thus the chances of mutual interference among the large number of discriminations, as well as the forgetting of subtle differentiations due to the passage of time, were greatly increased. Finally it should be remembered that the details of the scoring system were evolved only as more and more stories were evaluated. Thus a story scored Neutral on the basis of prior criteria might be scored differently when the investigator had a more comprehensive grasp of the range of feelings actually projected by the groups.

Results

Two different approaches were used in analyzing the results. One was the more traditional procedure of regarding the three groups as samples of similar but larger groups of psychosomatically ill, neurotic, and physically ill mother-child pairs. The focus here is upon the number of people evidencing a particular kind of attitude, and the differences obtained can be generalized to hypothetical populations. Because of the non-normality of much of the data, the Wallis H Test was used to test such differences.

The other approach was to regard the data as a self-contained, finite population of responses, and focus attention on the differences which characterize these data. Thus one deals with the characteristic features of a population of responses, and does not claim generality of results. Chi-square was used for such analyses.

These two approaches were employed in a complementary manner. The H test was always regarded as the principal measure of group differences. Chi-square results were used to supplement the findings in the cases of significant H results, or, more important, to highlight the magnitude and focus of differences within the groups when the H test showed a trend which was theoretically important but not statistically significant.

Table 31 presents the analysis of the data using the H statistic. With a single exception, the entries represent the mean number of stories for a given group. The exception is the Deviant Interpretations category. Here the entries represent the number of children having such interpretations, and the statistic used is chi-square.

Table 31

MEAN NUMBER OF STORIES FOR GIVEN GROUPS

	PSYCHOSOMATIC	NEUROTIC	ILLNESS	H	P
CONTENT					
Positive	2.65	3.19	3.46	3.87	.15
Negative	1.08	1.46	.85	2.45	.30
Neutral	1.38	1.27	1.31	1.30	.50
Mixed Themes	.65	.11	.27	6.15	.05
PERCEPTION OF FEELING					
Mother positive	3.27	3.42	4.19	9.11	.01
Mother negative	1.46	1.19	.65	6.92	.035
Mother positive to child	1.65	1.42	2.23	8.79	.015
Mother negative to child	.88	.61	.46	2.82	.25
Child positive to mother	.23	.50	.58	6.96	.035
Child negative to mother	.50	.38	.30	1.95	.38
DEVIANT INTERPRETATIONS	14	5	10	6.69	.04
WITCH PICTURES					
Traumatic content	3.42	1.5	2.58	7.59	.02

Table 32 presents the chi-square analysis of data from the children's stories.

As can be seen, the use of many scoring categories and two methods of analysis produced complex results. The basic decision in respect to interpretation was whether to capitalize upon this diversity by regarding each category as having a distinct psychological meaning, or whether to combine categories in order to get an over-all picture. The latter decision was made for several reasons. First, the separate categories themselves did not seem rich enough to justify assigning them distinct meanings. The exceptions to this were the Mixed Themes and their psychological brethren, the Controlling Mother-Surreptitious Child Negative Content. A methodological objection to individual interpretation of categories was that Content and Perception of Feeling are probably positively correlated, so that assigning separate meanings to each would not be justified. The most persuasive reason, however, arose from the number of hypotheses which have to be introduced to account for the diversity. The investigators found no way

Table 32

DATA FROM CHILDREN'S STORIES

	PSYCHOSOMATIC	NEUROTIC	ILLNESS	X^2	P
CONTENT	(n = 150)[a]	(n = 157)	(n = 153)		
Positive	69	83	90		
	— (1.09)[b] — (.95) —				
	— (2.13) —				
Negative	28	38	22		
	— (1.03) — (2.04) —				
Neutral	36	33	34		
Mixed Themes	17	3	7	16.43	.015
	— (3.13) —			df = 6	
PERCEPTION OF FEELING	(n = 130)[c]	(n = 127)	(n = 129)		
Mother positive	85	89	109		
Mother neutral	7	7	3		
Mother negative	38	31	17	13.32	.01
				df = 4	
	(n = 66)[d]	(n = 53)	(n = 70)		
Mother positive to child	43	37	58		
	— (.34) — (1.49) —				
Mother negative to child	23	16	12	5.80	.057
	— (2.16) —			df = 2	
	(n = 19)[d]	(n = 23)	(n = 23)		
Child positive to mother	6	13	15		
	— (1.34) — (.31) —				
Child negative to mother	13	10	8	4.95	.13
	— (1.92) —			df = 2	
	(n = 130)	(n = 130)	(n = 130)		
DEVIANT INTERPRETATIONS	23	17	20	9.94	.01

[a] Total n differs in each group since a story was scored twice if the inquiry produced a theme different from that of the original story. Also nine stories had to be discarded because of unreliability.

[b] Numbers in parentheses represent z scores between two groups. As is customary, any score above 1.96 is considered significant. All scores have been corrected for continuity.

[c] Total n is not equal in all groups since a few subjects resisted the inquiry questions.

[d] The Neutral category was dropped since it contained too few stories to warrant analysis.

to avoid bringing in a good many of them. There is nothing intrinsically wrong with this process; in fact it can be both exciting and fruitful if the speculation serves to enrich the understanding of the data. In the present case just the opposite happened—the total effect was of disjointed and muddled hypothesizing.

For these reasons a more conservative approach was used in interpreting results. Instead of attributing a specific attitude to each specific scoring category, the categories were grouped under general headings—Positive and Negative Content, Mixed Themes, Traumatic (Witch) Fantasies, and Deviant Interpretations. Thus, for example, Positive Content, mother perceived as feeling positive, mother feeling positive toward the child, and the child feeling positive toward the mother, were all taken as manifestation of generally positive feelings about the mother-child interaction, rather than being evaluated individually. Interpretation within each general category was also conservative. When there was a certain amount of inconsistency among the component categories (e.g., much Negative Content but few Negative Perceptions of Feeling in the mother) or between the two statistical treatments of the results, this was regarded as evidence against a pervasive or strongly felt underlying attitude. It was only when a group consistently received high or low scores within a general category that a clearly differentiated attitude was inferred.

Table 33

ANALYSIS OF SPECIFIC NEGATIVE CONTENT

Specific Content	Psychosomatic	Neurotic	Illness
Am	10	11	4
am	1	4	6
Dc	1	6	2
De	0	1	1
Der	0	2	3
P	0	3	0
Lm	0	2	2
Bm	2	3	0
Im	2	1	1
Cm	6	0	1
Ac	4	2	4
ac	4	2	4
Sc	4	3	2
Misc.	1	0	0

ANALYSIS OF SPECIFIC NEGATIVE CONTENT

The Specific Negative Content was analyzed in detail because of the prediction of possible qualitative differences between groups. The total number of each kind of Negative Content is presented in Table 33.

Clearly, most individual categories have too few entries to warrant analysis. However, the combination of Controlling Mother (Cm) and Surreptitious Child (Sc) was of interest because of its relevance to the Mixed Themes. The chi-square on this combination was 7.41 which, with two degrees of freedom, is significant at the .025 level of confidence.

Inspection of the table revealed that there were other interesting combinations of Specific categories. The chi-square for the combination of Mildly Angry, Realistically Delaying mother (am and Der) with Mildly Angry child (ac) was 5.27, which is significant at the .072 level of confidence. Thus the Psychosomatic group tends to have fewer themes of mild antagonism between mother and child. Also, the chi-square for combining Depriving and Delaying mothers (Dc, De, and Der) was 7.23, which was significant at the .04 level of confidence. Thus the Psychosomatic group has fewer themes of deprivation and delay.

These last two analyses are subject to all the objections raised by post hoc analysis. That is why the results were not heavily weighted in the interpretative chapter. However, they seem interesting and suggestive enough to include at this point.

There is also an important methodological consideration at this point. Generally speaking, findings concerning negative thema are not as clear-cut or as statistically significant as those in other categories. The nature of the pictures with their neutral-to-pleasant atmospheres might have contributed to this. Therefore it is impossible to tell how much the results reflect the feelings of the children and how much they reflect the bias of the stimulus material. Using the wisdom of hindsight one can say that a few clearly negative Realistic pictures might have made the results more definitive.

ANALYSIS OF UNSPECIFIED MOTHER DATA

The Unspecified Mother scoring is defined as a failure to designate the older female figure in the Realistic pictures as "mother." There were three kinds of failure to specify.

1. Omissions, in which the female figure was completely omitted

in the original story. Two degrees of resistance to including the mother figures were scored:

0 —Mother figure omitted in the original story.

0*—Not only omission in the original story, but continued blocking on the inquiry. This consisted of saying, "I don't know" when specifically asked who the figure was, designating her as someone other than a mother, or being unable to attribute any feeling to her even though specifically asked to do so.

2. Undifferentiated stories, in which there was an identity of mother and child. Again there were different degrees:

UDc—A complete identity with mother and child totally undifferentiated. The story was told throughout in terms of "we" or "they."

UDp—Poorly differentiated roles. The main portion of the story was in terms of "they," even though one figure may be differentiated somewhere along the way.

(UD)—"They" used as part of a one-sentence, inhibited story. It is doubtful whether this category really belongs with the others since it seems to reflect severe constriction rather than a real identity of mother and child. Fortunately there were very few stories here.

3. Surrogate stories in which the female figure was included but designated as someone other than mother. Sometimes the figure was simply called "she" and was scored Fs, sometimes it was called "a lady" and scored Fl, and sometimes it was a relative such as an aunt, and was scored Fr. If the figure were given a maternal role such as calling the child "her boy" an additional scoring of m was added.

The total number of stories in each category is as follows:

	Psychosomatic	Neurotic	Illness
OMITTED			
0	7	2	7
0*	4	0	0
IDENTITY			
UDc	2	0	0
UDp	3	0	1
SURROGATE			
Fs	2	0	6 (2m)
Fl	0	2 (2m)	1 (1m)
Fr	1	2	3

Because of the few cases in the N group and the danger of distorting the results because of zero scores, this group was eliminated from the analysis. Also the chi-square was run only on the total number of stories in the three major categories, since there were too few in each of the more differentiated categories. The result of the chi-square analysis yielded a value of 6.74 which, with two degrees of freedom, is significant at the .04 level of confidence. The Psychosomatic group has more Identity and Omission stories, and fewer Surrogate stories, than does the Illness group.

The more differentiated scoring furnished qualitative evidence that the disturbances within the Omitted and Identity classifications are also more serious in the Psychosomatic group.

A number of further analyses were made to understand more clearly the nature of Unspecified Mother stories.

1. Pictures on which Unspecified Mother stories occurred. The number of such stories told to each picture was tabulated for the three groups, but inspection of the results showed no evidence of a differential increase on any particular picture.

2. Thematic analysis of stories with Unspecified Mothers. The original stories containing Unspecified Mothers were examined to see if there were any thematic differences between the groups. The stories fell into three general categories: There were Positive stories, in which a positive theme was clearly stated and received at least a minimal amount of elaboration. There were Defensive stories which took the form either of an absence of feeling (U) or such brief positively toned clichés as "OK," "Fine," or "Happy" (P). Finally there were Negative themes, either implicitly or explicitly stated.

The number of such stories in each group was as follows:

	P	N	I
Positive	5	4	7
Defensive P	7	2	3
Defensive U	2	0	0
Negative	6	0	9

Again the Neurotic group was eliminated and both Defensive categories combined in order to use chi-square appropriately. The value obtained was 4.14 which, with two degrees of freedom, achieves a P of .15. The Psychosomatic group has more Defensive stories, but the difference in Positive and Negative themes is negligible. From the qualitative point of view it is interesting to note that the neurotics concentrated their few stories on Positive or Defensive Positive themes.

3. Thematic analysis of all pictures. In order to determine whether the Unspecified Mother stories were part of a characteristic context, all ten pictures were analyzed in terms of the general attitude toward being mothered. Unfortunately there was so much variety and so few entries for each category that statistical analysis was not possible. Five out of the twelve Psychosomatic children and two out of the four Neurotic children fell into the category of brief, superficial, "nice" mothers with traumatic witch stories. Five of the Psychosomatic children had the kind of relationship seen in Mixed Themes—either an alteration of strong positive and negative feeling or an insincere, deceptive mother.

4. Each group was divided into children who had Unspecified Mother stories and those who did not in order to see if any significant intragroup differences would emerge. The following results were obtained:

On Realistic pictures: There was no difference in Positive or Negative themes in both Illness groups. There was a tendency ($p = .15$) for the Unspecified Mother subgroup to have more Positive and fewer Negative themes in the Neurotic group.

On the Witch pictures: There was a significant decrease in Traumatic Witch themes in the Neurotic subgroup which had Unspecified Mother stories. The Psychosomatic group showed a trend in this direction, but it was not so striking.

A few conclusions can be drawn from this labyrinth of data. The Neurotic group presents the clearest picture. They not only have the fewest stories with Unspecified Mothers, but these are given in the context of skimming the surface, superficial pleasantness, and playing safe. Intense positive or negative feelings are avoided. The Psychosomatic group is quantitatively and qualitatively more disturbed in their Unspecified Mother stories, and such stories tend to take place in a context reminiscent of Mixed Themes. However, clearly positive or negative attitudes are also present in many cases. The Illness group resembles the Psychosomatic one, although it is less extreme.

17---Methodology of Studies of Personality Characteristics of Psychosomatic Children

Selection of Rorschach Signs of Emotional Emptiness

A somewhat different population was used for the Rorschach study because the schedule for the first two sessions was often so tight that the test could not be administered routinely. In addition, a number of protocols of children with psychosomatic disorders had been collected previously and these records could be readily matched with cases from the extensive files of the Institute for Juvenile Research. This meant that only certain members of the Illness group had to bear the burden of a prolonged session. Nine children from this group were used and three older children were obtained from Spalding School in order to widen the range.

Table 34 includes the pertinent data on this special population.

The following instructions were given to five clinical psychologists with considerable experience in interpreting children's Rorschach records:

Psychosomatic children have been described as having a peculiar kind of emotional distance. For example, ward personnel often complain that "They are hard to get close to." This does not mean that they are with-drawn in the usual sense of the word, since they are often adept at certain social techniques (such as carrying on cute or interesting conversations), are often intellectually bright, can manipulate their peers to get what they want, and have ways of calling attention to themselves. However, this seems to be a kind of shell and the real emotional vitality one associates with children is often lacking. Instead of the feelings of affection, anger, anxiety,

Table 34

POPULATION FOR RORSCHACH STUDY

	PSYCHOSOMATIC	NEUROTIC	ILLNESS
AGE			
Mean	9–5	9–11	9–6
Range	5–9 to 14–0	6–1 to 16–1	6–0 to 15–6
SEX			
Male	6	6	6
Female	6	6	6
RACE			
White	10	10	10
Negro	2	2	2
INTELLIGENCE			
Average	8	7	7
High average	0	1	2
Superior	4	4	3
SOCIOECONOMIC STATUS			
Middle	7	8	8
Lower	5	4	4
INTACT FAMILY	12	12	12
DIAGNOSES	4 Ulcerative colitis	5 Aggressive	4 Poliomyelitis
	3 Asthma	4 Anxiety	3 Congenital cardiac
	2 Rheumatoid arthritis	2 Delinquent	malformation
	1 Eczema	2 Withdrawn	2 Legg-Perthes
	1 Ulcer	2 Sex problem	1 Sickle cell anemia
	1 Ulcer and ulcerative	1 Immaturity	1 Charcot-Marie tooth disease
	colitis		1 Bronchiectasis

etc., which are usually expressed so readily in children, there is an emptiness, a coldness, an emotional sterility. It is almost as if the psychosomatic symptom is a physiological substitute for the feelings which should be expressed psychologically.

The Rorschach is a test which is sensitive to this kind of character structure. Would you please do the following:

1. Pick out the 5 scoring categories you think would be the most sensitive to such personality variables, list them in order of sensitivity, and write down what you would expect to happen to each of them (e.g., "increased x," "decreased y," "absence of z").

2. List 5 qualitative signs which you would consider as especially sensitive to this kind of character structure.

NOTE: please make your ratings in terms of the character structure (which might be found in many children) rather than in terms of your knowledge of psychosomatic children.

Criteria listed by at least three of the judges were selected as signs of emotional emptiness. These signs were as follows:

Formal Signs. (1) Low Sum C. (2) No shading or decreased shading. (3) High F%. (4) Low M. (5) Decreased Humans, with Hd greater than H.

Qualitative Signs. (1) Fewer and dehumanized humans; humans not interacting; few ordinary humans; threatening or undifferentiated humans when used; distanciated humans. (2) Limited fantasy, with few elaborations of responses; less animation. (3) Impersonal Content; increased inanimate content such as water, clouds, landscape. For purposes of simplification (1) was labeled Dehumanized Responses, (2) was called Unelaborated Responses, and (3) Impersonal Responses.

Three of the judges agreed on the Formal Signs, while four agreed on the Qualitative Signs.

Development of Specific Criteria

Tabulating the Formal Signs presented few problems, after one investigator had rescored all the records in order to insure consistency. However, specific criteria had to be developed for the Qualitative Signs.

(1) The specific criteria for scoring Dehumanized Responses were:

a. Distanciated humans: people from foreign countries, distant eras, from novels or movies; people without heads; Hd's other than the head, such as feet or fingers.

b. Dehumanized figures: mythological characters, fairy tale characters, scarecrows, skeletons, statues, clowns; people described as weird, strange, funny, upside down; vacillation between human and animal percept.

c. Undifferentiated figures: inability to go further than describing the percept as "a person," or inability to decide the sex of a figure.

(2) Specific criteria for Unelaborated Responses were quite extensive. The purpose was to eliminate any response which went beyond the mere statement of an unadorned percept and the factual description of same. To achieve this, a long list of "No's" had to be devised. This included no M, FM, or m, no z between two responses or within a single response, no reference to personal experiences in relation to the response, no expression of delight, or disgust, no adjectives of unusual size, no similes, no present participles implying movement (e.g., legs sticking out), no unusual adjectives such as "squirmy," "jagged," no adjectives expressing affect (e.g., pretty, ugly), no unusual specification of a percept (such as Scottie, starfish, bronco). Surprisingly enough, this scale had a reliability of 88 per cent agreement when a random sample of 12 records was rescored two months later by the same investigator.

(3) Specific criteria for Impersonal Responses were as follows.

a. Nature responses—water, clouds, landscape, maps, mountains, rocks.

b. Impersonal objects—(following Beck's system) household objects, implements, architecture, art, religion, travel, recreation.

c. Personal objects—clothing.

Responses with special symbolic meaning were not scored. These included fire, food, explosions, earthquakes. X rays were not scored as they were considered too close to Anatomy Responses, and masks were not scored as being too similar to Human Responses. However, the number of these last two responses was quite small.

Results

With a single exception the results in the following table represent mean values. A non-parametric test of significance, the "H" test, was used because of the lack of normality of the data. The exception is the "violent C" category, which was scored on a present-absent basis; the tabled values represent the number of children having this sign, and the P value is for chi-square.

	Psychosomatic (n = 12)	Neurotic (n = 12)	Illness (n = 12)	H	P
FORMAL SIGNS					
F per cent	77.75	69.83	60.50	5.66	.06
Y+T per cent	5.16	9.75	19.25	6.78	.04
M	2.58	2.30	2.08	.36	.85
H per cent	14.75	15.83	14.08	.14	.94
H vs. Hd	2.16–1.41	2.75–.75	1.91–1.67	3.61	.15
Sum C	1.83	2.37	3.33	3.16	.20
C responses	2.33	2.92	4.42	7.07	.03
"Violent C"	2	6	9	7.80	.02
QUALITATIVE SIGNS					
Dehumanized	3.42	2.67	2.42	.05	n.s.
Unelaborated	7.67	4.92	7.08	2.26	.35
Impersonal	2.5	2.92	2.67	.50	.75

The investigators are well aware of the interdependence of many of the formal signs. Once one hypothesizes an increased F% there is bound to be a decrease in measures of affectivity. Therefore the analyses of Y + T, M, and C should be regarded as steps designed to pinpoint which measures had decreased, rather than findings with independent importance.

It should also be added that the number of responses was analyzed and there was no evidence of significant group differences. The H obtained was .67, which has a P value of .72.

Signs of Early Trauma

The following is a detailed description of the criteria used for the different signs of early trauma.

(1) Oral trauma. The majority of the responses here were oral aggressive ones, in which orality and aggressive destruction were combined. Teeth, biting, chewing, or cannibalism were included in the response; e.g., a dragon trying to bite somebody; a bug with pinchers on his mouth; a glove that has been chewed up by a dog. The primitive oral activity of sucking and spitting were also regarded as symbolic of early trauma. Examples of this are witches sucking something; pigs spitting at each other; bats that suck your blood.

More positively toned oral responses, such as food, eating, and talking, were omitted.

(2) Depression. The three kinds of responses included here were (a) those referring to death (such as dead animals, trees, etc.), (b)

anergic responses (percepts characterized as wilted, crumbling, old, or barren, as well as snow and mud responses), and (c) "heavy" shading responses with no form element (such as "midnight," "inside of the heart," "shadows").

(3) Suspiciousness. This sign included masks, hidden people, pretense ("tigers pretending they are girls"), Janus, and unusual emphasis on the eye ("a monster with one big eye," or "a man with red eyes"). Animals seen as preying, stalking, and watching were included but not those actually killing, chasing, or biting their victim. Manipulatory instruments like hooks and tweezers were also scored although these were very rare.

The investigators decided to exclude animals which might or might not symbolize stealth and slyness, such as panthers and foxes, unless such activity were specifically included in the response by the child.[1]

Results

The number of signs of early trauma was tabulated for each case, and an H test of significance was used. The mean number of signs for each group was 3.0 for the Psychosomatic, 1.25 for the Neurotic, and 1.25 for the Illness. The H of 4.15, with two degrees of freedom, is significant at the .13 level of confidence. Thus there is a tendency for the Psychosomatic children to have more signs of early trauma in their Rorschach records.

A breakdown of the number of signs in each category reveals the following:

	PSYCHOSOMATIC	NEUROTIC	ILLNESS
Oral Trauma	9	5	5
Depression	13	5	8
Suspiciousness	14	5	2

The apparent increase in Depression in the Illness group should not be taken too seriously, since a single case contributed five of the eight responses.

Since Suspiciousness was a category of special interest, a chi-square was run on the number of records containing such signs. There were

----

[1] The investigators were greatly helped by Drs. Sternberg and Wieman in devising criteria for Rorschach signs of early trauma. In doubtful cases, agreement by two of the three judges was used as a basis for scoring.

eight such protocols on the Psychosomatic group, four in the Neurotic group, and two in the Illness group. A chi-square of 6.5 was obtained, which is significant at the .05 level of confidence. Thus signs of suspiciousness, while rare in all groups, are found most frequently in the Psychosomatic group.

WORLD TEST

Procedure

A 200-piece World Test was assembled following the description given by Charlotte Bühler.[2] The pieces were presented to the subject in a large box with the instructions that he should "make something with them—anything you want," on a table top. A record was kept of the sequence of construction and observations were made of the child's behavior during construction. When he had finished, the examiner inquired as to what the entire construction represented and what was going on in the different parts of the World. This inquiry was fairly exhaustive. As is usually the case with this technique, motivation was high in the majority of cases.

Scoring Signs of Emotional Disturbance

The principal use of the data was as a measure of emotional disturbance. Criteria were based on those described by Bühler, Lumry, and Carrol. In some cases such criteria were objective and easily scored; in other cases the investigators had to devise more specific guides for scoring.

The following is a description of the scoring categories:

1. Empty World (E-sign). This is a World which contains no people, or fewer than fifty pieces, or fewer than six different kinds of pieces. The scoring here can be completely objective.

2. Aggressive World (A-sign). This includes themes of fighting, fires, accidents (e.g., people drowning, being run over, storms destroying property), and wild animals biting. Again the scoring could be objective because of the inquiry.

3. Distorted World (CRD-sign). This includes three categories of distortions.

a. Closed World (C-sign). Bühler et al. state that fences, walls, or

----

[2] Charlotte Bühler, Gayle K. Lumry, and Helen S. Carrol, World-Test Standardization Studies (New York: Child Care Publications, 1951).

hedges should enclose the "major part of the world . . . although there may be quite a number of single elements outside." Since "quite a number" is not too specific, the investigators arbitrarily decided that no more than 20% of the pieces could remain without the enclosure.

b. Rigid World (R-sign). Bühler *et al.* define this as "unusually schematic" arrangements and refer to unnatural rows or exaggerated order. The investigators had to expand such descriptions and make them more specific. Two kinds of Rigid Worlds were noted. One contained what was labeled "Primitive Rigidity," and consisted either of rows of houses squashed together to make a solid line, or animals lined up in unnaturally long rows (not in parades or circuses). This was called "primitive" because it is like the constructions of young children. Next was "Compulsivity," which was defined as exaggerated orderliness expressed by repetition of a pattern (e.g., house, tree, house, tree, etc.). A very neat block with a certain variety was not included here.

A rigorous standard was set for this scoring. Isolated little islands of rows or briefly repeated patterns were not included; they had to be a major part of the construction. Also, Closed and Empty Worlds were not scored Rigid since the orderliness here seemed secondary to the extreme inhibition. Descriptions of the child's behavior were used to decide doubtful cases, e.g., whether the child was or was not described as striving for orderliness and perfection.

In spite of this elaboration, an element of subjectivity remained. Rigidity seems to be a continuum, and the cutoff point was not determined with complete objectivity. However, the records of the Worlds were randomized and evaluated "blind," so that no one group would be penalized by the vagueness of the criteria.

c. Disorganized World (D-sign). Here Bühler *et al.* emphasize placing elements chaotically and discontinuity or disarrangement of items. Since there were no completely disorganized Worlds in the present groups, criteria again had to be made more specific.

Inspection of the Worlds revealed two kinds of disorder. The first was called Disorganization, which was evidenced in several ways. There could be incongruous integration of pieces; e.g., a swan swimming on the roof of a building, or an alligator walking down the street. Care had to be taken to make sure that this was not animism, and that the alligator was regarded as a realistic animal in a realistic setting. Another kind of faulty integration was that of grouping wild and domestic animals together; e.g., a cow eating grass while a nearby leopard was looking for its father. This seemed a marginal case of disorganization compared with the others, since it was more like two independent activities happening side by side. However, the decision was made to retain it. There were a few obviously bizarre fantasies, such as "a blind elephant waiting outside a house," which were quite deviant from the general tenor of fantasy. The most frequent single sign was affectively determined disorganization. This was the use of illogical elements to express a single strong feeling, usually anger. Examples here are, animals trying to escape and break down a stop light; soldiers shooting wild and domestic animals because some will bite, some will not give milk, some ran away, and one had a white nose; a cow who wants to break into a house and eat the people. In such cases the intensity of the feeling usurps the child's capacity for rational organization.

The second kind of disorder was called Primitivism. This partakes of some qualities of Disorganization and some of the infantile quality of Primitive Rigidity. In its crudest form it consisted of piling different kinds of pieces on the table in a glob. A little more organized, but still quite crude, was the use of different kinds of pieces in a completely undifferentiated manner to form an undifferentiated group. For example, wild and domestic animals could be grouped together with no regard for their individuality, and referred to just as "animals" or "they." Finally there were two cases of children who used the houses as building blocks and proceeded to construct buildings with them.

It should be noted that animism as such was not scored as disorganization. To begin with, it is to be expected in the younger children, and, more important, the inquiry often encouraged it. The children would be asked what animals were thinking about or how they got along together in order to obtain fantasy material.

Results

The investigators were interested both in the general measure of adjustment obtained from combining all the signs, and in an analysis of the individual signs themselves, since these have different degrees of importance as indices of disturbance. The number of signs of disturbance was tallied for each individual, and an H test was used to evaluate group differences.

Thus there is evidence of more signs of disturbance in the Psychosomatic group whether one uses an over-all measure of this or takes

	Psychosomatic (n = 21)	Neurotic (n = 21)	Illness (n = 20)	H	P
Total number of signs (E, A, CRD)	54	43	35	5.03	.08
Total number of empty signs	15	7	15	3.82	.16
Total number of aggressive signs	25	29	12	8.51	.015
Total number of distorted signs	14	7	8	6.66	.04

each sign separately. The difference in CRD signs is particularly important since such distortions are most sensitive to deep disturbances.

Supplementary Evaluations

The World Test was also used to supplement some of the Rorschach findings as to emotional emptiness and suspiciousness.

1. Suspiciousness. The principal themes here were ones of hiding, secretiveness, and spying. Examples are, "a burglar listening to private secrets," "a man sneaking around," "a man hiding behind a hedge," and a thief disguised as someone else.

The number of Worlds with such themes were six in the Psychosomatic group, four in the Neurotic group, and zero in the Illness control group. A chi-square of 6.31 was obtained which, with two degrees of freedom, is significant at the .05 level of confidence. However, the theoretical frequencies were less than 5, so another measure had to be used. It was decided that the number of pieces in each World devoted to depicting the theme of suspiciousness would be an adequate substitute. This number was thirty-five pieces for the Psychosomatic group, nine for the Neurotics, and zero for the Illness group. An unsettling large chi-square of 41.08 was obtained, which is far beyond the .01 level of significance. Making allowances for the fact that the data might not be ideally suited to the statistic, one might still feel fairly certain that the Psychosomatic group has more signs of suspiciousness than the other groups.

2. Emptiness. The World Test is much less sensitive than the Rorschach to the particular kind of emotional emptiness described in the first section of Chapter 8. This is because, with the World Test, it is more difficult to distinguish lack of responsiveness from defensive or hostile holding back. Therefore, the following analyses should be regarded primarily as suggestive rather than conclusive supplementary

data. The criteria themselves derive from the monograph by Bühler *et al.*

a. Number of Human Pieces. Following Bühler's suggestion, soldiers were not included in the calculations since many children consider them in quite a different class than civilian humans.

First, the number of Worlds with no humans was tallied. There were six such Worlds in the experimental group, none in the Neurotic group, and two in the Illness control group. A chi-square of 7.83 was obtained, which is significant at the .02 level of confidence. Unfortunately, the theoretical frequencies were less than five, so the results can be regarded only as suggestive.

Next, the number of humans in each World was calculated. The mean number was 12.86 for the Psychosomatic group, 14.9 for the Neurotics, and 14.4 for the Illness group. An H of 2.83 was obtained which, with two degrees of freedom, is significant at the .25 level of confidence. This indicates only a very slight trend in the direction of fewer human pieces in the Psychosomatic group.

b. Number of Fences. The number of fences used in each World was calculated. The mean number was 14.81 for the Psychosomatic group, 9.24 for the Neurotic group, and 12.30 for the Illness control group. An H of 4.62 yielded a P of .10. Thus there is a tendency for the Psychosomatic group to use more fences in the construction of their Worlds.

These results can be taken as supporting the Rorschach findings in regard to emotional emptiness in the Psychosomatic child. However, the lack of impressive significance in some cases and the lack of appropriate statistical techniques in others, means that one should accept such findings with caution.

One final methodological point. There was no significant difference in the number of pieces used by each group in constructing their Worlds. This corresponds to the lack of significant difference in the number of Rorschach responses. It also justifies the use of absolute number of pieces rather than percentage in the above calculations.

RESPONSE TO PRESENT

The procedure here was quite simple. Ten pieces of hard candy, wrapped in cellophane, were placed in a gold box, and the box put on a shelf in a cabinet so as to be out of sight during the experimental session. After the child had been given the Realistic and Witch pictures he was told, "You did a very fine job on those stories, and I want you to have a present. You will find it inside the gold box in the cabinet over there." After this there was no more communication with the child except to tell him, "You can have all you like" if he failed to take all the candy.

The child's behavior was observed and recorded throughout this sequence, although the examiner did his best to look as though he were writing about other matters. The period of observation ranged from about one minute for the decisive outgoing children to five minutes for the more inhibited or conflicted ones.

The first and simplest measure of the Psychosomatic child's ambivalence about receiving presents was the number of pieces of candy taken. Because of the skewed nature of the data, an H test was used. The mean number of pieces for each group was 5.96 for the Psychosomatic, 6.60 for the Neurotic, and 6.57 for the Illness. Although the results are in the predicted direction, the obtained H of .18 failed to approach significance.

Next the data were analyzed for qualitative signs of difficulty in receiving. The criteria for this were established beforehand and consisted of the following: Rejection of the candy, Hesitation in taking it, and no overt evidence of Reactivity. After the data had been collected, these criteria could be defined more specifically. Rejection was evidenced by two types of reaction. One was excessive inhibition as compared with the rest of the children. There was much delay, extraneous activity, and signs of discomfort, all of which indicated the situation was quite uncomfortable for the child. The second evidence of Rejection was the child's taking three or fewer pieces of candy. Sometimes this was done with almost no sign of conflict, the child quickly and definitely stating, "That's all I want." Sometimes it was done with evidence of uneasiness, or with the feeling that the situation was too hot to handle. Hesitation represented less severe disturbance or definite rejection; rather it was more of a generalized holding back. The two criteria were that the child took only one piece of candy before he was encouraged to take more (but then was free to do so), or that he asked how many pieces he could have and was too inhibited to act before being told. Lack of Reactivity means the absence of any sign of feeling during the interval, no change of expression, no communication except perhaps a perfunctory "Thank you." These children were not inhibited in their actions, they just failed to show any evidence of feeling.

There were 23 signs of difficulty over receiving in the Psychosomatic group, 14 in the Neurotic group, and 10 in the Illness group. A "goodness of fit" chi-square yielded a value of 5.66 which, with two degrees of freedom, is significant at the .06 level of confidence. Thus, there is evidence of more difficulty over receiving in the Psychosomatic children than in the others.

Although no specific predictions were made, the data were further analyzed to ascertain if other differentiating kinds of behavior could be discovered. The following classification of responses was found to be descriptive of the children's behavior.

Dependency. There were two different manifestations of this. One was active dependence which consisted of strong demands for more attention and more gifts. The child would continually ask questions demanding to know what to do next, wanted to take the box as well as the candy, interfered with the examiner's note-taking, and could be aptly described as "pestering." Other children were passively dependent. They seemed to need permission to do everything—to go to the cabinet, to take the box out, to open it up—and they were constantly looking at the examiner with a questioning expression. Such children also had to show the examiner what they were doing (e.g., how many pieces of candy they were taking), as if they needed reassurance it was all right. The common denominator of both types of dependence was the fact that the child made a persistent attempt to draw the observer into the situation. This was not particularly characteristic of any of the other kinds of behavior.

Masochism. This label stems as much from the pessimism of the clinician as from the behavior of the child. Others might call it altruism. These were children who could not allow themselves to take candy for their own enjoyment, but could take it to give to someone else, such as a sibling. They were also concerned that other children might not have enough if they helped themselves. The impression they conveyed was that they did not feel worthy of the pleasure and self-indulgence implicit in the present.

Greediness. Some children seemed concerned over being greedy, especially when told they could have all the candy they wanted. They reacted strongly to "All," as if it implied unbridled indulgence. Quite often they would limit themselves to less than the ten pieces of candy, as if to control such impulses.

Escape. Evidence for this was an abrupt change in the ongoing behavior after the child had taken the candy, giving the impression that the child wanted to divert attention from what he had done. Some children would immediately start an animated conversation about outside activities, some would ask to leave the room, a few would go and stand looking out of the window instead of returning to the table where the candy had been.

Miscellaneous. Some children evidenced a high degree of choosiness or pickiness when taking the candy out; some were secretive in that they used the cabinet door to screen the box from the observer's sight or turned their backs to him while taking the candy; a couple of the physically ill children explained their reluctance in terms of being warned not to eat candy because of the harm to their health; and, finally, there was some indirect hostility expressed in the form of mild criticism of the present. There were relatively few children in all these categories.

Inspection of the data indicated that Dependency merited further analysis. There were eleven such cases in the Psychosomatic group, five in the Neurotic, and eight in the Illness control group. A chi-square of 3.32 was obtained which is significant at the .20 level of confidence. This shows a slight tendency for the Psychosomatic group to be more dependent in the sense of making more demands on the experimenter. Such a finding, while of little significance in itself, fits nicely with some of the observed interactions between mother and child, indicating an unhealthy kind of closeness.

TOY CHOICE

This technique was devised to obtain evidence of unsatisfied longings for maternal affection in Psychosomatic children—a very difficult hypothesis to verify. Although there seemed no way to approach this matter directly, observation of the ward children's behavior furnished a clue for an indirect verification. These children seemed to be unusually intrigued with sensory experiences, especially the very primitive olfactory and tactual ones. Thus they would become deeply engrossed in feeling, stroking, and petting different materials or in smelling pungent odors such as airplane dope. This seemed to represent a kind of hunger for such primitive stimulation. It was speculated that the children were trying to obtain the basic sensory gratification denied them because of inadequate mothering during infancy.

The Toy Choice technique was designed to test the hypothesis of an unusually strong need for sensory stimulation in Psychosomatic children.

Procedure. Eight small tables were arranged in a semicircle in a playroom with a one-way mirror. On four of these tables were constructive toys—crayons and paper, building blocks which could be snapped together, a pegboard on which miniature houses and trees could be placed, toy cars for the boys and miniature living room furniture for the girls. On the other four tables were objects with strong sensory appeal—a foam rubber pillow, bottles containing peppermint extract, airplane dope, and cologne, a handwarmer sewn into a flannel case, and pieces of velvet, satin, and rabbit fur. Placement of the toys was randomized.

Before the procedure began, one observer was stationed behind the one-way mirror to record the child's behavior. The child was brought into the room by the other observer and was told, "See all these different things? You can do whatever you like with them. But first let me show you what they are." The investigator then went from table to table, calling the child's attention to each object. This was to make sure the child was made aware of the different toys. The investigator then said, "You are going to have a lot of time and you can do anything you like. But just play with one thing at a time. I am going to be over here doing some work of my own, but you go on and play with all the things you want to." He then sat down in a far corner and began to observe and record the child's behavior. The pretense of being busy doing work of his own discouraged communication from the child. After five minutes he said, "I'm going to have to leave you for a while because I still have some other things to do. But you go right on playing with whatever you like. I will be back in a little while." He then joined the observer behind the one-way mirror and they both observed and recorded the child's behavior for fifteen minutes. The child was left alone on the assumption that he would feel freer to play with the sensory material under these circumstances.

At the end of this 15-minute period the investigator returned to the playroom and asked the child which toy he liked best, the next best, and so on, until all the toys had been ranked.

The investigators made a running account of the child's activities during his twenty minutes in the playroom. Particular attention was paid to describing his response to the sensory toys. In addition, the time in seconds which a child spent playing with each toy was recorded, and the intensity of his involvement in the play activity was rated on a five-point scale. If an activity lasted more than one minute it was rated once a minute.

Thus, there were three measures of attraction to the sensory toys as compared with the constructive ones—the total amount of time spent playing with these toys, the ratings of intensity of involvement, and the preference ranking at the end. It was predicted that the Psychosomatic children would show significantly greater attraction to the sensory toys than would the children in the other groups.

Results. Tabulated results revealed no group differences on any of the measures. The groups were so obviously similar that statistical tests were not·necessary. The descriptions of sensory activity were scored to differentiate constructive use of these toys (e.g., making a hat out of the rabbit pelt or a skirt out of the velvet) from pure sensory activity (e.g., stroking the material, kneading the pillow). Again no group differences were found.

In spite of a certain elegance of design, then, the technique failed to yield evidence of increased sensory needs in the Psychosomatic children.

It is not clear why such negative results were obtained. Perhaps the original observations on the ward children were not evaluated correctly and what appeared to be deep sensory needs were a more or less transitory interest. Observation of the behavior of subsequent children who came on the ward would lend a certain amount of credence to this possibility.

It is certainly more difficult to find flaws within the research design itself. It is possible that the children's behavior in the playroom was inhibited by the fact that this technique came early in the first session and the situational anxiety had not dissipated. Being left alone in the room would increase such uneasiness and this might inhibit freedom of play. Since strong sensory indulgence may well be embedded in feelings of guilt and anxiety, perhaps Toy Choice should have been postponed until the second session when the child was definitely more relaxed.

At this point however, it seems that further pursuit of this approach would not be warranted.

One final analysis of the data was undertaken after the "High" and "Low" Psychosomatic mothers had been established as distinct subgroups. The data on all the techniques described in this chapter as well as those on the thematic material discussed in the previous chapter were divided into two groups depending on whether the Psycho-somatic child had a "High" or a "Low" mother. However, none of the comparisons yielded significant differences. In all probability the pro-cedures tapped the child's reaction to the common denominator of the Psychosomatic mothers, their lack of motherliness, rather than the effects of the specific kinds of faulty relationships which they estab-lished with their child. Only the qualitative analysis of the Mixed Themes in Chapter 8 reflects the kinds of patterns typical of the "High" and "Low" subgroups of mothers.

18---Methodology of Studies of Children's Fantasies Concerning Etiology of Illness

Construction of Techniques

GIFT

The purpose of the Garner Illness Fantasy Technique (GIFT) was to present the children with a variety of situations whose affective implications might be relevant to their fantasies concerning sickness. Theoretically, the specific situations designated by a child as causing illness would be the ones which resonated to his specific fantasy life.

The principal psychological dimensions of the pictures are as follows: (1) Emotions involved—pleasure, anxiety, guilt, depression, and love; (2) Interpersonal situation—whether the child is alone or with a parent, and the particular parent involved; (3) Responsibility— whether the child provokes a negative response or is an innocent victim; and (4) Punishment—whether transgressions are detected and punished or not.

Using this schema, the pictures in the GIFT represent the following situations:

1. Interpersonal pleasure, father involved.

2. Unintentional transgression, undetected, mother referred to but not present.

3. Anxiety, non-personal.

4. Intentional transgression, detected and punished, mother involved.

5. Intentional transgression, undetected, father referred to but not present.

6. Neglect, mother involved.

7. Non-personal pleasure.

8. Innocent victim of anger, mother involved.

9. Unintentional transgression, detected and punished, father involved.

10. Love, mother involved.

11. Depression, mother referred to but not present.

12. Anger, mother involved.

Procedure

The following instructions were given the child as the GIFT pictures were placed in front of him.

I am going to show you some pictures of a little boy (girl) doing a lot of different things. Listen carefully so you will remember what is happening in each picture. [Picture 1 presented] The first picture shows the boy having *lots of fun* playing ball with his father. See, here he is having *lots of fun* playing ball with his father. In the next picture [Picture 2 presented] the little boy broke his mother's best vase but he *didn't mean to do it*. In this picture [Picture 3] the little boy gets caught in a storm and is *very scared*. See, here he is in the storm and he is *very scared*. Here [Picture 4] he got hold of his mother's lipstick and started drawing on the wall and she caught him doing it. See him drawing on the wall with his mother's lipstick, and she caught him doing it. In this picture [Picture 5] he is taking money out of his father's wallet; he's not supposed to but *no one is watching*. See, he is taking money from his father's wallet although he knows he is not supposed to, but *no one is watching*. Next [Picture 6] he is crying but his mother is talking on the phone and *won't pay him any attention*. See him crying here, and his mother is on the phone and *isn't paying any attention to him*. In the next picture [Picture 7] he is at the circus and he is just *having the time of his life*. See him at the circus, and he's *having a wonderful time*. Here [Picture 8] his mother is fussing at him although he is sure he *hadn't done anything to make her so mad*. Here she is fussing away although he is sure he *didn't do anything to make her that mad*. [Picture 9] His daddy is angry because the boy scratched the car, although he was *just playing and didn't mean to*. See how mad his daddy is even though the boy was *just playing and didn't mean* to scratch the car. Here [Picture 10] his mother is giving him a big hug and kiss and saying how much she loves him. See how she is hugging and kissing him, and she's telling him how much she loves him. Here [Picture 11] the boy's mother has gone shopping and he feels *sad and lonely* all by himself. See him by himself because his mother is shopping, and he feels very *sad and lonely*. In this picture [Picture 12] he gets *real mad* at his mother. See him there—he's just *real mad* at his mother.

Then, that night, this little boy did not feel so good. In fact, he began to feel worse and worse until he got very, very sick. Now, look at all these pictures and pick out the thing that made him sick. [After first choice is made, the child is asked what else could have made the boy sick, until three pictures are chosen. Then the following inquiry is made if the information is not given spontaneously.] What is this picture about? How does he feel? Why did that make him sick?

The emphasis on memory and repetition in the instructions was an effort to impress the child with the important psychological dimensions of the picture and to insure against memory failures in the younger and less intelligent subjects.

OTHER TECHNIQUES

When GIFT had been completed, a felt doll was placed in front of the child and he was told, "Now let's suppose that this is the little sick boy, and the doctor is coming to see him. Here comes the doctor. The doctor is going to try to find out what is the matter with the little boy. Now let's pretend the doctor can look inside the little boy. What does the doctor see when he looks inside the little boy?"

The child was encouraged to fantasy about what the doctor would see, and was asked specifically what the doctor would find in the head, body, stomach, arms, and legs. He was also asked, "What does the sickness look like?" and was encouraged to fantasy about this. All his responses were taken down verbatim.

Next, the child was presented with a box of colored pencils and a drawn outline of a child. He was told to draw what the child would look like on the inside and also to draw the sickness. To the investigator's surprise, the latter request was regarded as quite sensible. Again the child was encouraged to fantasy about the causes and nature of illness.

Finally, the child was asked about his own illness and how it was caused. The first responses were usually in terms of clichés or parroted medical explanations. However, as the investigator would continue to ask, "But why would that make you sick?" (or phrases to that effect), more personalized material was obtained.

Results

None of the analyses of picture choice on GIFT was fruitful. The number of choices of each picture was calculated for the groups, but inspection indicated very meager results. The Psychosomatic group had significantly fewer choices of Picture 6 (maternal neglect), but such an isolated finding is hardly noteworthy. Tabulation of first, second, and third choices proved equally barren.

However, two minor insights into the technique were furnished. Picture 3 (the boy in the storm) was overwhelmingly favored by children in all groups and accounted for about one quarter of all choices made. However, the reason for this choice was not the fear involved, but the colds the boy would catch. The only unsuccessful picture was the one of maternal affection (10), which was chosen only once. The rest of the pictures showed a nice distribution of choices. The second finding was that the children, in their answers to the questions about what was going on and how the boy felt, showed that the situations depicted were grasped and remembered. Thus the intellectual demands placed on the child were not too great.

The technique proved fruitful only when answers to the question "Why did that make him sick?" were examined.

Attention was first directed to the question of whether Psychosomatic children had more fantasies about interpersonal situations causing illness. To obtain a measure of this, all those responses which included a reference to parents were scored. At times such responses merely restated the theme of the picture ("Because she got mad at her mother"), at times they introduced novel elements ("She would be afraid to face her mother and father after that"). The Psychosomatic group had 19 of such responses out of a total of 54 responses, the Neurotics had 8 out of a total of 48, and the Illness group had 14 out of a total of 51 responses. A chi-square of 4.37 was obtained which, with two degrees of freedom, is significant slightly beyond the .10 level of confidence. (An H test yielded a value of 3.74 which is a little beyond the .15 level of confidence). Thus there is a tendency for both illness groups to give reasons for illness which involve interpersonal relations.

More data on this subject were obtained from the non-GIFT techniques. The number of children giving interpersonal reasons was not significantly different (11 out of 19 in the Psychosomatic, 9 out of 18 in the Neurotic, and 9 out of 20 in the Illness group), but the kinds of reasons were quite different. There were three general classifications of situations—those involving relationships with people, those involving God, and those involving contagion. The number of children in each category was as follows:

	PSYCHOSOMATIC	NEUROTIC	ILLNESS
Interpersonal	10	3	4
God	0	1	5
Contagion	1	6	1

The chi-square of 19.47, with four degrees of freedom, was significant far beyond the .01 level of confidence. Although many of the theoretical frequencies are less than five, such striking results cannot be disregarded. Thus there is evidence that different kinds of interpersonal situations are seen as causing illness: the Psychosomatic children project specific interpersonal interactions, the Neurotic refer more to contagion, while the children in the Illness group refer to God as the cause.

A brief description of the principal reasons in each category might be helpful in making the differences more vivid.

PSYCHOSOMATIC	NEUROTIC	ILLNESS
PARENTS		
Mother let her watch too much TV	Using money mother did not give her	Not telling mother of illness
She gulped forbidden food so mother would not see	Not being nice to mother	Not paying attention to mother
Parents failed to warn of danger		
Mother put something bad in food, although she thought it was good		
Mother gave her disease		
Took pills when parents not looking		
Neglected to tell mother of illness		
OTHERS		
Not knowing answer when teacher calls on child	Defending friend in a fight	Someone threw dirt on sore
No one loved her because of what she did		Kids pushed him around
Brother rolled log on leg		
Fear of doctor		Fighting with friend
Someone hit her on the head		
No one paid any attention to him		
Someone stepped on her toe		

PSYCHOMATIC	NEUROTIC	ILLNESS
GOD	God punished her for not being nice to mother	God "borned her" too small for hole in heart to heal
		Jesus makes her sick when she is mean and nasty
		God made child that way so doctors could learn how to treat the disease
		God did not want him to fight like other children did
		God picked him; if everyone had the illness it would be terrible

Contagion for all groups consisted of a general statement that a person gets sick from being with others who are sick. The people are always non-specific.

The most important contribution of GIFT was the so-called Primary and Secondary expression of affect. The criterion for the Primary category was that the emotional state of the child per se was seen as the cause of the illness. Sixteen such reasons were found in the Psychosomatic group (three mad, three scared, three sorry, three afraid, one lonely, one uneasy, one worried, one feel bad), six in the Neurotic group (one mad, one scared, one afraid, one feeling that he did something wrong, one "would be on her mind," one "knew it wasn't right"), and five in the Illness group (two mad, one guilty conscience, one lonesome, one real sorry). A chi-square of 8.36 was obtained which yielded a P of .015.

Criteria for the Secondary category were a bit more complicated. They included all cases in which the physical expression of emotion made the child sick; e.g., yelling made him hoarse, stamping made him hurt his foot. Care was always taken to make sure that it was the action itself and not the underlying affect (such as anger) which produced sickness. The most frequent case was crying. Many children thought crying per se made one sick, others blamed such consequences of crying as sore eyes, headaches. If crying were an expression of an emotional state (such as loneliness or separation), it was not scored, and the reason was placed in the Primary category. Three such Secondary reasons were found in the Psychosomatic group, thirteen in the Neurotic group, and ten in the Illness control group. A chi-square of 7.22 was obtained, which was significant at the .025 level of confidence.

Thus there is evidence that the Psychosomatic children give significantly more Primary reasons and significantly fewer Secondary reasons for illness.

Next, Guilt and Aggression as causes of illness were examined, since these variables figured so prominently in the original designing of the technique. Examination of the data revealed that there were three kinds of Guilt. Guilt I (G-I) was a simple statement that illness was due to transgressing—the child did something he was not supposed to do. Guilt II (G-II) went one step beyond this and made the emotional reaction to wrongdoing the cause. Thus, a child would "feel bad" over doing something wrong, would fear to face his parents, would have a guilty conscience. This category carried a stronger flavor of self-punishment than does G-I. Finally, Guilt III (G-III) is a special case of getting sick because of direct aggression against the mother in the form of getting mad and yelling at her. In the case of Aggression, the child can be seen either as the aggressor (A-I) or as aggressed against (A-II), depending on whether he is mad and doing the hollering, or whether he is being hollered at, scolded, fussed at. There were eighteen such Guilt and Aggression reasons in the Psychosomatic group, five in the Neurotic, and fourteen in the Illness group. A chi-square yielded a value of 5.86 which is significant slightly beyond the .05 level of confidence. Thus, both illness groups see Guilt and Aggression as a cause of sickness more frequently than do neurotic children.

Another category of reasons was concerned with eating. In almost all cases the reason was "eating too much," although the Psychosomatic group had two references to eating poison or harmful substances. Nine such reasons were given by the Psychosomatic group, eight by the Neurotic, and only three by the Illness. A chi-square yielded a value of 3.10 which is significant slightly beyond the .20 level of confidence. This finding can be considered as only suggestive.

By far the most common reasons for illness were those connected with catching cold, such as being out in the rain, not dressed warmly, sitting on the cold ground. These accounted for from 23% to 31% of all the reasons given, with the three groups sharing about equally.

There were other reasons given, but their frequencies were rather low, and they failed to differentiate the groups. There was fear of the storm, neglect by the mother, separation from the mother with the child feeling sad, lonely, or frightened, too much activity such as running or playing, and one reference to having too much fun.

One final methodological point. Aside from the Primary and Secondary reason analyses, all the chi-squares were obtained by the "goodness of fit" method. This was done to decrease the possibility of obtaining significant results by chance on the basis of running a large number of chi-squares.

These findings from the children were compared with the mothers' response to the question, "How do you understand your child's present illness [or "trouble" in the case of the Neurotic group]?"

The largest number of reasons fell under the rubric of Psychological. These included the mother blaming herself, her husband, or other relatives, the mother blaming the child or playmates, trauma (e.g., being scared by a dog), and psychologizing (e.g., references to "complexes"). The Psychosomatic group had twelve such reasons, the Neurotic seventeen, and the Illness three. A chi-square of 10.87 was significant at the .005 level. Thus the Psychosomatic and Neurotic mothers share an emphasis on psychological causation.

In contrast to this, the Illness group tended to describe the illness in response to the question, indicating they focused on understanding the process rather than the cause of the illness. There were nine such responses in the Illness group, with only three in the Psychosomatic and two in the Neurotic. The chi-square here was 5.09, which is significant between the .05 and .10 levels of confidence.

Religious reasons were of special importance, in light of the findings with the children. As with the children, there was a concentration of such responses in the Illness group, who referred to God, God's will, or such fatalistic concepts as "it was meant to be." There were six such reasons in this group, and none in the other two. The chi-square of 10.82, with its resounding significance beyond the .01 level is questionable, therefore, but the finding is too meaningful to be overlooked.

There were a number of Physiological reasons. These included the child's internal state (such as bad tonsils), heredity, unelaborated reference to congenital factors, and such external factors as accidents. However, the totals of six, three, and five in the Psychosomatic, Neurotic, and Illness groups respectively were not significantly different.

There were a number of miscellaneous reasons, all having relatively low frequencies. Some mothers blamed the doctors, a few became defensive over their own care of the child (e.g., saying she always kept the child clean), a few did not know, and one referred to chance.

A methodological point should be made here similar to that made with the children's data. The chi-squares were obtained by the "goodness of fit" method in order to decrease the possibility of obtaining significance on the basis of running a number of computation on a related series of categories.

Finally, the data on communication of knowledge about psychosomatic etiology from physician to mother to child will be presented. These pertain only to the Psychosomatic mothers and children.

Data obtained from referring agencies or from the mother's interview material indicated that nineteen of the twenty-six mothers had been told that emotional factors contributed to the etiology of their child's illness. Care was taken that the explanation had been in terms of etiology and not in terms of emotional consequences of illness. No data could be obtained in regard to the other seven mothers.

Fourteen of the nineteen informed mothers mentioned psychological etiology either to the psychologists or to the social worker on the present research. Whether they accepted the idea or not is of no concern here. The remaining five mothers gave other reasons, and there was no evidence in any of the data that they ever had been informed. It was on this basis that the investigators speculated that, because of personality factors, some mothers completely fail to grasp or to assimilate the information.

Next, the relationship between the number of mothers giving psychological reasons for etiology and the number of their children giving Primary Affect and Interpersonal Relationships as causing illness was tested. The results are as follows:

	CHILD			
	(I) PRIMARY AFFECT	OTHER	(II) INTERPERSONAL	OTHER
MOTHER				
Psychological reason	7	5	6	7
Non-psychological reason	3	4	5	3

A chi-square on (I) yielded a value of 1.27, which is significant beyond the .50 level of confidence; (II) was deemed to be nonsignificant by inspection.

A supplementary analysis was made to answer the objection that a mother may still retain the information about psychological etiology even though she does not tell the psychologists and social worker on the project. Therefore, data on children of informed mothers were examined. Roughly half of these children gave Primary Affect and half gave Other Reasons on GIFT; in a like manner, roughly half the children gave Interpersonal Reasons and half gave Other Reasons. Therefore it can be concluded that there is no one-to-one relationship between a mother's being informed about emotional factors producing illness and her child's fantasies about negative feelings and interpersonal situations producing illness.

Index